Discrete Algorithms and Complexity

PERSPECTIVES IN COMPUTING, Vol. 15

(Formerly "Notes and Reports in Computer Science and Applied Mathematics")

W. Rheinboldt and D. Siewiorek, editors

Discrete Algorithms and Complexity

Proceedings of the Japan-US Joint Seminar
June 4 – 6, 1986, Kyoto, Japan

Edited by

David S. Johnson
AT&T Bell Laboratories
Murray Hill, New Jersey

Akihiro Nozaki
International Christian University
Tokyo, Japan

Takao Nishizeki
Tohoku University
Sendai, Japan

Herbert S. Wilf
University of Pennsylvania
Philadelphia, Pennsylvania

ACADEMIC PRESS, INC.
Harcourt Brace Jovanovich, Publishers

Boston Orlando San Diego
New York Austin London Sydney
Tokyo Toronto

Academic Press, Inc.
Orlando, Florida 32887

United Kingdom Edition published by
ACADEMIC PRESS INC. (LONDON) LTD.
24-28 Oval Road, London NW1 7DX

Library of Congress Cataloging-in-Publication Data
Discrete algorithms and complexity; proceedings
    of the Japan-US Joint Seminar, June 4–6, 1986,
    Kyoto, Japan.

    (Perspectives in computing ; vol. 15)
    1. Electronic digital computers—Programming—
Congresses. 2. Algorithms—Congresses. 3. Computational
complexity—Congresses. I. Johnson, David S., Date
        II. Japan-US Joint Seminar on Discrete
Algorithms and Complexity Theory (1986 : Kyoto, Japan)
III. Series.
QA76.6.D577 1987   511   86-33469
ISBN 0-12-386870-X (alk. paper)

87 88 89 90   9 8 7 6 5 4 3 2 1
Printed in the United States of America

Contents

* Speakers

Contributors

Akeo Adachi (311), *IBM Science Institute, 5-19 Sanban-cho, Chiyoda-ku, Tokyo 102, Japan*

Leonard Adleman (237), *Department of Computer Science, University of Southern California, Los Angeles, CA 90089-0782, USA*

Michael Albertson (35), *Department of Mathematics, Smith College, Northampton, MA 01063, USA*

Takao Asano (51), *Department of Mechanical Engineering, Sophia University, Tokyo 102, Japan*

Tetsuo Asano (51, 65), *Osaka Electro-Communication University, Neyagawa, Osaka 572, Japan*

F.R.K. Chung (351), *Bell Communications Research, Morristown, New Jersey 07960, USA*

Toru Fujiwara (263), *Department of Information and Computer Sciences, Faculty of Engineering Science, Osaka University, Toyonaka 560, Japan*

Shafi Goldwasser (287), *MIT, Laboratory for Computer Science, Cambridge, MA 02139, USA*

R.L. Graham (351), *Bell Laboratories, Murray Hill, New Jersey 07974, USA*

E. Hare (437), *Department of Mathematical Sciences, Clemson University, Clemson, SC 29631, USA*

Stephen T. Hedetniemi (437), *Department of Computer Science, Clemson University, Clemson, SC 29631, USA*

John Hopcroft (201), *Department of Computer Science, Cornell University, Ithaca, NY 14853, USA*

Juraj Hromkovič (389), *Department of Theoretical Cybernetics, Comenius University, 842-15 Bratislava, Czechoslovakia*

Joan Hutchinson (81), *Department of Mathematics, Smith College, Northampton, MA 01063, USA*

Toshihide Ibaraki (185), *Department of Applied Mathematics and Physics, Faculty of Engineering, Kyoto University, Kyoto 606, Japan*

Yoshihide Igarashi (161), *Department of Computer Science, Gunma University, Kiryu 376, Japan*

Hiroshi Imai (417), *Department of Computer Science and Communication Engineering, Kyushu University, Fukuoka 812, Japan*

Katsushi Inoue (389), *Department of Electronics, Faculty of Engineering, Yamaguchi University, Ube 755, Japan*

Masao Iri (417), *Department of Mathematical Engineering and Instrumentation Physics, Faculty of Engineering, University of Tokyo, Tokyo 113, Japan*

Kazuo Iwama (223), *Kyoto Sangyo University, Kyoto 603, Japan*

Shigeki Iwata (405), *Information Science Laboratory, Tokai University, Hiratsuka 259-12, Japan*

Yoji Kajitani (5), *Department of Electrical and Electronic Engineering, Tokyo Institute of Technology, Tokyo 152, Japan*

Anna R. Karlin (459), *Computer Science Department, Stanford University, Stanford, CA 94305, USA*

Richard M. Karp (1), *Computer Science Division, University of California, Berkeley, CA 94720, USA*

Takumi Kasai (311, 405), *Department of Computer Science, University of Electro-Communications, Chofu, Tokyo 182, Japan*

Tadao Kasami (263), *Department of Information and Computer Sciences, Faculty of Engineering Science, Osaka University, Toyonaka 560, Japan*

Kojiro Kobayashi (325), *Department of Information Sciences, Tokyo Institute of Technology, O-okayama, Meguro-ku, Tokyo 152, Japan*

Renu Laskar (437), *Department of Mathematical Sciences, Clemson University, Clemson, SC 29631, USA*

Hajime Machida (107), *Department of Computer Science, University of Electro-Communications, Chofu, Tokyo 182, Japan*

Mark S. Manasse (459), *DEC Systems Research Center, Palo Alto, CA, USA*

Kevin S. McCurley (237), *Department of Mathematics, University of Southern California, Los Angeles, CA 90089-1113, USA*

Silvio Micali (287), *MIT, Laboratory for Computer Science, Cambridge, MA 02139, USA*

Gary L. Miller (81), *Department of Computer Science, University of Southern California, Los Angeles, CA 90089, USA*

Takao Nishizeki (99), *Department of Electrical Communications, Faculty of Engineering, Tohoku University, Sendai 980, Japan*

Takao Ozawa (5), *Department of Electrical Engineering, Kyoto University, Kyoto 606 Japan*

Ken Peters (437), *Department of Mathematical Sciences, Clemson University, Clemson, SC 29631, USA*

Carl Pomerance (119), *Department of Mathematics, The University of Georgia, Athens, Georgia 30602, USA*

Ronald L. Rivest (287), *MIT, Laboratory for Computer Science, Cambridge, MA 02139, USA*

Larry Rudolph (459), *Computer Science Department, Hebrew University, Jerusalem, Israel*

Kakuhiro Sado (161), *Department of Computer Science, Gunma University, Kiryu 376, Japan*

Nobuji Saito (99), *Department of Electrical Communications, Faculty of Engineering, Tohoku University, Sendai 980, Japan*

M.E. Saks (351), *Bell Communications Research, Morristown, New Jersey 07960, USA*

Daniel D. Sleator (459), *Computer Science Department, Carnegie-Mellon University, Pittsburgh, PA 15213, USA*

Hitoshi Suzuki (99), *Department of Electrical Communications, Faculty of Engineering, Tohoku University, Sendai 980, Japan*

Naofumi Takagi (145), *Department of Information Science, Faculty of Engineering, Kyoto University, Kyoto, 606, Japan*

Itsuo Takanami (389), *Department of Electronics, Faculty of Engineering, Yamaguchi University, Ube 755, Japan*

Ken-ichi Taniguchi (263), *Department of Information and Computer Sciences, Faculty of Engineering Science, Osaka University, Toyonaka 560, Japan*

Godfried T. Toussaint (65), *School of Computer Science, McGill University, Montreal, Canada*

Shuichi Ueno (5), *Department of Electrical and Electronic Engineering, Tokyo Institute of Technology, Tokyo 152, Japan*

Herbert S. Wilf (341), *Department of Mathematics, University of Pennsylvania, Philadelphia, PA 19104, USA*

T.V. Wimer (437), *Department of Mathematics, Clarion University of Pennsylvania, Clarion, PA 16214, USA*

Shuzo Yajima (145), *Department of Information Science, Faculty of Engineering, Kyoto University, Kyoto, 606, Japan*

Hiroto Yasuura (145), *Department of Information Science, Faculty of Engineering, Kyoto University, Kyoto, 606, Japan*

Nancy A. Yoshimura (341), *Department of Computer and Information Science, University of Pennsylvania, Philadelphia, PA 19104, USA*

Foreword

The Japan-US Joint Seminar on Discrete Algorithms and Complexity Theory was held 4 – 6 June, 1986, in Kyoto, Japan. It was jointly organized by A. Nozaki and H.S. Wilf and generously sponsored by the Japan Society for Promotion of Sciences and the U.S. National Science Foundation. Thirty-three of the participants were invited to give talks. This volume contains most of the papers presented there.

Some papers describe the state of the art in specific fields, some explore new problems, and others present new results that will soon appear in more detailed form in scientific journals. We expect that the reader will come away from this volume with a better understanding of and insight into Discrete Algorithms and Complexity.

The editors wish to thank all delegates; their efforts made the seminar stimulating and fruitful. Especially we would like to express our gratitude to the executive committee of the Seminar: Takao Asano, Tetsuo Asano, Kazuo Iwama, Shigeki Iwata, Takumi Kasai and Hajime Machida. Finally, we would like to thank the staff of Academic Press Boston for their cooperation in producing this volume.

David S. Johnson
Takao Nishizeki
Akihiro Nozaki
Herbert S. Wilf

An Upper Bound on the Expected Cost of an Optimal Assignment

Richard M. Karp†

Computer Science Division
University of California,
Berkeley, California 94720

Introduction

An instance of the $n \times n$ assignment problem (AP) is specified by a $n \times n$ matrix (c_{ij}) of real numbers. The problem is to find a permutation that minimizes

$$A^* = \sum_{i=1}^{n} c_{i,\sigma(i)}.$$

When n is fixed and the c_{ij} are drawn independently from the uniform distribution over $[0,1]$, A^* becomes a random variable. Computational experiments indicate that, when $n > 100$, $E[A^*]$ is close to 1.6. Lazarus [1979] shows that

$$E[A^*] \geq 1 + \frac{1}{e} + O\left(\frac{1}{n}\right) \approx 1.37,$$

and Walkup [1979] shows that

$E[A^*] < 3$ for all n. Our main result is

Theorem 1. For all n, $E[A^*] < 2$.

A Regularity Condition

Call the matrix (c_{ij}) <u>regular</u> if no two distinct subsets of its elements have the same sum. This implies in particular that the optimal assignment σ is unique. Under the stated assumptions about the probability distribution of the c_{ij} the matrix (c_{ij}) is regular with probability 1. Throughout the paper we restrict attention to regular instances of the AP.

†Research supported by NSF Grant MCS-8105217

DISCRETE ALGORITHMS AND
COMPLEXITY

1

The Transportation Problem and its Dual

The proof of Theorem 1 is based on well-known properties of the following dual pair of linear programming problems ([1]).

PRIMAL

$\min \sum_{i=1}^{m} \sum_{j=1}^{n} c_{ij} x_{ij}$

subject to

$x_{ij} \geq 0$

$\quad 1,2,...,m$

$\quad j = 1,2,...,n$

$\sum_{j} x_{ij} = a_i \quad i = 1,2,...,m$

$\sum_{i} x_{ij} = b_j \quad j = 1,2,...,n$

DUAL

$\max \sum_{i=1}^{m} a_i u_i + \sum_{j=1}^{n} b_j v_j$

subject to

$c_{ij} - u_i - v_j \geq 0$

$\quad i = 1,2,...,m$

$\quad j = 1,2,...,n.$

Here the a_i and b_j are nonnegative real numbers satisfying $\sum_{i=1}^{m} a_i = \sum_{j=1}^{n} b_j$. The AP is the special case in which $m = n$ and all a_i and b_j are equal to 1. In this special case the primal and dual have A^* as their common optimal value. Also, every basic feasible solution to the primal has all x_{ij} equal to 0 or 1; for every such basic feasible solution there is a permutation σ of $\{1,2,...,n\}$ such that $x_{ij} = 1$ and only if $j = \sigma(i)$.

In general, the basic solutions of the primal and dual can be characterized in graph-theoretic terms. Let G be the complete bipartite graph with vertex set

$\{s_1,s_2,...,s_m\} \cup \{t_1,t_2,...,t_n\}$

and edge set

$\{\{s_i, t_j\}, i = 1,2,...,m, j = 1,2,...,n\}.$

Let T be the edge set of a spanning tree of G. There is a unique solution of the primal satisfying: if $\{s_i, t_j\} \notin T$ then $x_{ij} = 0$. There is a unique solution of the dual satisfying: $u_1 = 0$ and if $\{s_i, t_j\} \in T$ then $c_{ij} - u_i - v_j = 0$. The solutions obtained in this way from spanning trees of G are the basic solutions of the primal and dual. Call T *feasible* if the associated basic solution of the primal satisfies $x_{ij} \geq 0$ for all i and j; call T *dual feasible* if the associated basic solution of the dual satisfies $c_{ij} - u_i - v_j \geq 0$ for all i and j. If T is both feasible and dual feasible we say that T is *optimal*; in this case the basic solutions associated with T are optimal for the primal and dual respectively.

In the special case of the AP there are in general many optimal spanning trees of G. If the AP satisfies our regularity hypothesis there is a unique optimal tree which remains feasible when the a_i and b_j are perturbed by setting

$a_i = 1 + n\varepsilon$ $i = 1$, $i = 2,...,n$

and $b_j = 1 + \varepsilon$, $j = 1,2,...,n$. Let us call this unique tree the canonical optimal tree.

Proof of Theorem 1: Each regular instance (c_{ij}) of the AP determines a 3-tuple $<T, u, v>$. Here T is the canonical optimal tree and the n-vectors $u = (u_1, u_2,...,u_m)$ and $v = (v_1, v_2,...,v_n)$ are the associated optimal solution of the dual; call this 3-tuple the *optimality data* for (c_{ij}).

Now assume that the c_{ij} are drawn independently from the uniform distribution over $[0,1]$. Define the following two random variables

over the sample space of instances (c_{ij}):

$$X = \sum_{i=1}^{n} \sum_{j=1}^{n} c_{ij}$$

and $Y = <T, u, v>$, the optimality data for (c_{ij}). The proof of Theorem 1 will emerge from consideration of the identity

$$E[X] = E[E[X|Y]].$$

Clearly $E[X] = \dfrac{n^2}{2}$, since the expected value of each c_{ij} is $\dfrac{1}{2}$. Let us compute $E[X|Y]$, where $Y = <T, u, v>$ is fixed. The matrices from our sample space having $<T, u, v>$ as optimality data are precisely those satisfying

$$c_{ij} - u_i - v_j = 0, \quad \{s_i, t_j\} \in T$$
$$c_{ij} - u_i - v_j \geq 0 \quad \{s_i, t_j\} \in T$$

The a priori distribution of each c_{ij} is uniform over $[0,1]$. The a posteriori distribution of c_{ij} given $<T, u, v>$ is uniform over $[\max(0, u_i + v_j), 1]$, and its conditional expectation given $<T, u, v>$

is therefore $\dfrac{1}{2} + \dfrac{1}{2}$

$\max(0, u_i + v_j)$. Hence,

$\square$

Dyer, Frieze and McDiarmid (1984) have recently used the proof

$$E[\sum_{i=1}^{n} \sum_{j=1}^{n} c_{ij} | <T, u, v>]$$

$$= \sum_{\{s_i,t_j\} \in T} (u_i + v_j)$$

$$+ \sum_{\{s_i,t_j\} \notin T} (\frac{1}{2} + \frac{1}{2} \max(0, u_i + v_j)).$$

Noting that $u_i + v_j = c_{ij} \geq 0$ when $\{s_i, t_j\} \in T$,   that

$\max (0, u_i + v_j) \geq u_i + v_j$ and

that $\sum_{i=1}^{n} u_i + \sum_{j=1}^{n} v_j = A^*$,   we

obtain

$$E[\sum_{i=1}^{n} \sum_{j=1}^{n} c_{ij} | <T, u, v>] \geq$$

$$\frac{1}{2} \sum_{\{s_i,t_j\} \in T} (u_i + v_j) + \sum_{\{s_i,t_j\} \notin T} (\frac{1}{2} + \frac{1}{2} (u_i + v_j))$$

$$= \frac{1}{2} \sum_{i=1}^{n} \sum_{j=1}^{n} (u_i + v_j) + \frac{n^2 - 2n + 1}{2}$$

$$= \frac{n}{2} A^* + \frac{n^2 - 2n + 1}{2}.$$

Applying $E[X] = E[E[X|Y]]$ we obtain

$$\frac{n^2}{2} \geq \frac{n}{2} E[A^*] + \frac{n^2 - 2n + 1}{2},$$

giving $E[A^*] \leq \frac{2n - 1}{n} < 2$

technique introduced in this paper to obtain a broad generalization of Theorem 1.

Acknowledgement

Thanks to Colin McDiarmid for suggesting a major simplification in the proof.

References

[1]   G. B. Dantzig, *Linear Programming and Extensions*, Princeton University Press (1963).

[2]   M. E. Dyer, A. M. Frieze and C. J. H. McDiarmid, "On Linear Programs with Random Objective Functions," private communication (1984).

[3]   A. Lazarus, *The Assignment Problem with Uniform (0,1) Cost Matrix*, B. A. Thesis, Department of Mathematics, Princeton University (1979).

[4]   D. W. Walkup, "On the Expected Value of a Random Assignment Problem," *SIAM J. Computing* 8, 440-442 (1979).

The Principal Partition of Vertex-Weighted Graphs and Its Applications

Takao Ozawa

Department of Electrical Engineering

Kyoto University

Kyoto 606, Japan

Yoji Kajitani and Shuichi Ueno

Department of Electrical and Electronic Engineering

Tokyo Institute of Technology

Tokyo 152, Japan

Abstract   The principal partition of vertex-weighted graphs is utilized to solve certain assignment problems or flow problems which are formulated using such graphs. The well-known labeling algorithm or labyrinth algorithm for augmenting flows is used to find the principal partition and to solve the first three problems. The fourth problem which is originated from a routing problem in three-dimensional integrated circuits, requires, in addition to the flow augmentation step, a step of finding an optimal flow assignment for a part of the graph.

1. Introduction.

The principal partition introduced by Kishi and Kajitani is a partition of a graph into three parts satisfying certain minimality

DISCRETE ALGORITHMS AND
COMPLEXITY

5

conditions with respect to a pair of spanning trees in the graph.[1] It has been generalized by Bruno and Weinberg[2] and further by Tomizawa[3] and Narayanan[4] to a partition of a graph or a matroid into more than three parts. Further extensions of the concept and various applications have been presented by many authors. An excellent survey of results on the principal partition from a point of view of maximization/minimization of supermodular/submodular functions was given by Tomizawa and Fujishige.[5]

In this paper we utilize the techniques for obtaining the general principal partition to solve certain assignment problems or flow problems which are formulated using vertex weighted-graphs. The weights given to vertices represent assignment or flow requirements, and minimization of an index is sought under the constraint that all the requirements be satisfied. This index represents the number of machines if the problems are regarded as those of job assignment to machines, or the number of layers if the problem are regarded as those of routing wires in three-dimensional integrated circuits. The principal partition of the graphs is defined with respect to the weights and the index.

Our problems are formulated using vertex-weighted graphs as follows.

Problem 1. Let G be an undirected graph with vertex set V and edge set E. Each vertex v in V is given a weight $w(v)$, a non-negative integer. Let $A(v)$ denote the set of edges which are incident to vertex v in V. Each vertex v in V is assigned to edges in $A(v)$ in such a way that the total number of assignments of v is equal to $w(v)$. The multiple use of edges is allowed, and both of the end-vertices of an edge can be assigned to the edge. The total number of assignments to edge e is called the multiplicity of assignments to e and is denoted by $m(e)$. The maximum of $m(e)$ taken over all edges in E is call the multiplicity of G and is denoted by $m(G)$.

The problem is to find an overall assignment of vertices to edges which achieves the minimum of m(G).

The number of assignments to an edge and thus m(G) is a non-negative integer. For example if G and the weights of vertices are as shown in Fig. 1 (a), we can get an overall assignment of vertices to edges as indicated by the figures attached to the edges. Thus m(1)=6+6=12, m(2)= 7+0=7, m(3)=7+2=9, m(4)=6+1=7, m(5)=2+2=4 and m(G)=12. Another example of assignment is given in Fig. 1 (b). This assignment gives the minimum of m(G) of all possible overall assignments, since the total of weights is 20+12+3+4=39 and there are five edges and m(G)$\geq$39/5.

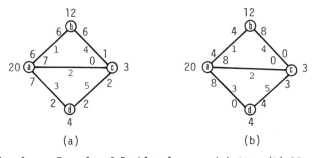

(a)   (b)

Fig. 1   Example of Problem 1.   w(a)=20, w(b)=12,
    w(c)=3, w(d)=4. (a) m(1)=12, m(2)=7, m(3)=9, m(4)=7,
    m(5)=4. (b) m(1)=8, m(2)=8, m(3)=8, m(4)=8, m(5)=7.

Problem 2. Let G be a bipartite graph with vertex sets V and U, and let A(v) be the set of vertices in U which are adjacent to vertex v in V. For vertex v in V a weight w(v), a non-negative integer, is specified. Vertex v in V is assigned to vertices in A(v) so that the total number of assignments of v is equal to w(v). The total number of assignments to vertex u in U is denoted by m(u), and the maximum of m(u) taken over all vertices of U is denoted by m(G). The problem is to find an overall assignment of vertices in V to vertices in U such that the minimum of m(G) is attained.

Problem 1 can be regarded as a special case of Problem 2. In other words, Problem 1 can be converted to a problem on a bipartite graph as follows. Let a vertex v in V and a vertex u in U of the bipartite graph correspond to a vertex v and an edge e, respectively, in the graph defined for Problem 1, and let u be adjacent to v if and only if e is incident to v in the graph for Problem 1. Each vertex in U of the bipartite graph has exactly two adjacent vertices in V.

Problems 1 and 2 can be viewed as supply-and-demand problems of single commodity where only the demands are specified and the maximum of the supplies are to be minimized.

Problem 2 can be extended to a problem in a directed graph with three vertex sets V, U and P. Let us state Problem 3 using the term "flow" instead of "assignment". The sources of flows are vertices of V and sinks are those of U. The flows through the edges of the graph take integer values.

Problem 3. Let G be a directed graph with three vertex sets V, U and P. The flows originating at a vertex v in V go through vertices in P and terminate at vertices in U. For each vertex v in V a weight w(v), a non-negative integer, is specified and the total of the flows originating at v must be w(v). The total of flows going through a vertex p in P and the total of flows terminating at a vertex u in U are denoted by m(p) and m(u) respectively. The maximum of m(p) and m(u) taken over all vertices of P and U is denoted by m(G). The problem is to find an overall flow distribution in G which achieves the minimum of m(G).

The flows going through a vertex in P must satisfy the flow conservation law. The above problem is closely related to the independent-flow problem solved by Fujishige.[6]

We further introduce a graph G with three sets V, U and Q of vertices. The roles of vertices in V and U are essentially the same, respectively, as those of Problem 3, and flows in G take integer values.

Problem 4. Let G be a directed graph with three vertex sets V, U and Q.
Vertex set V is constituted by three subsets V_1, V_2 and V_3. A vertex q
in Q has two sets of incoming edges and a set of outgoing edges as
illustrated in Fig. 2. The first set consists of two incoming edges
(called upper edges hereafter) from vertices in V_1, the second set
consists of two incoming edges(called lower edges hereafter) from vertices in V_2, and the third set consists of a single outgoing edge to a
vertex in U. G has the form as illustrated in Fig. 4. Each vertex v in V
is given a weight w(v), a non-negative integer, and the total of flows
originating at v must be w(v). The flows coming into q through the upper
edges are added and those through the lower edges are added separately.
The larger of the two sums thus attained becomes the flow of the outgoing
edge, which is defined to be the multiplicity of q. The multiplicity m(u)
of a vertex u in U is the total of its incoming flows, and the multiplicity of G is the maximum of m(u) taken over all u in U. The problem is to
find an overall distribution of flows which minimizes m(G).

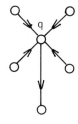

Fig. 2 A Q vertex.

2. The Principal Partition of Vertex-Weighted Graphs and Solution

Algorithms For Problem 2

Since Problem 1 can be regarded as a special case of Problem 2, let us now consider Problem 2. (The principal partition of the graph defined for Problem 1 has its own meaning, though.) Let V_s be a subset of V and let us define:

$$A(V_s) := \bigcup_{v \in V_s} A(v), \quad a(V_s) := |A(V_s)|, \quad w(V_s) := \sum_{v \in V_s} w(v). \qquad (2.1)$$

$$i(V_s) := \lceil w(V_s)/a(V_s) \rceil. \qquad (2.2)$$

(In general $|A|$ is the cardinality of A, and $\lceil x \rceil$ is the least integer not less than x.) We call $i(V_s)$ the assignment index of V_s.

Let min(G) be the minimum of m(G). Then we have:

Theorem 1.

$$\min(G) = \max_{V_s \subseteq V} i(V_s) \qquad (2.3)$$

Obviously $w(V_s) \leq \min(G) \cdot a(V_s)$ must hold for any $V_s \subseteq V$. The maximum of the assignment index and an overall assignment satisfying the condition of the problem can be obtained at the same time by using algorithms for determining the principal partition of G, which we are going to describe.

First we define a function

$$\sigma(V_s, c) := w(V_s) - c \cdot a(V_s) \qquad (2.4)$$

where c is a positive constant. It is easy to show that $\sigma(V_s, c)$ for a fixed value of c is a supermodular function of V_s, and then it is known that there exist a unique minimal subset and a unique maximal subset of V for which the maximum of σ is attained.[5] Here the maximum is taken over all subsets of V. These two subsets define a partition of V into three subsets, and the tri-partition of V induces a tri-partition of U, and thus of G. The partition depends on the value of c. This partition of G is called the principal (tri-)partition of G with respect to w and c, and the three subgraphs are called the principal subgraphs.

Principal Partition of G:

$V^+(c)$:= the minimal subset of V such that

$$\sigma(V^+,c) = \max_{V_s \subseteq V} \sigma(V_s,c).$$ (2.5)

$V^-(c)$:= the minimal subset of V such that

$$\sigma(V-V^-,c) = \max_{V_s \subseteq V} \sigma(V_s,c).$$ (2.6)

$$V^0(c) := V - V^+(c) - V^-(c).$$ (2.7)

$$U^+ := A(V^+), \quad U^- := U - A(V-V^-), \quad U^0 := U - U^+ - U^-.$$ (2.8)

G^+(resp. G^-; G^0):= the subgraph of G which consists of the vertices of V^+(resp. V^-; V^0) and U^+(resp. U^-; U^0) and the edges connecting them.

Note that $V-V^-$ is the maximal subset for which the maximum of σ is attained. It may happen that one or even two of $V^+(c)$, $V^-(c)$ and $V^0(c)$ are null sets.

It may be possible that each of G^+ and G^- is further partitioned in the same way as above but with respect to a different value of c, and it may be possible the resulting subgraphs are further partitioned, and so on. In this way we get the general principal partition of the original graph G.[3] To solve Problem 2 we only have to consider the partition of G^+, and min(G) can be determined by the following algorithm. In this algorithm GG(VV,UU) is a subgraph of G which is constituted by the vertices of subsets VV V and UU U and the edges connecting them.

Algorithm SOL-2

Step 1. Set $GG(VV,UU):=G(V,U)$ and $c:=i(V)$.

Step 2. Obtain the principal subgraph $GG^+(VV^+(c),UU^+(c))$ of $GG(VV,UU)$.

Step 3. If $GG^+(VV^+(c),UU^+(c))$ is a null graph, then return $c(=min(G))$

and stop. Otherwise, set $GG(VV,UU):=GG^+(VV^+(c),UU^+(c))$,

$c:=i(VV^+(c))$ and go to Step 2.

Note that the value of c used in SOL-2 is the average of weights per vertex in UU. It is a lower bound for the multiplicity, and there may be cases where an overall flow assignment satisfying the condition of the problem is possible with this lower bound. Now one way to obtain GG^+ of Step 2 is as follows.

Algorithm PARTITION

Step 1. Construct a flow network by adding to GG a source vertex s, a sink vertex t, edges from s to the vertices of VV and edges from vertices of UU to t. The capacity of edge (s,v) for v∈VV is set to w(v) and the capacity of edge (u,t) for u∈UU is set to c. The capacity of an edge originally in GG is set to a very large positive integer.[7]

Step 2. Obtain a maximal flow from s to t through the flow network by using the well-known labeling algorithm or labyrinth algorithm. (The algorithm searches for an augmenting flow by labeling vertices. It stops when the search ends without breakthrough to the sink and no more augmentation is possible. At this time a maximal flow is obtained.). The labeled vertices in VV and UU constitute VV^+ and UU^+, and the flows through the remaining vertices in VV and

UU give desired assignments.

A part of an optimal overall flow assignment is obtained at Step 2 of PARTITION at each iteration of Step 2 in SOL-2. Algorithm SOL-2 is applied to the example of Fig. 3 (a). For the first iteration c=36/6=6 and we get VV^+={3,4}, UU^+={3,4,5} and GG^+ as shown in Fig. 3 (b). For the second iteration c=27/3=9 and we get VV^+={4}, UU^+={4,5} and GG^+ as shown in Fig.3 (c). Finally for the third iteration c=10 and VV^+=ϕ, and thus min(G)=10. The figures attached to the edges are the flows(assignments of vertices in V to those in U) determined by Algorithm PARTITION.

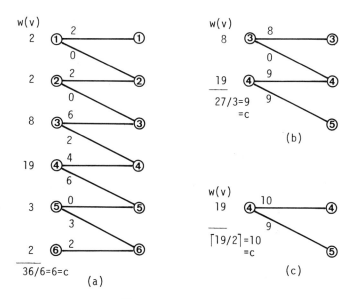

Fig. 3   Example of Problem 2.

We can solve Problem 3 similarly to Problem 2. We construct a flow network by adding to G a source vertex s and a sink vertex t. Edges connecting s and vertices of V and those connecting t and vertices of U are also added.

Theorem 2

$$\min(G) = \max_{V_s \subseteq V} i(V_s) \quad \text{where} \quad i(V_s) := \lceil w(V_s)/k(V_s) \rceil \tag{2.9}$$

and $k(V_s)$ is the vertex connectivity between vertices s and t of the subnetwork which consists only of vertices reachable from s through the vertices in V_s and edges connecting them.

The minimum value min(G) and flows satisfying the conditions given in Problem 3 can be obtained by algorithms the same as SOL-2 and PARTITION except the graph which is dealt with in the algorithms. The bipartite graph of Problem 2 is replaced by the graph defined for Problem 3.

3. Flow Assignment In The Graph Defined For Problem 4: Part 1

The main frame of the solution algorithm for Problem 4 is the same as Algorithm SOL-2 for Problem 2. Initially vertices of V and those of U are regarded as sources and sinks of flows, respectively. At a source it is required that the total of flows outgoing from it be equal to its weight. The maximum amount of flows which can be absorbed by a sink is called the capacity of a sink. Thus, the constraint at a sink is that the total of flows coming into it must not exceed its capacity. The capacity of sinks is set uniformly to c, and c is increased step by step until the source requirement and sink constraint are satisfied at all sources and sinks respectively. Because of the special structure of the graph defined for Problem 4, we take a different approach to Problem 4 from that to Problem 2. As is stated in Algorithm SOL-4 below, sources and sinks are redefined in the steps which follow the initialization steps.

A vertex in Q(resp. V_1; V_2; U) is called a Q(resp. V_1; V_2; U) vertex. Let n be the number of Q vertices, that is, $|Q| = n$. Then $|V_1| = n+1$,

$|V_2|=n+1$ and $|U|=n$. Q(resp. V_1; V_2; U) vertices are labeled q_1, q_2, .., q_n(resp. v_{11}, v_{12}, .., v_{1n+1}; v_{21}, v_{22}, ..., v_{2n+1}; u_1, u_2, .., u_n) from left to right. The directed edge from vertex x to vertex y is denoted by (x,y), and the flow assigned to edge (x,y) is denoted by f(x,y). The subgraph of G consisting of the vertices in Q, V_1, V_2 and U and the edges incident to Q vertices is denoted by G_Q. (To get G_Q the vertices of V_3 are removed from G together with the edges incident to them. See Fig. 5).

The following SOL-4 is a solution algorithm to Problem 4.

Algorithm SOL-4

Step 1.   Determined flows in G_Q so that the source requirement is satisfied at every vertex in V_1 and V_2 and the total of flows from G_Q is minimum.

Step 2.   Determine the sink capacity c of vertices in U.

Step 3.   Assign flows to edges from vertices in V_3 to vertices in U so that the source requirement is satisfied at every vertex in V_3.

Step 4.   If none of the total flows going into vertices in U exceeds c, stop.

Step 5.   Redefine sources and sinks and augment flows.

Step 6.   If the source requirement is satisfied at every redefined source, stop. Otherwise determine new sink capacity c and go to Step 5.

Steps 1, 2 and 3 are the initialization steps. Flows are assigned to edges so that the source requirement is satisfied at every vertex in V. In general, then, the sink constraint is violated at some vertices in U. These vertices are redefined as new sources whose source requirement is the amount of flow exceeding the sink capacity. Flow augmentation from new sources to sinks is sought at Step 5. Steps 5 and 6 are repeated similarly to Steps 2 and 3 of Algorithm SOL-2. The details of the steps are given below.

<u>Step 1</u>. First let us consider Step 1 of SOL-4 and present two algorithms for determining a minimum flow assignment in G_Q. Let us define

$$d(j):=f(v_{1j},q_j)-f(v_{2j},q_j) \tag{3.1}$$

$$e(j):=f(v_{1j+1},q_j)-f(v_{2j+1},q_j) \tag{3.2}$$

$$g(j):=f(v_{1j},q_j)+f(v_{1j+1},q_j)-(f(v_{2j},q_j)+f(v_{2j+1},q_j)) \tag{3.3}$$

$$f(Q_s):= \sum_{q_j \in Q_s} f(q_j,u_j). \tag{3.4}$$

It can be easily shown that for any overall flow assignment

$$f(Q)= w(V_1)- \sum_{g(j)<0} g(j) = w(V_2)+ \sum_{g(j)>0} g(j). \tag{3.5}$$

The following algorithm MINIQFLOW-R determines flows in G_Q from left to right. The readers are referred to Fig. 4 for the suffixes of vertices.

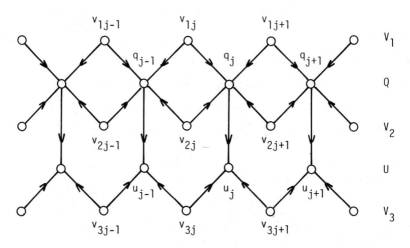

Fig. 4   Graph for Problem 4.

Algorithm MINIQFLOW-R

Step 1.   Set $j:=1$ and

$$f(v_{11},q_1):=w(v_{11}), \ f(v_{21},q_1):=w(v_{21}),$$
$$f(v_{1n+1},q_n):=w(v_{1n+1}), \ f(v_{2n+1},q_n):=w(v_{2n+1}).$$

Step 2.   If $d(j)<0$, then go to Step 4-1.

Step 3-1. $\{d(j)\geqq 0\}$ Set

$$f(v_{1j+1},q_j):=0, \ f(v_{1j+1},q_{j+1}):=w(v_{1j+1}), \ f(q_j,u_j):=f(v_{1j},q_j).$$

Step 3-2.   If $d(j)<w(v_{2j+1})$, then set

$$f(v_{2j+1},q_j):=d(j), \ f(v_{2j+1},q_{j+1}):=w(v_{2j+1})-d(j). \ \{Note:g(j)=0\}$$

Otherwise set

$$f(v_{2j+1},q_j):=w(v_{2j+1}), \ f(v_{2j+1},q_{j+1}):=0. \ \{Note:g(j)>0\}$$

Step 3-3.   Go to Step 5.

Step 4-1. $\{d(j)<0\}$ Set

$$f(v_{2j+1},q_j):=0, \ f(v_{2j+1},q_{j+1}):=w(v_{2j+1}), \ f(q_j,u_j):=f(v_{2j},q_j).$$

Step 4-2.   If $-d(j)<w(v_{1j+1})$, then set

$$f(v_{1j+1},q_j):=-d(j), \ f(v_{1j+1},q_{j+1}):=w(v_{1j+1})+d(j). \ \{Note:g(j)=0\}$$

Otherwise set

$$f(v_{1j+1},q_j):=w(v_{1j+1}), \ f(v_{1j+1},q_{j+1}):=0. \ \{Note:g(j)<0\}$$

Step 5.   If $j=n-1$, set

$$f(q_n,u_n):=\max(f(v_{1n},q_n)+f(v_{1n+1}\cdot q_n),f(v_{2n},q_n)+f(_{2n+1},q_n))$$

and stop. Otherwise set $j:=j+1$ and go to step 2.

The following algorithm MINIQFLOW-L determines flows in G_Q from right to left.

Algorithm MINIQFLOW-L

Step 1.   Set $j:=n$ and

$$f(v_{11},q_1):=w(v_{11}), \ f(v_{21},q_1):=w(v_{21}),$$
$$f(v_{1n+1},q_n):=w(v_{1n+1}), \ f(v_{2n+1},q_n):=w(v_{2n+1}).$$

Step 2.   If $e(j)<0$, then go to Step 4-1.

Step 3-1. $\{e(j)\geq0\}$ Set

$$f(v_{1j},q_j):=0, \; f(v_{1j},q_{j-1}):=w(v_{1j}), \; f(q_j,u_j):=f(v_{1j+1},q_j).$$

Step 3-2.   If $e(j)<w(v_{2j})$, then set

$$f(v_{2j},q_j):=e(j), \; f(v_{2j},q_{j-1}):=w(v_{2j})-e(j). \; \{Note:g(j)=0\}$$

Otherwise set

$$f(v_{2j},q_j):=w(v_{2j}), \; f(v_{2j},q_{j-1}):=0. \; \{Note:g(j)>0\}$$

Step 3-3.   Go to Step 5.

Step 4-1. $\{e(j)<0\}$ Set

$$f(v_{2j},q_j):=0, \; f(v_{2j},q_{j-1}):=w(v_{2j}), \; f(q_j,u_j):=f(v_{2j+1},q_j).$$

Step 4-2.   If $-e(j)<w(v_{1j})$, then set

$$f(v_{1j},q_j):=-e(j), \; f(v_{1j},q_{j-1}):=w(v_{1j})+e(j). \; \{Note:g(j)=0\}$$

Otherwise set

$$f(v_{1j},q_j):=w(v_{1j}), \; f(v_{1j},q_{j-1}):=0. \; \{Note:g(j)<0\}$$

Step 5.   If $j=2$, set

$$f(q_1,u_1):=\max(f(v_{12},q_1)+f(v_{11},q_1),f(v_{22},q_1)+f(v_{21},q_1))$$

and stop. Otherwise set $j:=j-1$ and go to step 2.

Examples of flow assignment obtained by MINIQFLOW-R and MINIQFLOW-L are shown Fig. 5 (a). We have:

Theorem 3.

The total flow $f(Q)$ of the flow assignments obtained by MINIQFLOW-R (or MINIQFLOW-L) is minimum.

(proof)   If $g(j)>0$(resp. <0) for all $j=1,2,..,n$, then $f(Q)=w(V_1)$(resp. $w(V_2)$ from eq.(3.5), and thus $f(Q)$ is minimum. Suppose there exist j and k such that $g(j)>0$, $g(j+1)=0$, .., $g(k)<0$. We see that $g(j)$ and $-g(k)$ and thus $f(Q)$ could be decreased by $\Delta f>0$ if it were possible to change flows through upper edges as follows:

$f(v_{1m},q_{m-1}):=f(v_{1m},q_{m-1})-\Delta f$, $f(v_{1m},q_m):=f(_{1m},q_m)+\Delta f$ for $m=j+1,..,k$;

or to change flows through lower edges as follows:

$f(v_{2m},q_{m-1}):=f(v_{2m},q_{m-1})+\Delta f$, $f(v_{2m},q_m):=f(v_{2m},q_m)-\Delta f$ for $m=j+1,..,k$.

This flow change, however, is not possible because $g(j)>0$ and thus $f(v_{1j+1},q_j)=0$ and $f(v_{2j+1},q_{j+1})=0$ are assigned by MINIQFLOW-R(Steps 3-1, 3-2). Likewise suppose there exist j and k such that $g(j)<0$, $g(j+1)=0$, .., $g(k)>0$, Then $-g(j)$ and $g(k)$ and thus $f(Q)$ could be decreased by $\Delta f>0$ if it were possible to change flows through upper edges as follows:

$f(v_{1m},q_{m-1}):=f(v_{im},q_{m-1})+\Delta f$, $f(v_{1m},q_m):=f(_{1m},q_m)-\Delta f$ for $m=j+1,..,k$;

or to change flows through lower edges as follows:

$f(v_{2m},q_{m-1}):=f(v_{2m},q_{m-1})-\Delta f$, $f(v_{2m},q_m):=f(v_{2m},q_m)+\Delta f$ for $m=j+1,..,k$.

This flow change is not possible because $g(j)<0$ and thus $f(v_{2j+1},q_j)=0$ and $f(v_{1j+1},q_{j+1})=0$(Steps 4-1, 4-2). Therefore in any case $f(Q)$ cannot be decreased.

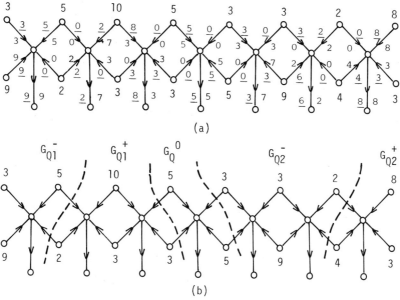

(a)

(b)

Fig. 5 (a) Flows assigned by MINIQFLOW-R and MINIQFLOW-L(smaller figures with and without a underline, respectively). (b) The principal partition of G_Q.

Using the two different overall flow assignments determined by MINIQFLOW-R and MINIQFLOW-L, we can get a partition of G_Q into G_Q^+, G_Q^- and G_Q^0 as follows. This partition is the principal partition of G_Q.

Principal Partition of G_Q.

G_Q^+: A subgraph of G_Q^+ is constituted by vertices q_j, q_{j+1}, $\cdots$, q_k together with vertices v_{1j+1}, $\cdots$,v_{1k}; v_{2j}, v_{2j+1}, $\cdots$, v_{2k}, v_{2k+1}; u_j, u_{j+1}, $\cdots$, u_k (and the edges connecting these vertices) satisfying the following conditions:

[1+] $f(v_{1j},q_j)=0$, $f(v_{2j},q_{j-1})=0$, $f(v_{1k+1},q_k)=0$, $f(v_{2k+1},q_{k+1})=0$ are obtained by both of the algorithms,

[2+] $g(m)\geqq 0$ for m=j,..,k-1 and g(k)>0 are obtained by MINIQFLOW-R, and

[3+] $g(j)>0$ and $g(m)\geqq 0$ for m=j+1,..,k are obtained by MINIQFLOW-L.

There can be more than one set of Q vertices q_j, q_{j+1}, $\cdots$, q_k satisfying the above condition, and G_Q^+ is constituted by the subgraphs defined by such sets. A special case of G_Q^+ is that the left or right end of G_Q is included in it. In this case the zero-flow condition [1+] for $q_j(j=1)$ or $q_k(k=n)$ is neglected.

G_Q^-: A subgraph of G_Q^- is constituted by vertices q_j, q_{j+1}, $\cdots$, q_k together with vertices v_{1j}, v_{1j+1}, $\cdots$, v_{1k}, v_{1k+1}; v_{2j+1}, $\cdots$, v_{2k}; u_j, u_{j+1}, $\cdots$, u_k (and the edges connecting these vertices) satisfying the following conditions:

[1-] $f(v_{1j},q_{j-1})=0$, $f(v_{2j},q_j)=0$, $f(v_{1k+1},q_{k+1})=0$, $f(v_{2k+1},q_k)=0$ are obtained by both of the algorithms,

[2-] $g(m)\leqq 0$ for m=j,..,k-1 and g(k)<0 are obtained by MINIQFLOW-R, and

[3-] $g(j)<0$ and $g(m)\leqq 0$ for m=j+1,..,k are obtained by MINIQFLOW-L.

There can be more than one set of Q vertices q_j, q_{j+1}, $\cdots$, q_k satisfying the above conditions, and G_Q^- is constituted by the subgraphs defined by such sets. A special case of G_Q^- is that the left or right

end of G_Q is included in it. In this case the zero-flow condition [1-]
for $q_j(j=1)$ or $q_k(k=n)$ is neglected.

G_Q^0:

$$G_Q^0 := G_Q - G_Q^+ - G_Q^-. \tag{3.6}$$

If q_j, q_{j+1}, .., q_k are Q vertices belonging to a subgraph of G_Q^0,
then

[1-01] $f(v_{1j}, q_{j-1})=0$, $f(v_{2j}, q_j)=0$, $f(v_{1k+1}, q_k)=0$, $f(v_{2k+1}, q_{k+1})=0$ and
$g(m)=0$ for $m=j, j+1, .., k$ are obtained by both of the algorithms;

or

[1-02] $f(v_{1j}, q_j)=0$, $f(v_{2j}, q_{j-1})=0$, $f(v_{1k+1}, q_{k+1})=0$, $f(v_{2k+1}, q_k)=0$ and
$g(m)=0$ for $m=j, j+1, .., k$ are obtained by both of the algorithms.

[1-01](resp. [1-02]) holds when q_{j-1} belongs to G_Q^+(resp. G_Q^-) and
q_{k+1} belongs to G_Q^-(resp. G_Q^+).

For a subgraph of G_Q^+

$$\sum_{m=j+1}^{k} w(v_{1m}) = \sum_{m=j+1}^{k} f(v_{1m}, q_m) + \sum_{m=j}^{k-1} f(v_{1m+1}, q_m)$$

$$> \sum_{m=j}^{k} f(v_{2m}, q_m) + \sum_{m=j}^{k} f(v_{2m+1}, q_m) = \sum_{m=j}^{k+1} w(v_{2m}) \tag{3.7}$$

holds. Note that the number of V_1 vertices in this subgraph is less than
that of V_2 vertices, but the total of the weights given to the former
vertices is larger than that given to the latter vertices.

For a subgraph of G_Q^-

$$\sum_{m=j}^{k+1} w(v_{1m}) = \sum_{m=j}^{k} f(v_{1m}, q_m) + \sum_{m=j}^{k} f(v_{1m+1}, q_m)$$

$$< \sum_{m=j+1}^{k} f(v_{2m}, q_m) + \sum_{m=j}^{k-1} f(v_{2m+1}, q_m) = \sum_{m=j+1}^{k} w(v_{2m}) \tag{3.8}$$

holds. For this subgraph the number of V_1 vertices is more than that of V_2 vertices, but the total of the weights given to the former vertices is smaller than that given to the latter vertices.

An example of the principal partition of G_Q into G_Q^+, G_Q^- and G_Q^0 is shown in Fig. 5 (b). The partition is indicated by the dotted lines. Each of G_Q^+ and G_Q^- is constituted by two subgraphs.

4. Flow Assignment In The Graph Defined For Problem 4: Part 2.

In this section we present details of Steps 2, 3, 5 and 6 of SOL-4.

Step 2. After we have assigned flows to the edges in G_Q, we set the sink capacity of vertex u in U to

$$c := \lceil (f(Q) + w(V_3)) / |U| \rceil \tag{4.1}$$

where $f(Q)$ is the minimum flow value obtained by Algorithm MINIQFLOW-R or MINIQFLOW-L.

Step 3. This step of SOL-4 can be done almost in an arbitrary way. Of course an overall flow assignment such that the sink constraint is satisfied at as many vertices of U as possible, is desirable.

Step 5. For Step 5 of flow augmentation we redefine sources and sinks as follows. First, a vertex in U is regarded as a source or a sink depending on whether or not the total of flows coming into it exceeds its capacity c. Thus, if the total of flows into a vertex u_j exceeds c, then u_j is regarded as a source with the source requirement of

$$s(u_j) := f(q_j, u_j) + f(v_{3j}, u_j) + f(v_{3j+1}, u_j) - c, \tag{4.2}$$

and otherwise it is regarded as a sink with the sink capacity of

$$t(u_j) := c - f(q_j, u_j) - f(v_{3j}, u_j) - f(v_{3j+1}, u_j). \tag{4.3}$$

Second, suppose, for some flow assignment in G_Q, $g(j)>0$ holds at vertex q_j in Q. Then the flow coming into q_j through a lower edge, that is, $f(v_{2j},q_j)$ or $f(v_{2j+1},q_j)$ can be increased without increasing the outgoing flow $f(q_j,u_j)$ from q_j. In order to handle such an increase of a flow we regard vertex q_j as a special sink into which only flows from lower edges can go. The capacity of this sink is

$$t(q_j):=g(j). \tag{4.4}$$

Dually, if $g(j)<0$ for q_j, then we regard q_j a sink into which only flows through upper edges can go. The capacity of this sink is

$$t(q_j):=-g(j). \tag{4.5}$$

In the following $g(j)$ is a variable and so is the capacity of sink q_j.

A source whose source requirement has not been satisfied($s>0$) is called an unsatisfied source, and a sink which can absorb more flows($t>0$) is called an unsaturated sink.

Let $G_R(j)$(resp. $G_L(j)$) be the subgraph which is constituted by vertices u_j, q_j, v_{1j+1}, v_{2j+1}, v_{3j+1}, u_{j+1} and q_{j+1}(resp. u_j, q_j, v_{1j}, v_{2j}, v_{3j}, u_{j-1} and q_{j-1}) and the edges connecting these vertices. $G_R(j)$ or $G_L(j)$ is called a section of G.

Flow augmentation in G is classified into two categories. The flow augmentation of the first(resp. second) category proceeds in G from an unsatisfied source to an unsaturated sink in only one direction, to the right or left(resp. both directions, to the right and left.). The flow augmentation of the first category is tried first and then that of the second category.

AUG-1, AUG-2, AUG-11 and AUG-12 given below belong to the first category. AUG-1(R), AUG-2(R), AUG-11(R) and AUG-12(R)(resp. AUG-1(L), AUG-2(L), AUG-11(L) and AUG-12(L)) are flow augmentation for a section $G_R(j)$(resp. $G_L(j)$), beginning at u_j and ending at u_{j+1}(resp. u_{j-1}). (R)(resp. (L)) indicates flow augmentation which proceeds to the right (resp. left). When a breakthrough from an unsatisfied source to an unsaturated sink occurs, the flow augmentaton is repeated for the sections involved. Different types of flow augmentation may be combined. Thus, for example, AUG-1(R) may be followed by AUG-2(R) which, in turn, may be followed by AUG-11(R). The search for a breakthrough proceeds from u_j to u_{j+1}(resp. to u_{j-1}). If u_{j+1}(resp. u_{j-1}) is a sink, it terminates with breakthrough. Otherwise, it proceeds from u_{j+1} to u_{j+2}(resp. u_{j-1} to u_{j-2}), and so on, if any of the conditions specified in AUG-1(R), AUG-2 (R), AUG-11(R) and AUG-12(R)(resp. AUG-1(L), AUG-2(L), AUG-11(L) and AUG-12(L)) is satisfied. If none of the specified conditions is satisfied, it terminates without breakthrough.

AUG-1.

(R) Condition: $f(v_{3j+1},u_j)>0$.

$f(v_{3j+1},u_j):=f(v_{3j+1},u_j)-\Delta f$, $f(v_{3j+1},u_{j+1}):=f(v_{3j+1},u_{j+1})+\Delta f$.

(L) Condition: $f(v_{3j},u_j)>0$.

$f(v_{3j},u_j):=f(v_{3j},u_j)-\Delta f$, $f(v_{3j},u_{j-1}):=f(v_{3j},u_{j-1})+\Delta f$.

AUG-2.

(R) Condition: $f(v_{1j+1},q_j)>0$ and $f(v_{2j+1},q_j)>0$.

$f(q_j,u_j):=f(q_j,u_j)-\Delta f$,

$f(v_{1j+1},q_j):=f(v_{1j+1},q_j)-\Delta f$, $f(v_{1j+1},q_{j+1}):=f(v_{1j+1},q_{j+1})+\Delta f$,

$f(v_{2j+1},q_j):=f(v_{2j+1},q_j)-\Delta f$, $f(v_{2j+1},q_{j+1}):=f(v_{2j+1},q_{j+1})+\Delta f$,

$f(q_{j+1},u_{j+1}):=f(q_{j+1},u_{j+1})+\Delta f$.

(L) Condition: $f(v_{1j},q_j)>0$ and $f(v_{2j},q_j)>0$.

$f(q_j,u_j):=f(q_j,u_j)-\Delta f$,

$f(v_{1j},q_j):=f(v_{1j},q_j)-\Delta f$, $f(v_{1j},q_{j-1}):=f(v_{1j},q_{j-1})+\Delta f$,

$f(v_{2j},q_j):=f(v_{2j},q_j)-\Delta f$, $f(v_{2j},q_{j-1}):=f(v_{2j},q_{j-1})+\Delta f$,

$f(q_{j-1},u_{j-1}):=f(q_{j-1},u_{j-1})+\Delta f$.

<u>AUG-11.</u>

(R) Condition: $g(j)>0$, and $f(v_{1j+1},q_j)>0$.

$f(q_j,u_j):=f(q_j,u_j)-\Delta f, \quad g(j):=g(j)-\Delta f,$

$f(v_{1j+1},q_j):=f(v_{1j+1},q_j)-\Delta f, \; f(v_{1j+1},q_{j+1}):=f(v_{1j+1},q_{j+1})+\Delta f,$

$f(q_{j+1},u_{j+1}):=f(q_{j+1},u_{j+1})+\Delta f, \; g(j+1):=g(j+1)+\Delta f.$

(L) Condition: $g(j)>0$ and $f(v_{1j},q_j)>0$.

$f(q_j,u_j):=f(q_j,u_j)-\Delta f, \quad g(j):=g(j)-\Delta f,$

$f(v_{1j},q_j):=f(v_{1j},q_j)-\Delta f, \; f(v_{1j},q_{j-1}):=f(v_{1j},q_{j-1})+\Delta f,$

$f(q_{j-1},u_{j-1}):=f(q_{j-1},u_{j-1})+\Delta f, \; g(j-1):=g(j-1)+\Delta f.$

<u>AUG-12.</u>

(R) Condition: $g(j)<0$, and $f(v_{2j+1},q_j)>0$.

$f(q_j,u_j):=f(q_j,u_j)-\Delta f, \quad g(j):=g(j)+\Delta f,$

$f(v_{2j+1},q_j):=f(v_{2j+1},q_j)-\Delta f, \; f(v_{2j+1},q_{j+1}):=f(v_{2j+1},q_{j+1})+\Delta f,$

$f(q_{j+1},u_{j+1}):=f(q_{j+1},u_{j+1})+\Delta f, \; g(j+1):=g(j+1)-\Delta f.$

(L) Condition: $g(j)<0$ and $f(v_{2j},q_j)>0$.

$f(q_j,u_j):=f(q_j,u_j)-\Delta f, \; g(j):=g(j)+\Delta f,$

$f(v_{2j},q_j):=f(v_{2j},q_j)-\Delta f, \; f(v_{2j},q_{j-1}):=f(v_{2j},q_{j-1})+\Delta f,$

$f(q_{j-1},u_{j-1}):=f(q_{j-1},u_{j-1})+\Delta f, \; g(j-1):=g(j-1)-\Delta f.$

In the above Δf is the amount of flow change, and $\Delta f>0$.

The search for breakthrough must take the following into consideration. Suppose $g(j)>0$ and AUG-11(R) is possible. Then $g(j+1)$ will be strictly positive after the flow augmentation, even if $g(j+1)=0$ at present. Thus the condition $g(j+1)>0$ at u_{j+1} will be automatically satisfied, and another AUG-11(R) can follow if $f(v_{1j+2},q_{j+1})>0$. The same can be said regarding the condition of AUG-11(L), AUG-12(R) and AUG-12 (L).

Note that if AUG-11(R)(resp. AUG-12(R)) for $G_R(j)$ is followed by another AUG-11(R)(resp. AUG-12(R)) for $G_R(j+1)$, then $f(q_{j+1}, u_{j+1})$ and $g(j+1)$ remain the same. Thus the flow augmentation essentially proceeds along the upper edges(resp. lower edges) in G_Q. The same can be said for the flow augmentation to the left.

An example of AUG-1(R)(resp. AUG-2(R); AUG-11(R); AUG-12(R)) is shown in Fig. 6(resp. Fig. 7, Fig. 8, Fig. 9). The thick lines indicate the augmenting path. The underlined figures are flows after the augmentation.

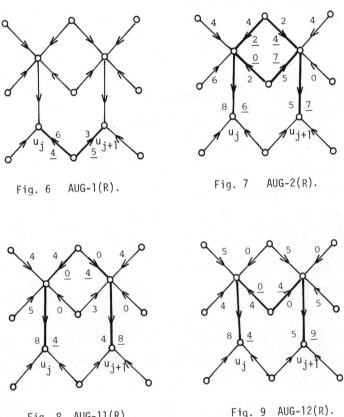

Fig. 6   AUG-1(R).   Fig. 7   AUG-2(R).

Fig. 8   AUG-11(R).   Fig. 9   AUG-12(R).

The following AUG-21, AUG-22, AUG-31 and AUG-32 belong to the second category of flow augmentation. Breakthrough to sinks, in Q or U, in both directions must occur for the flow augmentation. Aug-21 initiates flow augmentation to both directions. It may be followed by AUG-31(flow augmentation to the right by AUG-31(R), and flow augmentation to the left by AUG-31(L)). Likewise AUG-22 initiates flow augmentation to both directions, and it may be followed by AUG-32.

AUG-21

Condition: $f(v_{1j+1},q_j)>0$ and $f(v_{2j},q_j)>0$.

$f(q_j,u_j):=f(q_j,u_j)-\Delta f$,

$f(v_{1j+1},q_j):=f(v_{1j+1},q_j)-\Delta f$, $f(v_{1j+1},q_{j+1}):=f(v_{1j+1},q_{j+1})+\Delta f$,

$f(v_{2j},q_j):=f(v_{2j},q_j)-\Delta f$, $f(v_{2j},q_{j-1}):=f(v_{2j},q_{j-1})+\Delta f$,

Case 1R: If $g(j+1)\geq0$, then

$f(q_{j+1},u_{j+1}):=f(q_{j+1},u_{j+1})+\Delta f$, $g(j+1):=g(j+1)+\Delta f$;

Case 2R: If $g(j+1)<0$, Δf is absorbed by sink q_{j+1}, and

$g(j+1):=g(j+1)+\Delta f$.

Case 1L: If $g(j-1)\leq0$, then

$f(q_{j-1},u_{j-1}):=f(q_{j-1},u_{j-1})+\Delta f$, $g(j-1):=g(j-1)-\Delta f$;

Case 2L: If $g(j-1)>0$, Δf is absorbed by sink q_{j-1}, and

$g(j-1):=g(j-1)-\Delta f$.

AUG-22

Condition: $f(v_{2j+1},q_j)>0$ and $f(v_{1j},q_j)>0$.

$f(q_j,u_j):=f(q_j,u_j)-\Delta f$,

$f(v_{2j+1},q_j):=f(v_{2j+1},q_j)-\Delta f$, $f(v_{2j+1},q_{j+1}):=f(v_{2j+1},q_{j+1})+\Delta f$,

$f(v_{1j},q_j):=f(v_{1j},q_j)-\Delta f$, $f(v_{1j},q_{j-1}):=f(v_{1j},q_{j-1})+\Delta f$,

Case 1R: If $g(j+1)\leq0$, then

$f(q_{j+1},u_{j+1}):=f(q_{j+1},u_{j+1})+\Delta f$, $g(j+1):=g(j+1)-\Delta f$;

Case 2R: If $g(j+1)>0$, Δf is absorbed by sink q_{j+1}, and

$g(j+1):=g(j+1)-\Delta f$.

Case 1L: If $g(j-1)\geq0$, then

$f(q_{j-1}, u_{j-1}) := f(q_{j-1}, u_{j-1}) + \Delta f$, $g(j-1) := g(j-1) + \Delta f$;

Case 2L: If $g(j-1) < 0$, Δf is absorbed by sink q_{j-1}, and

$g(j-1) := g(j-1) + \Delta f$.

AUG-31.

(R)　Condition: $g(j) > 0$, and $f(v_{1j+1}, q_j) > 0$.

$f(q_j, u_j) := f(q_j, u_j) - \Delta f$, $g(j) := g(j) - \Delta f$,

$f(v_{1j+1}, q_j) := f(v_{1j+1}, q_j) - \Delta f$, $f(v_{1j+1}, q_{j+1}) := f(v_{1j+1}, q_{j+1}) + \Delta f$,

Case 1R: If $g(j+1) \geqq 0$, then

$f(q_{j+1}, u_{j+1}) := f(q_{j+1}, u_{j+1}) + \Delta f$, $g(j+1) := g(j+1) + \Delta f$.

Case 2R: If $g(j+1) < 0$, Δf is absorbed by sink q_{j+1}, and

$g(j+1) := g(j+1) + \Delta f$.

(L)　Condition: $g(j) < 0$ and $f(v_{2j}, q_j) > 0$.

$f(q_j, u_j) := f(q_j, u_j) - \Delta f$, $g(j) := g(j) + \Delta f$,

$f(v_{2j}, q_j) := f(v_{2j}, q_j) - \Delta f$, $f(v_{2j}, q_{j-1}) := f(v_{2j}, q_{j-1}) + \Delta f$,

Case 1L: If $g(j-1) \leqq 0$, then

$f(q_{j-1}, u_{j-1}) := f(q_{j-1}, u_{j-1}) + \Delta f$. $g(j-1) := g(j-1) - \Delta f$.

Case 2L: If $g(j-1) > 0$, Δf is absorbed by sink q_{j-1}, and

$g(j-1) := g(j-1) - \Delta f$.

AUG-32.

(R)　Condition: $g(j) < 0$, and $f(v_{2j+1}, q_j) > 0$.

$f(q_j, u_j) := f(q_j, u_j) - \Delta f$, $g(j) := g(j) + \Delta f$,

$f(v_{2j+1}, q_j) := f(v_{2j+1}, q_j) - \Delta f$, $f(v_{2j+1}, q_{j+1}) := f(v_{2j+1}, q_{j+1}) + \Delta f$,

Case 1R: If $g(j+1) \leqq 0$, then

$f(q_{j+1}, u_{j+1}) := f(q_{j+1}, u_{j+1}) + \Delta f$, $g(j+1) := g(j+1) - \Delta f$.

Case 2R: If $g(j+1) > 0$, f is absorbed by sink q_{j+1}, and

$g(j+1) := g(j+1) - \Delta f$.

(L)　Condition: $g(j) > 0$ and $f(v_{1j}, q_j) > 0$.

$f(q_j, u_j) := f(q_j, u_j) - \Delta f$, $g(j) := g(j) - \Delta f$,

$f(v_{1j},q_j):=f(v_{1j},q_j)-\Delta f,\ f(v_{1j},q_{j-1}):=f(v_{1j},q_{j-1})+\Delta f,$

Case 1L: If $g(j-1)\geqq0$, then

$f(q_{j-1},u_{j-1}):=f(q_{j-1},u_{j-1})+\Delta f.\ g(j-1):=g(j-1)+\Delta f.$

Case 2L: If $g(j-1)<0$, f is absorbed by sink q_{j-1}, and

$g(j-1):=g(j-1)+\Delta f.$

As was remarked for the flow augmentation of the first category, it may be unnecessary to check, in the search for breakthrough, the condition $g(j)>0$ or $g(j)<0$. Thus essentially the search for AUG-21 followed by AUG-31 proceeds along the upper edges in G_Q to the right and along the lower edges to the left. Likewise, the search for AUG-22 followed by AUG-32 proceeds along the lower edges in G_Q to the right and along the upper edges to the left.

An example of AUG-21 followed by AUG-31 is shown in Fig. 10. The underlined figures are flows after the augmentation.

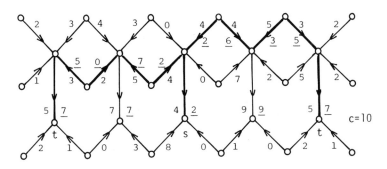

Fig. 10 AUG-21 followed by AUG-31. s: source, t: sinks.

The flow augmentation to the right(resp. the left) of AUG-21, AUG-22, AUG-31(R) or AUG-32(R)(AUG-31(L) or AUG-32(L)) may be followed by AUG-1(R)(resp. AUG-1(L)). Furthermore AUG-1 may be followed by another AUG-21 or AUG-22. An example of such flow augmentation is shown in Fig. 11. Again the underlined figures show flows after the augmentation. Note that AUG-21 or AUG-22 may create a sink at q_{j+1} or q_{j-1}.

If both of the sinks of the flow augmentation of the second category are vertices in U, the total of the flows from G_Q, that is, $f(Q)$ increases by Δf, and $f(Q)$ is no more minimum.

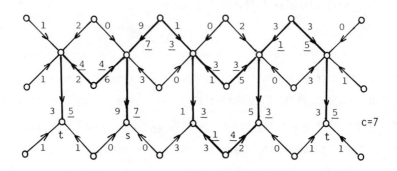

Fig. 11   AUG-21 followed by AUG-1 and AUG-21. s: source, t: sinks.

<u>Step 6.</u>   In the case of non-breakthrough, new sink capacity c should be calculated. Let U_s be the set of unsatisfied sources in U, and let

$$s(U_s) := \sum_{u_j \in U_s} s(u_j). \tag{4.6}$$

Also let U_1^+ and U_2^+ be the sets of saturated sinks in U reached by the search for the flow augmentation of the first category and second category, respectively. Then

$$c := c + \lceil s(U_s)/(|U_1^+| + 0.5|U_2^+ - U_1^+|) \rceil. \tag{4.7}$$

The reason for the coefficient 0.5 in eq.(4.7) is that the flow augmentation of the second category may require two unsaturated sinks in U.

5. Applications.

A special case of Problem 2 is the problem of scheduling unit-time parallel tasks on parallel processors.[8] A task must be assigned to a processor so that it is processed between its release time and due time. Tasks are sorted so that tasks with the same release time and due time are in one set. The vertices of V represent such task sets and the vertices of U, the time slots. The weight given to a vertex in V is the number of tasks in a task set and constant c of vertex in U is the number of processors. Graph G for this problem is a convex bipartite graph. Because of this special feature a simple algorithm for obtaining GG^+ can be constructed.

Problem 4 originated from a routing problem in three-dimensional integrated circuits. In Fig. 12 depicted is a model for this problem. The large rectangle in the figure represents a chip of a circuit. The small squares are cells (or buses) from which wires to outside the chip come out. For each cell the numbers of wires which must go to the upper edge and the lower edge of the chip, respectively, are specified. The spaces between columns of cells are routing channels where wires can go through. A wire from a cell can go through either of the vertical channels on the left and right of the cell. A vertical channel between two adjacent cells allows a single wire going through it. The circuit, however, is constituted by layers(Thus it is three-dimensional. Fig. 12 shows one layer

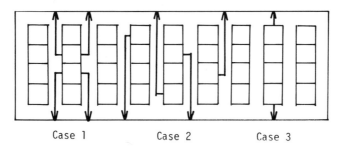

Case 1   Case 2   Case 3

Fig. 12 Chip model of 3-D integrated circuit.

only.), and therefore wires from a cell can go through channels on different layers. Let us consider a cell array of four rows and n+1 columns.

In Case 1 of Fig. 12 two wires(thick lines) can share a channel on one layer, but in Case 2 a wire occupies a channel on one layer. In Case 3 a wire requires no channel. Thus wires can be partitioned into four classes. A wire in the first class must go to the upper edge of the the chip, and can share a channel on one layer with a wire in the second class which must go to the lower edge of the chip. A wire in the third class occupies a channel by itself. A wire in the fourth class requires no channel, and can be neglected in channel assignment to wires.

A section of the graph defined for Problem 4 represents a section of the above circuits consisting of two adjacent vertical channels and a column of four cells between them. Such a section of the graph contains a V_1 vertex, a V_2 vertex, a V_3 vertex, two Q vertices and two U vertices. The V_1(resp. V_2; V_3) vertex represents the wires in the first(resp. second; third) class which belong to this section. The weight given to it is the number of such wires. The Q vertices and U vertices represent the channels. The flows through the edges represent wires assigned to channels. Then the total of flows coming into a U vertex is equal to the number of layers to let wires go through, and the minimum of $m(G)$ is the minimum number of layers to fulfil the wiring requirement.

6. Concluding Remarks.

Vertex-weghted graphs can be models of various systems. Then the fundamental technique used to attain the minimum of parameter c can be applied to minimization problems arising from such systems. The number of the iterations needed to solve problems like Problems 2 and 4 is expected to be log n in average where n is the number of vertices in V.

References

[1]   G. Kishi and Y. Kajitani, "On maximally distinct trees,"   Fifth Allerton Conference on Circuit and System Theory, pp.635-643, 1967.

[2]   J. Bruno and L. Weinberg, " The principal minors of a matroid," Linear Algebra and Its Applications, vol.4, pp.17-54, 1971.

[3]   N. Tomizawa, "Strongly irreducible matroids and principal partition of a matroid into strongly irreducible minors," Trans. Inst. Elec. Commun. Eng. of Japan, vol.J59-A, No.2, pp.83-91, 1976.

[4]   H. Narayanan, "Theory of Matroids and Network Analysis," Ph. D. Thesis, Department of Electrical Engineering, Indian Institute of Technology, Bombay, 1974.

[5]   N. Tomizawa and S. Fujishige, "Historical survey of extension of the concept of principal partition and their unifying generalization to hyper matroids," Systems Science Research Report No.5, Department of Systems Science, Graduate School of Science and Engineering, Tokyo Institute of Technology, 1982.

[6]   S. Fujishige, "Algorithms for solving the independent-flow problems," J. Operat. Res. Soc. of Japan, vol.21, No.2, pp.189-204, 1978.

[7]   L. R. Ford and D. R. Fulkerson, Flows in Networks, Princeton University Press, Princeton, NJ, 1962.

[8]   T. Ozawa, Y. Kajitani and S. Ueno, " Efficient algorithms for assigning parallel tasks to a minimum number of parallel processors," 1986 Japan-Korea Joint Conference on Circuits and Systems Proceedings, also in Technical Report, Inst. Elec. Commun. Eng. of Japan, CAS, Oct. 1986.

Generalized Colorings

Michael O. Albertson

Dept. of Mathematics

Smith College

Northampton, MA 01063 USA

<u>0</u>.   Introduction.

A homomorphism f from a graph G to a graph H is a
mapping from V(G), the vertex set of G, to V(H), the
vertex set of H which preserves edges i.e. if (u,v) is in
E(G), the edge set of G, then (f(u),f(v)) is in E(H), the
edge set of H. A convenient way to exhibit a graph
homomorphism is to assign distinct labels to the vertices
of the target graph H and let the homomorphism pull them
back to the domain graph G. As an example Figure 1
exhibits a homomorphism from the 7-cycle to the 5-cycle.

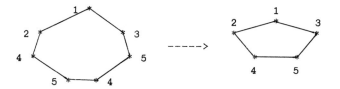

Figure 1.

research supported by NSF DMS-8513418

DISCRETE ALGORITHMS AND
COMPLEXITY

As a further example note that identifying the antipodal vertices of a dodecahedron is a homomorphism onto the Petersen graph. There is no homomorphism from the Petersen graph to the 5-cycle, since any such mapping must identify two non adjacent vertices and thus create a triangle.

Interpretations within Formal Languages and morphisms within the category of graphs are just graph homomorphisms in disguise. Many classic results have been obtained in these contexts: see [9,12,20,21,25,26,28,29]. This paper's point of view is colored by the most famous family of graph homomorphisms. Specifically a homomorphism from a graph G to the r-clique is just an r-coloring of G. In this context the preimage of any vertex is just a color class. Let $\chi(G)$ denote the chromatic number of G. Thus if $f : G \longrightarrow H$, then

$$\chi(G) \leq \chi(H).$$

There has been a flurry of activity on graph homomorphisms in the past few years. The four sections of this paper will survey recent work and suggest some directions for future work. First we discuss homomorphisms and parameters such as the chromatic number and independence. Second we consider algorithmic questions. Third we look at obstructions to the existence of homomorphisms. Finally we describe the homomorphism order.

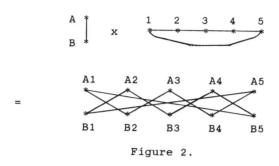

Figure 2.

1. Parameters.

The oldest open question concerning graph homomorphisms is the Hedetniemi Conjecture concerning the chromatic number of the weak product of graphs. Definition. Given H, K the weak product of H and K, denoted by H x K, has V(H x K) = {(x,y): x in H, y in K} and E(H x K) = {((x,y),(u,v)): (x,u) in #(H) and (y,v) in E(K)}. The "x notation" is suggestive since the weak product of 2 edges is a pair of independent edges. Figure 2 exhibits the weak product of an edge and a 5-cycle. The weak product's connection with graph homomorphisms is categorical. Specifically projection:H x K ---> H (or K) is a graph homomorphism. Consequently if H is r-colorable, then H x K is r-colorable for any K. Thus

$$X(H \times K) <= \min\{ X(H), \; X(K)\}$$

Conjecture. [19] $X(H \times K) = \min\{ X(H), X(K)\}$.

Graph Colorers are happy to attest to the apparent difficulty of the Hedetniemi Conjecture. This may have impeded the development of homomorphisms. While equality is straightforward for 3-colorable graphs, it is only within the last several years that there has been any progress for more difficult cases. El-Zahar and Sauer have proved the following.

Theorem [10].   If $\chi(H) = \chi(K) = 4$, then $\chi(H \times K) = 4$.

A (naive) generalization of the Hedetniemi Conjecture would be to think that

if H -X-> M and K -X-> M, then H x K -X-> M.

To see that this is false let H be a triangle and K be a 4-chromatic graph with odd girth at least 5. Let M = H x K. Clearly H x K ---> M. If H ---> H x K, then H ---> K by projection. Similarly if K ---> H x K, K ---> H. Since a homomorphism cannot reduce either the chromatic number or the odd girth, there cannot exist any mappings between H and K. Haggkvist, Hell, Miller, and Neumann Lara have investigated this property of "multiplicativity". Using the methods of El-Zahar and Sauer (which earlier appeared in the papers of Vesztergombi [30,31]) they have shown that all cycles are multiplicative [18]. The question of what other classes of graphs are multiplicative suggests itself. The early Czech constructions can be used to show that certain classes are not multiplicative [20,21].

Definition.   The independence of a graph G, denoted by u(G), is defined to be the proportion of vertices in a maximum independent set of G.

If $\alpha(G)$ denotes the independence number of a graph G with V vertices, then $u(G) = \alpha(G)/V$.

Examples a) u(5-cycle) = 2/5, and b) u(Petersen's graph) = 2/5 c) Let ML(k) denote the k-th Mobius Ladder. This graph can be realized as a regular 2k gon together with all longest diagonals. Then u(ML(4)) = 3/8.

Definition. Let $\alpha(t,G)$ be the maximum number of vertices in an induced t-colorable subgraph of G. Set

$$u(t,G) = \alpha(t,G)/V$$

Examples a) if C = 5-cycle, then u(1,C) = 2/5, u(2,C) = 4/5, and u(3,C) = 1; b) if P = Petersen's graph, then u(1,P) = 2/5, u(2,P) = 7/10, and u(3,P) = 1; and c) if M = ML(4), then u(1,M) = 3/8, u(2,M) = 3/4, and u(3,M) = 1. It remains an open question as to what are the possible u sequences of a graph, though Albertson and Berman have necessary and sufficient conditions for graphs that can be 4-colored [1]. The connection with homomorphisms is given by the No Homomorphism Lemma "NHL" of Albertson and Collins.

NHL [6]. If f:G ---> H and H is symmetric (vertex transitive), then for all t, u(t,G) >= u(t,H).

The NHL was originally conceived of as a necessary condition for the existence of a homomorphism. For instance, one can use it to show that there does not exist a homomorphism from Petersen's graph to the 5-cycle, since u(2,P) = 7/10 and u(2,C) = 4/5. However, it can also be used to bound the independence. For example, Haggkvist has the following result.

Theorem [17]. If G is a triangle free graph whose minimum degree is more than 3V/8, then G maps to the 5-cycle.

As a corollary we get that if G is a triangle free graph whose minimum degree is more than $3V/8$, then $u(G) \geq 2/5$. Inspired by the Haggkvist result Albertson and Chan have proved the following.

Theorem [5]. If G contains no triangle and no 5-cycle, and the minimum degree of G is more than $V/4$, then $u(G) \geq 3/7$.

Questions in this area abound. Here are my favorites.

Albertson, Bollobas, and Tucker have conjectured that a planar triangle free graph with maximum degree 3 has independence at least $3/8$ [2]. Is there a proof of this using the NHL?

That $u(1,G) \geq u(2,G) - u(1,G)$ is immediate for any graph G. If one looks at $u(k,G) - u((k-1),G)$, it is well known that (contrary to naive expectation) this sequence is not monotonic. It is monotonic for comparability graphs but not for all perfect graphs [14,15]. Is it the case that for any symmetric graph,

$$u((k+1),G) - u(k,G) \geq u(k,G) - u((k-1),G)?$$

Suppose (instead of being symmetric) you know the orbit sizes of the target graph. Is there a useful generalization of the NHL?

Finally, homomorphisms preserve cliques. This suggests that there ought to be a clique version of the NHL. Is there?

2. Algorithmic Issues.

    Given that homomorphisms are generalizations of colorings the most natural question is the complexity of

    "For a fixed H, given G is there f:G ---> H?".

If H is bipartite then the mapping f exists precisely when G is bipartite, and that, of course, is easy to test for. If H is a triangle then the problem is NP-complete even when the class of G is severely restricted [13,24]. In 1981 Maurer, Sudborough, and Welzl showed that when H is a fixed odd cycle, this problem is NP-complete [27]. They further conjectured that it would be NP-complete for any H which is not bipartite. In the last five years there has been a lot of activity verifying the above conjecture for special classes of graphs [see 23]. Finally in 1986 Hell and Nesetril established this conjecture.

Theorem [23]. If H is any fixed non-bipartite graph, then given a graph G it is NP-complete to determine if there exists f:G ---> H.

    Their proof involves intricate arguments on the nature of a counterexample with the fewest vertices and the most edges. It would be nice to have a more illuminating proof.

    If both G and H are directed graphs there is not even a plausible conjecture concerning when the existence of a homomorphism is an NP-complete problem [7,23,27].

Even though the existence of a k-coloring is an NP-complete problem, it has recently been shown that backtracking will take on average O(1) time to settle the question of the existence of a k-coloring [34]. The reason that this is so is that almost all graphs have many small subgraphs that cannot be k-colored. Is it the case that a bactracking algorithm to test for homomorphism will take O(1) time on average?

Finally a graph G is said to be minimal if there is no homomorphism to a proper subgraph of G. How difficult is it to test if a graph is minimal?

There has been another interesting algorithmic facet to graph homomorphisms. Call a homomorphism f:G ---> H onto if whenever (u,v) is an edge of H, there is an x, y in V(G) with f(x) = u, f(y) = v, and (x,y) in E(G). The achromatic number of a graph G, denoted by a(G), is the number of vertices in a largest clique which G maps onto. A homomorphism from G to a clique of size a(G) represents a coloring of G in which every pair of color classes has a pair of adjacent vertices. Thus color classes cannot be combined. Yannakakis and Gavril have shown the following.

Theorem [35]. Given a graph G and an integer n, deciding if a(G) >= n is NP-complete.

In contrast Farber, Hahn, Hell, and Miller have produced a O(E) algorithm to decide if a(G) >= n for fixed n [11]. While there have been numerous attempts that have settled special cases (e.g. paths and caterpillars) the question of the complexity of determining the achromatic number of a tree remains open.

3. Obstructions.

Given a graph G and a target H, what can G contain that will prohibit a homomorphism from G to H. In light of the Nesetril and Hell result of the preceding section one should not expect a "good" solution to this problem. If H is a clique, then this problem asks for a characterization of critical graphs (forget it!). So the first interesting case will be the odd cycles.

Vesztergombi has shown that there exists a homomorphism from a 3-chromatic graph G onto the 5-cycle if and only if the chromatic number of the strong product of G with the 5-cycle equals 5 [30,31]. While this characterization seems to proceed from a hard problem to a harder problem, the paper is noteworthy for its introduction of the coloration graph. Albertson, Catlin, and Gibbons were able to find something like an obstruction.

Theorem [4]. If G does not map to an (odd) r-cycle, and does not contain an odd cycle with fewer than r vertices, then a subgraph of G maps to a homeomorph of a 4-clique in which each face has exactly r vertices on its boundary.

Catlin found a better obstruction using more restrictive hypotheses.

Theorem [8]. Suppose G has maximum degree three and no
pair of vertices of degree three is joined by a path of
length less than r (odd). Then if G does not map to the
r-cycle, then G is homeomorphic to 4-clique in which each
edge has been replaced by a path of length r.

Finally Gerards found:

Theorem [16]. If G is a non-bipartite graph that does not
contain a copy of either of the graphs in Figure 3, then G
maps to its shortest odd cycle.

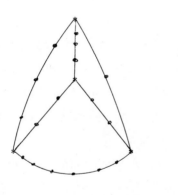   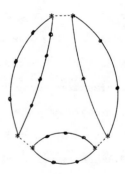

    odd 4-clique   odd 2-triangle

Figure 3.

4. The Homomorphism Order.

If there exists a homomorphism from H to K it is natural to say that H <= K. This does not quite produce a partial order on the set of graphs since it is easy to find pairs of distinct graphs, say H and K with both H <= K and K <= H. For example the 5-cycle and the truncated icosahedron (known to chemists as Buckminister Fullereen and to sports fans as the skeleton of a soccer ball) are so related. It is straightforward to show that the homomorphism order is a partial order on the set of minimal graphs.

If there exists a homomorphism from H to K but none from K to H, we write H < K. If G < H, let

$$I(G,H) = \{K: G < K < H\}.$$

I(G,H) is the "open interval" consisting of all graphs between G and H. About five years ago Welzl proved a density result for the homomorphism order.

Theorem [32,see also 12,28]. If H is not bipartite, then I(G,H) is not empty.

For example the dodecahedron fits properly between the 5-cycle and the Petersen graph. Somewhat later Welzl conjectured that if both G and H are symmetric, then K can be chosen to be symmetric also [33]. Welzl showed that this is true if G is a clique. He also showed that for each clique G, there exists an asymmetric H with I(G,H) containing no symmetric K. Albertson and Booth have

sharpened this contrast with the following two results.
Theorem [3]. If G is any symmetric non-bipartite graph,
then there exists a graph G~ such that G < G~ and I(G,G~)
does not contain any symmetric graph. {Note G~ is
asymmetric}

Theorem [3]. If G is an odd cycle and H is a symmetric
graph with the property that u(G) > u(H), then there
exists a symmetric K in I<G,H>.

The above theorem will probably push through for G an
arbitrary circulant. Is the reliance on independence in
the preceding theorem an artifice of the proof or could
the Welzl conjecture be false, (provided G and H have the
same (generalized) independence)? If G and H are
multiplicative and G < H, is there necessarily a
multiplicative K in I<G,H>?

REFERENCES

1. M. Albertson and D. M. Berman, "The chromatic difference
    sequence of a graph", J. Combinatorial Theory B 29 (1980)
    1-12.

2. M. Albertson, B. Bollobas, and S. Tucker, "The
    independence ratio and maximum degree of a graph",
    Congressus Numerantium 17 (1976) 43-50.

3. M. Albertson and V. Booth, "Homomorphisms of symmetric
    graphs", Congressus Numerantium (submitted).

4. M. Albertson, P. Catlin, and L. Gibbons,
    "Homomorphisms of 3-chromatic graphs, II", Congressus
    Numerantium, 47, 1986, 19-28.

5. M. Albertson and L. Chan, "Independence and graph homomorphisms" (in preparation).

6. M. Albertson and K. L. Collins, "Homomorphisms of 3-chromatic graphs", **Discrete Math.**, 54 (1985), 127-132.

7. G. Bloom and S. Burr, "On unavoidable digraphs in orientations of graphs", preprint.

8. P. A. Catlin, "Homomorphism as a generalization of graph coloring", **Congressus Numerantium** 50 (1985) 179-186.

9. K. Culik, F. E. Fitch, and A. Salomaa, "A homomorphic characterization of regular languages", **Discrete Applied Math.**, 4, 1982, 149-152.

10. M. El-Zahar and N. Sauer, "The chromatic number of the product of two four-chromatic graphs is four", **Combinatorica**, 5 (1985), 121-126.

11. M. Farber, G. Hahn, P. Hell, and D. Miller, "Concerning the achromatic number of graphs", **J. Combinatorial Theory B** 40 (1986) 21-39.

12. W. D. Fellner, "On minimal graphs", **Theoretical Computer Science** 17, 1982, 103-110.

13. M. R. Garey and D. S. Johnson, **Computers and intractibility: a guide to the theory of NP-completeness,** Freeman, San Francisco, 1979.

14. C. Greene, "Some partitions associated with a partially ordered set", **J. Combinatorial Theory A** 20 (1976), 69-79.

15. C. Greene and D. J. Kleitman, "The structure of Sperner k-families", **J. Combinatorial Theory A** 20 (1976), 41-68

16. A. M. H. Gerards, "Homomorphisms of graphs to odd cycles", preprint.

17. R. Haggkvist, "Odd cycles of specified length in non-bipartite graphs", **Annals of Discrete Math** 13 (1982)

89-100.

18. R. Haggkvist, P. Hell, D. J. Miller, and V. Neumann Lara, "On multiplicative graphs and the product conjecture", preprint.

19. S. Hedetniemi, "Homomorphisms of graphs and automata", University of Michigan Technical Report 03105-44-T, 1966.

20. Z. Hedrlin and A. Pultr, "Symmetric relations with given semigroup", **Monatsh. fur Math.** 68, 1965, 318-322.

21. P. Hell, "On some strongly rigid families of graphs and the full embeddings they induce", **Algebra Universalis 4**, 1974, 108-126.

22. P. Hell and D. J. Miller, "Graphs with forbidden homomorphic images", **Annals of the New York Academy of Sciences**, 319, 1979, 270-280.

23. P. Hell and J. Nesetril, "On the complexity of H-coloring", preprint.

24. D. S. Johnson, "The NP-completeness column: An ongoing guide" **J of Algorithms** especially 3 (1982).

25. H. A. Maurer, A. Salomaa, and D. Wood, "Colorings and interpretations: a connection between graphs and grammar forms", **Discrete Applied Math 3**, 1981, 119-137.

26. ----, "On predecessors of finite languages", **Information and Control**, 50, 1981, 259-275.

27. H. A. Maurer, I. H. Sudborough, and E Welzl, "On the complexity of the general coloring problem", **Information and Control**, 51 (1981), 128-145.

28. A. Salomaa, "On color-families of graphs", **Annales Academia Scientiarum Fennicae**, Series A. I. Mathematica, 6, 1981, 135-148.

29. A. Salomaa, Jewels of formal language theory, Computer Science Press, Rockville MD, 1981.

30. K. Vesztergombi, "Chromatic number of strong product of graphs" in Algebraic Methods in Graph Theory, ed. by Lovasz and Sos, North-Holland, NY, 1981, 819-826.

31. K. Vesztergombi, "Some remarks on the chromatic number of the strong product of graphs", Acta Cybernetica, 4, 1978, 207-212.

32. E. Welzl, "Color families are dense", Theoretical Computer Science, 17 (1982), 29-41.

33. E. Welzl, "Symmetric graphs and interpretations", J. Combinatorial Theory B, 37 (1984), 235-244.

34. H. S. Wilf, "Backtrack: an O(1) expected time algorithm for the graph coloring problem", Information Processing Letters, 18 (1984) 119-121.

35. M. Yannakakis and F. Gavril, "Edge dominating sets in graphs", SIAM J. Applied Math 38 (1980), 364-372.

Voronoi Diagram for Points in a Simple Polygon

Takao Asano

Department of Mechanical Engineering

Sophia University

Chiyoda-ku, Tokyo 102, Japan

and

Tetsuo Asano

Osaka Electro-Communication University

Neyagawa, Osaka 572, Japan

Abstract.

We present an algorithm for constructing the Voronoi diagram for a
set of n points in a simple polygon of m vertices in $O(mn + m \log\log m + n \log n)$ time and $O(m+n)$ space.

1. Introduction

For a set of n points v_i (i=1,2,...,n) in a simple polygon of m
vertices, the <u>Voronoi region</u> of v_i is defined by

$$V(v_i) = \{z \in R^2 \mid d(z,v_i) \leq d(z,v_h) \text{ for all } h, h=1,2,...,n\},$$

where $d(z,z')$ denotes the distance of the two points z and z', i.e., the
length of a shortest path between z and z' avoiding the obstacles. (Edges
of the polygon are considered as obstacles.) The skeleton formed by the
boundaries of $V(v_i)$ (i=1,2,...,n) is a planar graph and is called the
<u>Voronoi diagram</u> (Fig. 1). Points v_i (i=1,...,n) are called <u>generators</u> of
the Voronoi diagram. For the ordinary Voronoi diagram (i.e., the Voronoi

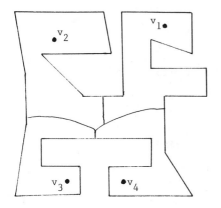

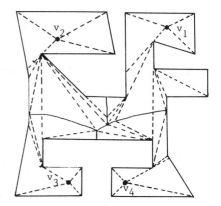

Fig. 1.   Voronoi diagram for points   Fig. 2.   Voronoi triangulation.
          in a simple polygon.

diagram without obstacles), an O(n log n) time algorithm based on the

divide-and-conquer method [SH] and an O(n^2) time algorithm based on the

incremental method [GS] have been proposed. Unlike the ordinary Voronoi

diagram, however, the Voronoi diagram considered in this paper contains

hyperbolic curves as well as straight line segments because of the

presence of obstacle edges. Furthermore, it requires O(m loglog m) time

to calculate the distance between two points [TV,GHLST], because it is

necessary to consider the visibility problem [LP], while it is trivial to

calculate the Euclidean distance in constructing the ordinary Voronoi

diagram. By these reasons, the Voronoi diagram for points in a simple

polygon cannot be easily constructed on the analogy of the ordinary

Voronoi diagram, and no polynomial time algorithm seems to have been

presented.

    In this paper, we present an algorithm for constructing the Voronoi

diagram for a set of n points in a simple polygon of m vertices. It

constructs the Voronoi diagram in O(mn + m loglog m + n log n) time and

O(m+n) space. The algorithm is based on the recent results of triangulating a simple polygon [TV] and of finding shortest paths from a point to all the vertices of a simple polygon [GHLST].

As an application, the following problems can be efficiently solved if the Voronoi diagram is constructed in $O(mn + m \log\log m + n \log n)$ time and $O(m+n)$ space.

(i) All nearest generators of all generators can be found in $O(m+n)$ time.

(ii) A furthest point from generators, which corresponds to the center of a maximum empty circle (i.e., circle containing no generators) in the ordinary Voronoi diagram, can be found in $O(m+n)$ time.

(iii) The post office problem of finding a nearest generator of a query point can be also solved in $O(\log m + \log n)$ time with additional $O(m+n)$ time preprocessing, because the Voronoi diagram can be further divided in $O(m+n)$ time into $O(m+n)$ pseudo triangles (i.e., regions each with three curves) satisfying the following (Fig. 2) (this structure will be called the Voronoi triangulation later).

(1) For each pseudo triangle, all the points inside it have the same nearest generator.

(2) A point-location query can be answered in $O(\log m + \log n)$ time.

(3) The distance of a shortest path between a point z and its nearest generator can be found in constant time and the actual shortest path can be found in time proportional to the number of the segments of the path, if the point z is already located.

2. Sketch of the algorithm

We give an informal description of our algorithm for constructing the Voronoi diagram for a set of points v_1, v_2, ..., v_n in a simple polygon of vertices u_1, u_2, ..., u_m. For a point z, let $v(z)$ denote a nearest generator of z, that is, z is in the Voronoi region $V(v(z))$

of $v(z)$. For simplicity, we assume that, for every vertex u_j of the
simple polygon, its nearest generator $v(u_j)$ is uniquely determined. This
implies that no vertices of the polygon are on the boundaries of two or
more Voronoi regions. (The argument below can be easily modified to work
even when $v(u_j)$ is not uniquely determined for some u_j.) Note that there
is exactly one shortest path between vertex u_j and its nearest generator
$v(u_j)$, because there is no hole in the polygon.

It is clear that, for any two points z and z' and their nearest
generators $v(z)$ and $v(z')$, two shortest paths $P(z,v(z))$ between z and
$v(z)$ and $P(z',v(z'))$ between z' and $v(z')$ may meet or branch only at
vertices of the polygon and the generators. Similarly, if point z' is on
the shortest path $P(z,v(z))$, then the subpath $P(z',v(z))$ of $P(z,v(z))$
connecting z' and $v(z)$ is a shortest path between z' and $v(z)$. Thus,
point z' has $v(z)$ as its nearest generator, i.e., $v(z')=v(z)$. Thus, we
have the following lemma.

Lemmma 1. Let $U(v)$ be the set of vertices of the polygon having v as
the nearest generator. Then the set of shortest paths from the vertices
of the polygon to their nearest generators can be represented by <u>shortest
path trees</u> $\{ T_v | v=v_1,\ldots,v_n \}$, where T_v is a rooted tree with root v and
$U(v)$ is the node set of T_v. (The unique path $P(u,v)$ from u to v in the
tree T_v is the shortest path from u to v inside the polygon.)
Furthermore, the total number of edges contained in the trees T_v
$(v=1,\ldots,n)$ is $\sum_v |U(v)| = |\bigcup_v U(v)| = m$.

We first find the shortest path trees rooted at the generators. Such
trees can be obtained by first finding the shortest paths from each
generator to the vertices of the polygon and then comparing the distances
from each vertex to the generators and choosing its nearest generator.

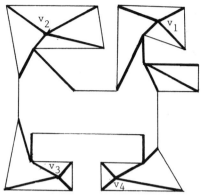

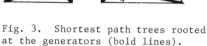

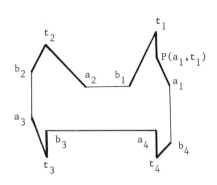

Fig. 3.   Shortest path trees rooted
at the generators (bold lines).

Fig. 4.   Face F.

Then we add all edges of the trees to the polygon and obtain a straight-
line-segment planar graph whose <u>edges</u> are the edges of the polygon and
the added edges of the trees, because edges in the trees are straight
line segments and they may meet only at vertices of the polygon and
generators (Lemma 1). The <u>nodes</u> of the graph are vertices and the
generators. Thus, the resulting planar graph has m+n nodes and 2m edges
(Fig. 3).

The boundary of a face consists of an alternating sequence of
polygon edges and the subpaths of shortest path trees (Fig. 4). Each
subpath $P(u,u')$ connecting u and u' can be divided into two paths $P(u,t)$
connecting u and t and $P(t,u')$ connecting t and u', where t is the unique
node on $P(u,u')$ that is an anscestor of all nodes on $P(u,u')$. Clearly, t
is the root of $P(u,u')$, i.e., the root of the subtree of the shortest
path tree containing $P(u,u')$ which is obtained by deleting all the other
nodes of the tree except the nodes on $P(u,u')$. It is possible that $P(u,t)$
or $P(t,u')$ is a null path, that is, $P(u,t)=t$ or $P(t,u')=t$. A node v
inside a face is also considered the shortest path tree with root v.

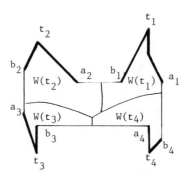

Fig. 5.   Weighted Voronoi diagram.

Thus, we can divide the nodes of a face into two types: <u>roots</u> and <u>non-roots</u> of the subpaths. Nodes of a face corresponding to roots are called <u>exits</u> of the face. Each exit t of a face has a weight $w(t)$ representing the distance between t and its nearest generator $v(t)$. For each point z in the face, the <u>weighted distance</u> $w(z,t)$ between z and exit t is defined by the sum of the weight of t and the distance between t and z, i.e., $w(z,t)=w(t)+d(z,t)$. Thus, the weighted distance $w(z,t)$ between z and t coincides with the distance between z and the nearest generator $v(t)$ of t.

For the set of exits t_i (i=1,2,...,j) of a face F and a point z inside F, the nearest exit of z with respect to the weighted distance is denoted by $t(z)$ and simply called the <u>nearest exit</u> of z. The <u>weighted Voronoi region</u> $W(t_i)$ of t_i is defined by the set of points z in F having t_i as a nearest exit $(t(z)=t_i)$, i.e.,

$W(t_i)=\{z|$ z is a point in the face F and

$w(z,t_i) \leq w(z,t_h)$ for all h, h=1,,2,...,j }.

The planar skeleton formed by the boundaries of $W(t_i)$ (i=1,2,...,j) is called the <u>weighted Voronoi diagram</u> (Fig. 5). For a point z inside a face, a shortest path between z and its nearest generator $v(z)$ always passes through some exit t of the face. Clearly, $t=t(z)$ and $v(z)=v(t(z))$

and the weighted distance $w(z,t(z))$ is equal to the distance between z and $v(z)$. Thus, we have the following lemma.

Lemma 2. The weighted Voronoi region $W(t_i)$ of exit t_i of a face is a subset of the Voronoi region $V(v(t_i))$ of $v(t_i)$ ($v(t_i)$ is the nearest generator of t_i). The Voronoi region $V(v)$ of generator v is the union of the weighted Voronoi regions $W(t)$ of all the exits t of faces with $v(t)=v$.

By Lemma 2, we can summarize our algorithm for constructing the Voronoi diagram for a set of points in a simple polygon.

Outline of the Voronoi diagram algorithm VDA

Step 1. Find the shortest path from a vertex of the polygon to its nearest generator and the shortest path trees rooted at the generators.

Step 2. Add the shortest path trees to the polygon and obtain a planar graph G_{SPT}.

Step 3. Construct the weighted Voronoi diagram for each face of the graph G_{SPT}.

Step 4. Merge the weighted Voronoi diagrams for all the faces and obtain the Voronoi diagram for the generators.

The correctness of the algorithm VDA is almost clear from Lemma 2. Note that the shortest path trees rooted at the generators can be found in $O(mn + m \log\log m)$ time and $O(m+n)$ space, because the shortest path problem from a point to the vertices of the simple polygon can be solved in $O(m)$ time and $O(m)$ space by the algorithm proposed in [HGLST] if the polygon is triangulated in advance in $O(m \log\log m)$ time and $O(m)$ space by the algorithm in [TV]. In the following sections we give a little more

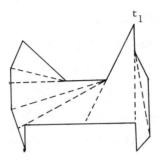

Fig. 6.   Shortest path triangulation
of F at t_1.

detailed description of the other steps and analysis of their complexity.

3. Constructing the weighted Voronoi diagram

We add the shortest path trees rooted at the generators to the polygon and obtain the straight-line-segment planar graph G_{SPT}. This is Step 2 in the algorithm VDA and can be done in $O(m+n)$ time. Each of the faces of the planar graph consists of alternating sequence of boundary edges of the polygon not contained in any shortest path trees and subpaths of shortest path trees. Let

$$P(a_1,t_1)P(t_1,b_1)(b_1,a_2)P(a_2,t_2)P(t_2,b_2)...P(a_q,t_q)P(t_q,b_q)(b_q,a_1)$$

be the counter-clockwise sequence of the boundary of a face F of the graph, where $P(a_i,t_i)P(t_i,b_i)$ $(i=1,...,q)$ is the subpath (subtree with root t_i) of a shortest path tree and (b_i,a_{i+1}) $(q+1=1)$ is an edge of the polygon not contained in any shortest path trees (Fig. 4). Clearly, t_1, t_2, ..., t_q are exits of F. Let t_{q+1}, ..., t_{q+r} be the other exits of F. That is, t_{q+1}, ..., t_{q+r} are generators inside the face F.

It can be easily observed that each $P(a_i,t_i)$ $(i=1,...,q)$ is <u>outward-convex</u>, that is, the convex hull of each subpath of $P(a_i,t_i)$ lies outside F. Similarly, each $P(t_i,b_i)$ is also outward-convex. Thus, if face F has only one exit t_1 on the boundary then there is no exit inside F and F itself is the weighted Voronoi diagram for the exit. To actually find the shortest path from a query point z to the exit t_1, however, we need a more refined structure. For a simple polygon P and a specified vertex t, the following structure, called a <u>shortest path triangulation of P at t</u> and denoted by SPT(t), may be suitable for such a query (Fig. 6).

(1) The vertices of each triangle are on the boundary of P and at least one of the three vertices of a triangle is a vertex of P or t.

(2) For each triangle Q and all points z on or inside Q, all the shortest paths from points z to t pass through the unique vertex of Q (such a vertex is called <u>gate</u> of Q and denoted by g(Q)), and

(3) Each g(Q) is a vertex of P or t.

Note that such a triangulation can be obtained in O(p) time, where p is the number of the vertices of the polygon if the polygon is already triangulated [GHLST]. From now on, we assume that all the faces have already been triangulated in O(m loglog m) time and O(m) space in total. The following properties of the weighted Voronoi diagram are of fundamental importance and play critical roles in the algorithm for constructing the weighted Voronoi diagram and in its complexity analysis.

<u>Lemma 3.</u> For each exit t_i (i=1,...,q) of face F, the weighted Voronoi region $W(t_i)$ is a simple polygonal region (simply connected region) containing $P(a_i,t_i)P(t_i,b_i)$ on its boundary and is a subset of the union of triangles of SPT(t_i) whose gates are on $P(a_i,t_i)P(t_i,b_i)$.

<u>Lemma 4.</u> For each exit t_i of face F, the boundary of the weighted Voronoi region $W(t_i)$ consists of O(p+r) curves, where p is the number of nodes on the boundary of F and r is the number of nodes inside F.

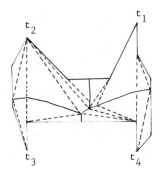

Fig. 7. Weighted Voronoi
triangulation of F.

For each weighted Voronoi region $W(t_i)$ and each curve C on the
boundary of $W(t_i)$, we add two edges connecting the two endpoints $z(C)$ and
$z'(C)$ of C and their gate $g_i(C)$ of the shortest path triangulation of F
at t_i. The resulting graph is a planar graph and is called the weighted
Voronoi triangulation of F (Fig. 7). $g_i(C)$ is also called a gate of the
pseudo triangle determined by curve C and two segments $g_i(C)z(C)$ and
$g_i(C)z'(C)$. The graph obtained by dividing each face into the weighted
Voronoi triangulation is called the Voronoi triangulation (see Fig. 2).

Now, we describe an algorithm for constructing the weighted Voronoi
triangulation (and the Voronoi triangulation). This step corresponds to
Step 3 in the algorithm VDA. The Voronoi diagram can be easily obtained
from the Voronoi triangulation. The algorithm for constructing the
weighted Voronoi triangulation is divided into the following three steps.

Step 3.1. Construct the weighted Voronoi triangulation of face F by
ignoring all exits t_{q+1}, ..., t_{q+r} inside F.

Step 3.2. Construct the ordinary Voronoi diagram for generators
t_{q+1}, ..., t_{q+r} inside F.

Step 3.3. Merge the weighted Voronoi triangulation and the ordinary Voronoi diagram obtained above and construct the weighted Voronoi triangulation of F.

Step 3.2 can be done in $O(r \log r)$ time and $O(r)$ space by the ordinary Voronoi diagram algorithm based on the divide and conquer method [SH]. So we first concentrate on Step 3.1 and then on Step 3.3. Step 3.1 is divided into two cases: (i) q=1; and (ii) q≥2.

case 1. q=1. In this case the weighted Voronoi triangulation coincides with $SPT(t_1)$, the shortest path triangulation of F at t_1. Thus, it can be done in $O(p)$ time and $O(p)$ space.

Case 2. q≥2. By restricting the exits of F to $t_1, t_2, \ldots, t_k$ (1≤k≤q), we can define the weighted Voronoi triangulation of F for the exits $t_1, \ldots, t_k$, which will be denoted by WVT(k). Clearly, WVT(1) coincides with $SPT(t_1)$, the shortest path triangulation of F at t_1. We construct WVT(q), the weighted Voronoi triangulation of F for the exits $t_1, \ldots, t_q$, based on the incremental method. Starting with WVT(1), the incremental method constructs WVT(q) through repeated modification of WVT(k-1) to WVT(k) (k≤q). WVT(k) is obtained from WVT(k-1) by cutting the Voronoi region $W(t_k)$ of t_k with an aid of the shortest path triangulation $SPT(t_k)$ at t_k. We omit the details, but WVT(q) can be obtained in $O(pq)$ time and $O(p+q)$ space by using Lemmas 3 and 4.

Step 3.3 can be carried out in a similar way as in Step 3.1. By using the ordinary Voronoi diagram for $t_{q+1}, \ldots, t_{q+r}$ instead of the shortest path triangulations, we construct the weighted Voronoi regions of $t_{q+1}, \ldots, t_{q+r}$ and modify the weighted Voronoi regions of $t_1, \ldots, t_q$. Thus, Step 3.3 can be done in $O(pr)$ time and $O(p+r)$ space and we have the following:

Lemma 5. The weighted Voronoi triangulation of face F with p nodes and q exits on the boundary and r exits inside can be constructed in $O(p(q+r) + r \log r)$ time and $O(p+q+r)$ space if F is already triangulated.

The Voronoi triangulation can be obtained from the weighted Voronoi triangulations of the faces of the planar graph G_{SPT} obtained in Step 2. Let $p(F)$, $q(F)$ and $r(F)$ be the number of nodes of F, the number of exits on the boundary of F and the number of exits inside F. Then the total complexity required to construct the Voronoi triangulation from graph G_{SPT} is

$$O(\Sigma_F (p(F)(q(F)+r(F)) + r(F) \log r(F) + p(F) \log\log p(F))) \text{ time,}$$
$$O(\Sigma_F (p(F)+q(F)+r(F))) \text{ space.}$$

Since $q(F) \leq p(F)$ and G_{SPT} is planar and has 2m edges (see Lemma 1),

$$O(\Sigma p(F))=O(m), \quad O(\Sigma q(F))=O(m) \text{ and } O(\Sigma(q(F)+r(F)))=O(n).$$

Thus, we have the following.

Theorem. The Voronoi triangulation for n generators in a simple polygon of m vertices can be constructed in $O(mn + m \log\log m + n \log n)$ time and $O(m+n)$ space.

5. Concluding remarks

We have presented $O(mn + m \log\log m + n \log n)$ time and $O(m+n)$ space algorithm for constructing the Voronoi diagram (Voronoi triangulation) for a set of n generators in a simple polygon of m vertices. As application, we can easily obtain (i)-(iii) in Section 1 by the same technique used in the ordinary Voronoi diagram. Note that, although the Voronoi triangulation contains hyperbolic curves, we can transform it into a straight-line-segment planar triangulation H by replacing each hyperbolic curve C of two endponts with the line segment of the same endpoints. We locate a query point z in the straight-line-segment planar triangulation H by the algorithm in [K,EGS] and then locate z in the Voronoi triangualtion using the triangle of H containing z. Thus, we obtain (iii).

The Voronoi diagram for a set of n generators in the plane of polygonal obstacles of m vertices can be also obtained in a similar way. The complexity of the algorithm in this case is $O(m^2 + mn + n \log n)$ time and $O(m^2 + n)$ space. It uses the algorithm in [AAGHI] for finding a Euclidean shortest path between two points in the presence of polygonal obstacles.

References

[AAGHI] T. Asano, T. Asano, L. Guibas, J. Hershberger and H. Imai, Visibility of disjoint polygons, Algorithmica, 1 (1986), pp.49-63.

[EGS] H. Edelsbrunner, L. Guibas and J. Stolfi, Optimal point location in a monotone subdivision, SIAM J. Comput., 15 (1986), pp.317-340.

[GHLST] L. Guibas, J. Hershberger, D. Leven, M. Sharir and R.E. Tarjan, Linear time algorithms for visibility and shortest path problems inside simple polygons, Proc. 2nd ACM Symp. Computational Geometry, Yorktown Heights, New York, 1986, pp.1-13.

[GS] P.J. Green and R. Sibson, Computing Dirichlet tessellation in the plane, The Computer Journal, 21 (1978), pp.168-173.

[K] Kirkpatrick, Optimal search in planar subdivisions, SIAM J. Comput., 12 (1983), pp.28-35.

[LP] D.T. Lee and F.P. Preparata, Euclidean shortest paths in the presence of rectilinear barriers, Networks, 14 (1984), pp.393-410.

[SH] M.I. Shamos and D. Hoey, Closest-point problems, Proc. 16th IEEE

Symp. Foundations of Computer Science, Berkeley, California, 1975, pp.151-162.

[TV] R.E. Tarjan and C.J. Van Wyk, A linear time algorithm for triangulating simple polygons, Proc. 18th ACM Symp. Theory of Computing, Berkeley, California, 1986, pp.380-388.

Computing the Geodesic Center of a Simple Polygon

by

Tetsuo Asano* and Godfried Toussaint**

* Osaka Electro-Communication University, Japan.

**McGill University, Canada.

ABSTRACT

This paper presents a polynomial-time algorithm for finding the **geodesic center** of a simple polygon, i.e., the point in the polygon whose greatest internal distance to any other point in the polygon is a minimum. The distance between two points in a simple polygon is measured as the length of the shortest internal path between them. The key idea is the construction of a geodesic farthest-point Voronoi diagram for a simple polygon which consists of straight lines and hyperbolic curve segments. The geodesic center of a simple polygon is either the center of its geodesic diameter or a vertex of the geodesic farthest-point Voronoi diagram. The proposed algorithm runs in $O(n^3 \log \log n)$ time, where n is the number of vertices of the given polygon.

1. Introduction

In this paper we consider the problem of finding the geodesic center of a simple polygon, which is defined to be a point in the polygon whose greatest internal distance to any

DISCRETE ALGORITHMS AND
COMPLEXITY

other point in the polygon is a minimum. The distance between
two points is measured as the length of the shortest internal
path between them. This problem is a generalization of the
smallest enclosing circle problem or the minimax facilities
location problem familiar in Operations Research, in which,
given a set of points in the plane, we seek the smallest
circle that encloses all the points, or a point whose greatest
distance to any point in the set is a minimum. In the
smallest enclosing circle problem the distance between two
points is given by the length of the straight line segment
connecting them while in our case it is measured as the length
of the shortest path between them within the polygon. The
geodesic center has applications to image processing and shape
description.

In this paper we present a polynomial-time algorithm for
finding the geodesic center of a simple polygon P. First of
all, we find a pair of vertices of the greatest distance
diam(P). The mid-point r of the shortest path between them is
a candidate for the geodesic center. Next, we check whether
there is a vertex p such that the distance between r and p is
greater than diam(P)/2. If there exists no such vertex then
the point r is the geodesic center. Otherwise, we construct a
geodesic furthest-point Voronoi diagram for the polygon which
consists of straight lines and hyperbolic curve segments. We
show that, in this case, the geodesic center of a simple
polygon must be a vertex of the diagram. The proposed
algorithm runs in $O(n^3 \log \log n)$ time where n is the number of
vertices of the polygon.

2. Uniqueness of Geodesic Center

In this section we show that the geodesic center of a simple polygon is unique. For this purpose we introduce some terminologies and investigate the properties of the geodesic center.

[Definition 1] For two points x and y in a simple polygon P, the geodesic distance, denoted by dist(x, y), is the length of a shortest internal path between x and y within P.

[Definition 2] For a point x in a simple polygon P, the locus of points reachable from v within the distance of d is denoted by $D(v, d)$. More formally, it is defined by

$D(v, d) = \{u|\ u$ is a point in P and $dist(u, v) < d\}$.

[Definition 3] Let x be a point in a simple polygon P.

(1) The (geodesic) furthest point of x is a point x^* in P such that the geodesic distance between x and x^* is a maximum.

(2) The geodesic distance between x and x^* is denoted by $d_{max}(x)$.

(3) The range of x, denoted by R(x), is the locus of points v in P such that $d_{max}(v) < d_{max}(x)$.

[Lemma 1] Let x be an arbitrary point in a simple polygon P. Then, the geodesic farthest point of x is some convex vertex of P.

[Lemma 2] Let $C = \{c_1, c_2, \ldots, c_m\}$ be a set of all convex vertices of a simple polygon P and x be a point in P. Then, the range R(x) of x is given by

$$R(x) = \bigcap_{i=1}^{m} D(c_i, d_{max}(x))|\ c_i \in C.$$

To compute the locus of points D(x, d), we decompose a simple polygon P based on the visibility from the point x by the following procedure.

[Algorithm Decomposition]

[input] A simple polygon P and a point x in its interior.

[output] Decomposition of P into disjoint regions P_0, P_1, ...,
P_m. For each region P_i, r_point(P_i) and gdist(x, P_i) are
computed:

   r_point(P_i): A representative point of P_i that is nearest
to the given point within P_i.

   gdist(x, P_i): The geodesic distance between x and the
representative point of P_i.

<u>begin</u>

   vis_decomp(x, 0, P);

<u>end</u>

procedure vis_decomp(w, distance, S)

<u>begin</u>

   (1) Find the visibility polygon Vis(w, S) of the polygon S
from the point w;

   (2) Enumerate all the vertices P_1, P_2, ... , P_m of S on the
boundary of Vis(w, S) such that each P_i is adjacent to both a
visible edge and an invisible edge from w in polygon S;

   (3) Remove the region Vis(w, S) from S and then let P_1, P_2,
..., P_m be the resulting regions such that each P_i contains
the vertex P_i;

   (4) Let P_0 be Vis(w, S) and let

         r_point(P_0) = w;

         gdist(w, P_0) = distance;

   (5) For each vertex P_i and the polygon P_i, call

         vis_decomp(P_i, distance+dist(w, P_i), P_i);

         where dist(w, P_i) is given by the straight line

distance   between w and p_i since p_i is visible from w
in P;

<u>end</u>

It is easy to see that the above procedure decomposes the
given simple polygon P with respect to the point x into
disjoint regions such that for each region P_i

(1)   there   exists   one   representative   point   denoted   by
$r\_point(P_i)$ which is either a vertex of P or the point x,

(2)   any   point   in P_i is visible from   its   representative
point,

(3)   the shortest path from x to any point v in P_i passes
through   the   representative   point of P_i and   does   not   pass
through   any other vertex of P on the way from $r\_point(P_i)$ to
v, and thus

(4)   the geodesic distance between x and any point v in P_i
is   given   by the sum of the straight line distance between   v
and $r\_point(P_i)$ and the geodesic distance $gdist(x, P_i)$ between
$r\_point(P_i)$ and x.

After the decomposition, we build a region adjacency tree
in the following way.   The root of the tree is the point x.   A
set   of sons of x is a set of representative points   lying   on
the boundary of the visibility polygon Vis(x, P).   Generally,
a   set   of sons of a node w of the tree is given by a   set   of
representative   points   enumerated at the second step   of   the
procedure vis_decomp(w,   distance, S).   An example is shown in
Fig. 1.

Using   this decomposition algorithm,   we can compute   the
locus of points D(x, d) by the following procedure.

[Procedure for Computing D(x, d)]

(Step 1) Decompose a simple polygon P with respect to the point x in P by the above described decomposition procedure.

(Step 2) Construct a region adjacency tree defined above.

(Step 3) v = x.

(Step 4) If the geodesic distance between x and v is greater than the specified distance d, then do nothing. Otherwise, let S be the visibility polygon associated with the representative point v. Compute the furthest point w of v in S. If the geodesic distance between w and x is greater than d, then the boundary of D(x, d) should pass through S, which is a circular arc of the radius d - dist(x,v) with its center at v. Thus, the boundary in S is given by the intersection of such a circle with S. After computing the intersection, apply the same procedure to every son of v in the region adjacency tree.

An example of the region D(x, d) is illustrated in Fig. 2

[Lemma 3] Let x be a point in a simple polygon P. Then, the range R(x) of x is empty if and only if x is the geodesic center of P.

[Lemma 4] Let x be a point in a simple polygon P such that the range R(x) is not empty. For any point y within the range R(x), the range of y is a proper subset of R(x). In other words,

$$y \in R(x) \implies R(y) \subset R(x).$$

[Lemma 5] The range of any point in a simple polygon is a connected region if it is not the geodesic center.

It follows from the above two lemmas that if we iterate choosing a point x in a region S and then computing the region

R(x) to be replaced with S again. then such region converges to a point, which is the geodesic center required. Formal description of the procedure is as follows.

[Procedure for computing the Geodesic Center]

```
    S := P;/* P is a simple polygon */
    repeat
        choose an arbitrary point x in S;
        compute the range R(x) of x;
        S = R(x);
    until(S is empty);
```

The above procedure may iterate infinitely many times, but it is important in proving the uniqueness of the geodesic center. Lemmas 4 and 5 may not be sufficient for convergence. We need an effective rule for choosing the new point x at each iteration. One such rule is to choose the center of a circle of the maximum radius $r(e^*)$ which is contained in the region R(x). Then, we can reduce the diameter of the region by at least $r(e^*)$.

Lemma 4 guarantees the convergence of the above procedure and Lemma 5 assures that it converges into one point. Therefore we have the uniqueness theorem.

Theorem 1: Any simple polygon has the unique geodesic center.

In this paper we consider the problem of computing the geodesic center of a simple polygon without holes in the L_2-metric. If we remove one of the conditions of simpleness and L_2-metricity, the uniqueness of geodesic center is not guaranteed. In fact we can construct examples with more than one geodesic center for a polygonal region with holes and for a simple polygon in the L_1 metric (see Fig. 3).

3. Geodesic Diameter of a Simple Polygon

For a simple polygon P with n vertices a geodesic farthest point of P is defined to be a point pair (u, v) having the greatest geodesic distance. By r(u, v) we denote the mid-point of the shortest internal path between u and v. The length of this shortest internal path is referred to as the geodesic diameter of P and denoted by diam(P). Several algorithms have been proposed for the problem, for example, $O(n^2)$ time and $O(n^2)$ space algorithm [Chazelle (1982)], $O(c^2 n \log n)$ time and $O(n)$ space algorithm [Toussaint (1985)] where c is the number of convex vertices, and $O(n^2)$ time and $O(n)$ space algorithm [Reif and Storer (1985)].

The mid-point r(u, v) for a geodesic farthest point pair (u, v) is a candidate for the geodesic center of P. So we check whether there is a vertex p such that the distance between r(u, v) and p is greater than diam(P)/2. If there exists no such vertex, then the point r(u, v) is the geodesic center. Note that a pair of vertices defining the greatest distance is not always unique.

4. Farthest-Point Voronoi Diagram

The Voronoi diagram of a set S of n points $\{p_1, p_2, \ldots, p_n\}$ in the plane is a partition of the plane such that each region of the partition is the locus of points which are closer to one member of S than to any other member. Many papers have been published concerning the Voronoi diagram which are summarized in [Preparata-Shamos (1985)]. The furthest-point Voronoi diagram has also received some attention [Bhattacharya-Toussaint (1985)]. In this paper we generalize the notion of the Voronoi diagram. We define a geodesic farthest-point Voronoi diagram for a simple polygon P to be a partition of the polygon so that each region of the partition is the locus of points which are furthest (in the geodesic sense) from one vertex of P than from any other vertex of P. An example is illustrated in Fig. 4. As is seen in the figure, the diagram consists of not only straight line segments but also hyperbolic curve segments.

Formally, we define a geodesic farthest-point Voronoi polygon $FV(p_i)$ for a vertex p_i of a simple polygon P by

$FV(p_i) = \{v|\ v$ is a point in P and

$\qquad dist(p_i,\ v) \geq dist(p_j,\ v)$

$\qquad$ for any vertex p_j of P, $j \neq i\}$,

where $dist(p,\ q)$ denotes the internal geodesic distance between two points p and q in P, that is, the length of the shortest path connecting p and q within P. In other words, $FV(p_i)$ is the locus of points v such that the vertex p_i is further from v than is any other vertex of P. Note that $FV(p_i)$ may be empty for some vertex p_i. An equivalent definition is

$FV(p_i) = \bigcap F(p_i,\ p_j),\ p_j \neq p_i,$

where $F(p_i,\ p_j)$ is the locus of points v such that the vertex p_i is farther from v than p_j, i.e.,

$F(p_i,\ p_j) = \{v|\ v$ is a point in P and

$\qquad dist(p_i,\ v) \geq dist(p_j,\ v)\}.$

The furthest-point Voronoi diagram FVOD(P) is defined as the collection of all such furthest-point Voronoi polygons of

P. A brute-force algorithm for computing the furthest-point Voronoi diagram for a simple polygon P is to compute the geodesic furthest-point Voronoi polygon for every vertex.

The fundamental problem here is described as follows.

(Problem) Given a simple polygon P with n vertices and two points u and v in its interior, find the region F(u, v), which is the locus of points w in P such that u is further from w than v.

An example is shown in Fig. 5.

This problem was first solved by Asano [Asano (1986)] in $O(n^2)$ time and then the algorithm was improved by Asano and Asano [Asano and Asano (1986)] into an O(n log log n)-time algorithm by using an O(n log log n)-time algorithm for computing a shortest path tree for a simple polygon [Guibas, Hershberger, Leven, Sharir, and Tarjan (1986)]. An important thing is that we can compute the collection of all shortest paths inside a simple polygon P from a given point to all the other vertices of P in O(n log log n) time. Thus, $O(n^2 \log \log n)$ time is sufficient to compute a geodesic furthest-point Voronoi polygon $FV(p_i)$ for a vertex p_i.   In this way we can construct a geodesic furthest-point Voronoi diagram in $O(n^3 \log \log n)$ time. What we have to do in the next step is to compute the greatest distance for each vertex of the Voronoi diagram and to find one with the smallest greatest distance, which is the geodesic center required. Thus we have an algorithm for computing the geodesic center of a simple polygon.

[Algorithm for computing the geodesic center]

(Step 1) Find the two convex vertices x and y of the greatest geodesic distance and then compute the mid-point r of the shortest internal path between x and y.

(Step 2) If there exists no vertex z such that $dist(r,z) >$ $dist(r,x)$, then r is the geodesic center required.

(Step 3) For every pair of convex vertices u and v, compute the internal boundary of the region $F(u, v)$.

(Step 4) Enumerate all the intersections of the internal boundaries of the regions $F(u, v)$'s for all pairs of convex vertices u and v, and then for each such intersection q compute the geodesic distance between q and its furthest vertex.

(Step 5) Find the intersection g of the smallest geodesic distance to its furthest vertex, which is the geodesic center required.

[Theorem 2] Given a simple polygon P with n vertices, we can find the geodesic center in $O(n^3 \log \log n)$ time in the worst case.

Proof: We evaluate the time complexity of the above algorithm. The first two steps can be done in $O(n^2)$ time using Reif and Storer's method. Step 3 may require $O(n^3 \log \log n)$ time since there are $O(n^2)$ vertex pairs and for each vertex pair (u, v) $O(n \log \log n)$ time is required to compute $F(u, v)$. At step 4 we enumerate all the vertices of the geodesic furthest-point Voronoi polygon $F(p_i)$ for each vertex p_i in $O(n^3 \log \log n)$ time in total. For every vertex of the polygons we can compute a furthest vertex in $O(n \log \log n)$ time. Thus, the latter half of Step 4 is done in $O(n^3 \log \log n)$ time in total.

The correctness of the above-stated algorithm is assured

by the following lemma.

[Lemma 6] Let P be a simple polygon.   If the mid-point of any geodesic furthest point pair of P is not the geodesic center of P,   then there exist three convex vertices u, v, and w such that the intersection point between the internal boundaries of the regions F(u, v) and F(u, w) is the geodesic center.

Proof: Let g be the geodesic center of a given simple polygon P.   Assume the condition described in the lemma. We define a furthest vertex to be a vertex of P that is furthest in a geodesic sense from g.

Suppose that the number of furthest vertices of P is only two, say u and v. Since the mid-point r(u, v) of the point pair (u, v) is not the geodesic center,   for any constant c such that $c < d_{max}(g) - dist(r(u, v), u)$ there exists a point g' such that $dist(g', u) = dist(g', v) = d_{max}(g) - c$. Let w be a third furthest vertex of P.   Then, for any constant $c' < d_{max}(g) - dist(g, w)$ there exists a point g'' such that $dist(g'', x) \leq d_{max}(g) - c'$ for any vertex x except for u and v.   Therefore, if we choose a constant c^* such that $c^* < \min\{d_{max}(g) - dist(r(u, v), u), d_{max}(g) - dist(g, w)\}$, there exists a point g^* such that $dist(g^*, x) \leq d_{max}(g) - c^*$ for any vertex x including u and v, which contradicts the assumption that g is the geodesic center of P.   So we can conclude that there exist at least three furthest vertices under the condition stated in the lemma.

Let FV be a set of all furthest vertices of P.   For each furthest vertex u we define the first visible point b(u) of u to be the first vertex on the shortest internal path from g to u.   Let B be a set of all different first visible points.   If

B contains only two elements, say b(u) and b(v), then it is easily seen that the geodesic center must coincide with the mid-point of u and v, which contradicts the assumption. So B contains at least three elements, say b(u), b(v), and b(w). Since those three points are all visible from g, the internal boundary of F(u, v) must meet with that of F(u, w) only at the point g. □

References

[Asano (1986)] Asano, Te., "Dividing a Simple Polygon into Two Territories", Trans. of IECE of Japan, vol. E-69, pp. 521-523, 1986.

[Asano and Asano (1986)] Asano, Ta. and Asano, Te., "Voronoi Diagram in a Simple Polygon", Abstracts of Japan U.S.A. Joint Seminar on Discrete Algorithms and Complexity Theory, Kyoto, 1986.

[Bhattacharya and Toussaint (1985)] Bhattacharya, B.K. and Toussaint, G.T., "On geometric algorithms that use the furthest-point Voronoi diagram", in Computational Geometry, G.T. Toussaint, Ed., North Holland, pp. 43-61, 1985.

[Chazelle (1982)] Chazelle, B., "A Theorem on Polygon Cutting with Applications", 23rd Annual IEEE Symposium on Foundations of Computer Science, pp.339-349, 1982.

[El Gindy and Avis (1981)] El Gindy, H. and Avis, D., "A Linear Algorithm for Computing the Visibility Polygon from a Point", Journal of Algorithms, vol.2, pp.180-197, 1981.

[Kirkpatrick (1983)] Kirkpatrick, D.G., "Optimal Search in Planar Subdivisions", SIAM Journal on Computing", vol. 12, pp.28-35, 1983.

[Lantuejoul and Maisonneuve (1984)] Lantuejoul, C. and
Maisonneuve, F.,"Geodesic Methods in Qualitative Image
Analysis", Pattern Recognition, vol. 17, pp.177-187, 1984.

[Lee and Preparata (1984)] Lee, D.T. and Preparata, F.P.,
"Euclidean Shortest Paths in the Presence of Rectilinear
Barriers", Networks, Vol. 14, pp. 393-410, 1984.

[Preparata and Shamos (1985)] Preparata, F.P. and Shamos,
M.I., "Computational Geometry: An Introduction", Springer-
Verlag, pp. 160-165, 1985.

[Reif and Storer (1985)] Reif, J. and Storer, J.A., "Shortest
Paths in Euclidean Space with Polyhedral Obstacles", Tech.
Rept. CS-85-121, Brandes University, April 1985.

[Toussaint] Toussaint, G.T., "Computing Geodesic Properties of
Polygons", manuscript in preparation.

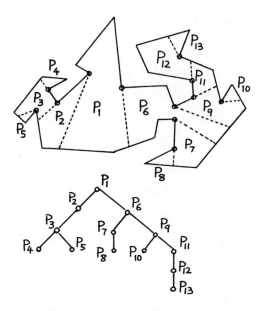

Fig. 1. Visibility decomposition of a simple
polygon and its region adjacency tree.

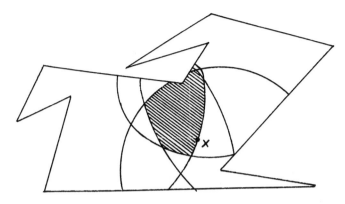

Fig. 2.   The range R(x).

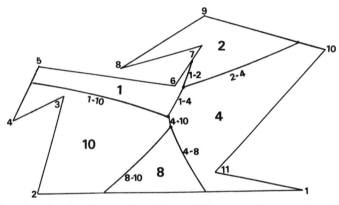

Fig. 3.   The furthest-point Voronoi diagram: A curve segment with a
pair of numerals attached is the equidistant portion from the
corresponding vertices.   A region having a big numeral k above is
FV(the vertex numbered k).

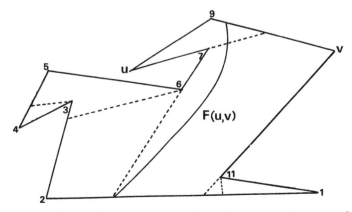

Fig. 4.   The equidistant portion from the two vertices u and v.

On deleting vertices to make a graph of positive genus planar

Joan P. Hutchinson[1]

Department of Mathematics, Smith College

Northampton, MA 01063

and

Gary L. Miller[1]

Department of Computer Science, University of Southern California

Los Angeles, CA 90089

Abstract. This paper contains a proof that an n-vertex graph of genus $g > 0$ contains a set of $O(\sqrt{gn})$ vertices whose removal leaves a planar graph.

1. Introduction

Many results for graphs of known or bounded genus $g > 0$ have been derived from related results for planar graphs. Sometimes planar results have pointed the way for graphs embedded on other surfaces; examples include embedding and isomorphism testing [7,8,12], and Kuratowski's theorem and the recent finiteness result of a forbidden subgraph characterization for every surface [14]. Sometimes planar results are actually central to the extended result; for example the separator theorem for graphs of bounded genus [9] relies on the planar separator theorem [11].

----

1. This research was done in part while both authors were visiting the Mathematical Sciences Research Institute, Berkeley, Calif., and was also supported in part by N.S.F. grants #DCR-8411690 and DCR-8514961, respectively.

Thus one approach to problems on graphs of positive genus is to reduce the graphs to planar ones, to use planar results and techniques, and to extend these results to the original graphs.

In this paper we consider the problem of finding a small set of vertices whose removal from an n-vertex graph of genus g leaves a planar graph. The results of [1] show that $g\sqrt{2n} = O(g\sqrt{n})$ vertices can always be removed from a graph on a surface of genus g to leave a planar graph. In [9] this result was improved to $O(\sqrt{gn}\, \log g)$, and it was conjectured that $O(\sqrt{gn})$ vertices are sufficient. In this paper we prove the latter conjecture. Similar results have been announced by H. N. Djidjev [3,6]; our work extends some ideas of [3] where a partial proof for finding a $O(\sqrt{gn})$ "planarizing" set is given.

<u>Theorem 1.</u> If G is an n-vertex graph embedded on a surface of genus $g > 0$, then there is a set of at most

$$26 \sqrt{gn} - 13 \sqrt{n/g} = O(\sqrt{gn})$$

vertices whose removal leaves a planar graph.

Most of the steps of this proof are constructive, and in a subsequent paper we will show how to implement these ideas as an algorithm that finds this set of vertices in an embedded graph. The algorithm runs in time linear in the number of edges of the graph.

The result of Theorem 1 is best possible up to constants since it is known that embedded graphs satisfy the following separator theorems and that up to constants these results are best possible.

Theorem 2. (Lipton and Tarjan [11]; Djidjev [4]) If G is a planar graph with n vertices, then there is a set of $O(\sqrt{n})$ vertices whose removal leaves no component with more than 2n/3 vertices.

Theorem 3. (Djidjev [5]; Gilbert, Hutchinson and Tarjan [9]) If G is a graph of genus g > 0 with n vertices, then there is a set of $O(\sqrt{gn})$ vertices whose removal leaves no component with more than 2n/3 vertices.

If there were a set of vertices in a graph of positive genus whose removal left a planar graph and whose order was smaller than $O(\sqrt{gn})$, then by removing these vertices and using the planar separator theorem one would have a smaller order separator for graphs of positive genus. This argument also shows that Theorems 1 and 2 imply Theorem 3; the algorithmic implementations are similarly related. However the proof of Theorem 1 and related algorithm are more intricate and involve constants larger than those in [9].

In section 2 we present background for this work, the graph theory lemmas and order arithmetic needed for the proof of Theorem 1, which is presented in section 3.

2. Background in topological graph theory and order arithmetic

We use the terminology of [2] and [15]. The main definitions follow. A graph is said to embed on a surface of genus g ≥ 0 if it can be drawn on the sphere with g handles, denoted S(g), so that no two edges cross. The genus of a graph G is the least integer g for which G embeds on S(g). A face of an embedding of G on S(g) is a connected component of S(g)\G and is called a 2-cell if it is contractible. An embedding is called a 2-cell embedding if every face is a 2-cell and a <u>triangulation</u> if every face is bounded by three edges. An example of a triangulation of the torus (g = 1) is shown in Figure 1a. These embedding terms can also be defined in a strictly combinatorial way. Indeed, they must be so defined for the algorithmic implementation.

A set of vertices whose removal from a graph G leaves a planar graph is called a <u>planarizing set for G</u>. An important planarizing set is a set of vertices whose induced subgraph leaves all other vertices in regions that are 2-cells.

Embedded graphs on nonplanar surfaces can contain three fundamental types of simple cycles. A cycle is called <u>contractible</u> if it can be continuously deformed on the surface into a point; otherwise it is called <u>noncontractible</u>. A simple noncontractible cycle may be either a <u>separating</u> cycle or a <u>nonseparating</u> cycle according as it does or does not divide the surface into two disjoint pieces. Figure 2 shows all three types of cycles in a graph on the double torus. The Euler-Poincaré Formula will be used to distinguish among these type of cycles; it is also crucial for other parts of the proof.

<u>Euler-Poincaré Formula.</u> If G has a 2-cell embedding on S(g), $g \geq 0$, then $n - e + f = 2 - 2g$ where n, e and f are, respectively, the number of vertices, edges and faces of the embedded graph.

The number, $2 - 2g$, is known as the Euler characteristic of S(g).

The proof of Theorem 1 will be by induction on g. First we look for a short, $O(\sqrt{n/g})$, noncontractible cycle in the embedded graph, and if such a cycle is present we can remove it and proceed by induction on graphs of smaller genus. If the graph contains no short noncontractible cycle, then we find a spanning

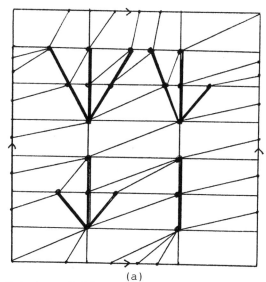

(a)
A triangulation of the torus with a
spanning forest of radius 2 with 4
components

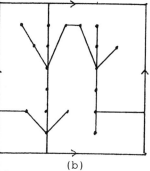

(b)
After deleting nonforest
edges until one 2-cell
remains

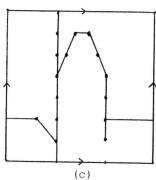

(c)
A planarizing subgraph

Figure 1.

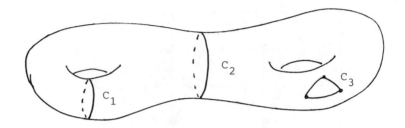

C_1: Noncontractible and nonseparating
C_2: Noncontractible and separating
C_3: Contractible

Figure 2.

forest of small radius and with few components. By a forest of
radius r we mean that every vertex is joined to a root by a path
with at most r edges. The next lemma is a generalization of a
result in [9] on spanning trees of embedded graphs.

<u>Lemma 4.</u>   Suppose the n-vertex graph G has a 2-cell embedding on
$S(g)$, $g > 0$, and suppose G has a spanning forest F of radius r
with $d \geq 1$ components. Then G contains a planarizing set of at
most $4gr + (d-1)(2r+1) + 1$ vertices.

Proof: We call the edges of F and $G \setminus F$ forest and nonforest
edges, respectively. We begin by deleting nonforest edges from G
one by one until the remaining graph is embedded with exactly one
face; as shown in [9] this can be accomplished so that the final
face is a 2-cell. (An example is shown in Figure 1 with $d = 4$,
$r = 2$ and $g = 1$.) Next we successively delete (nonroot) vertices of
degree one and their incident edge (necessarily a forest edge).
If G had originally e edges and f faces, we are left with a
subgraph G' of G with n' vertices, e' edges and f' faces where

$n' \leq n$, $e' \leq e$, $f' = 1$,   and $n' - e' + 1 = 2 - 2g$.

Let $F' = F \cap G'$ be the remaining spanning forest of radius $r' \leq r$ with $d' \leq d$ components. Thus

$$e' = n' - 1 + 2g = (n' - d') + (2g + d' - 1),$$

and the e' edges of G' consist of $(n' - d')$ forest edges and $(2g + d' - 1)$ nonforest edges.

Now the spanning forest F' has d' roots, and each nonforest edge of G' joins two vertices of F' at distance at most r' from a root. Furthermore, by construction every vertex of G' lies on some path from a nonforest edge to a root of F'. We estimate the number of vertices of G'. First there are d' roots of F'. Then to every nonforest edge $w = \{u_1, u_2\}$ we associate the at most $2r'$ (nonroot) vertices that lie on the path from u_i to a root, $i = 1, 2$. Thus

$$n' \leq d' + (2g + d' - 1)(2r')$$

$$\leq d + (2g + d - 1)(2r)$$

$$= 4gr + (d - 1)(2r + 1) + 1.$$

If these n' vertices of G' are removed, the remaining graph lies in the one 2-cell face of G' and so is planar. ∎

When the graph contains no $O(\sqrt{n/g})$ noncontractible cycle, we proceed by finding a breadth first spanning tree of presumably too large a radius and then break it into a spanning forest of small radius, $r = O(\sqrt{n/g})$, with few components, $d = O(g)$.

<u>Lemma 5.</u> If G is a connected graph with n vertices, then G has a spanning forest of radius r with at most $\lceil n/(r+1) \rceil$ components.

Proof: Let T be a spanning tree of G of radius s with root t; we are done if $s \leq r$. Pick a leaf z of T at distance s from t, and let x be the vertex at distance r from z along the path from z to t. Remove from G the vertex x and all its ancestors; this discarded part of G can be covered by one tree of radius r. The remaining graph is connected with at most $n - r - 1$ vertices and by induction its vertices can be covered by at most $\lceil (n-r-1)/(r+1) \rceil$ = $\lceil n/(r+1) \rceil - 1$ trees of radius at most r. Thus G can be covered by at most $\lceil n/(r+1) \rceil$ trees of radius r. ∎

Corollary 6. [3]   A graph G with n vertices and each connected component having at least m vertices has a spanning forest of radius r with at most $\lfloor n/(r+1) + n/m \rfloor$ components.

Proof: Suppose G has k connected components with $n_1, n_2, \ldots, n_k$ vertices each. Then $n_1 + \ldots + n_k = n$ and $n \geq km$. By Lemma 5 each component can be covered by at most $\lceil n_i/(r+1) \rceil$ trees and so G can be covered by at most

$$\sum_{i=1}^{k} \lceil n_i/(r+1) \rceil \; \leq \; \sum_{i=1}^{k} (n_i/(r+1)) + 1)$$

$$= \frac{n}{r+1} + k$$

$$\leq \frac{n}{r+1} + \frac{n}{m}. \quad \blacksquare$$

The next two lemmas give detailed information on the growth rate of the function $f(g,n) = 2\sqrt{gn} - \sqrt{n/g}$. This will be necessary for our induction steps.

Lemma 7.   For all $g > 1$ and $n > 0$

$$2\sqrt{(g-1)n} - \sqrt{n/(g-1)} + \sqrt{n/g} \leq 2\sqrt{gn} - \sqrt{n/g}.$$

Proof: Since

$$1/\sqrt{g} - 1/(2\sqrt{g-1}) < 1/(2\sqrt{g}) < 1/(\sqrt{g} + \sqrt{g-1}) = \sqrt{g} - \sqrt{g-1},$$

it follows that

$$2\sqrt{n/g} - \sqrt{n/(g-1)} < 2\sqrt{gn} - 2\sqrt{(g-1)n},$$

and the lemma follows. ∎

Lemma 8. Let g, n, x, y and d be positive integers satisfying $0 < g < n$, $0 < d \leq \sqrt{n/g}$, $0 < x < g$, and $0 < y < n-d$. Then

$$2\sqrt{xy} - \sqrt{y/x} + 2\sqrt{(g-x)(n-y-d)} - \sqrt{(n-y-d)/(g-x)} + d \leq 2\sqrt{gn} - \sqrt{n/g}.$$

Proof: Multiplying the inequality by $\sqrt{x}$, $\sqrt{g}$ and $\sqrt{g-x}$, we must show that

$$(2x-1)\sqrt{y}\sqrt{g-x}\sqrt{g} + (2g-2x-1)\sqrt{n-y-d}\sqrt{x}\sqrt{g} + d\sqrt{x}\sqrt{g-x}\sqrt{g}$$

$$\leq (2g-1)\sqrt{n}\sqrt{x}\sqrt{g-x}. \tag{1}$$

First we find the maximum value of the left hand side of (1) as a function of d: let $f(d) = (2g-2x-1)\sqrt{n-y-d}\sqrt{x}\sqrt{g} + d\sqrt{x}\sqrt{g-x}\sqrt{g}$. Then the maximum value of $f(d)$ occurs when $d = (n-y) - (g-x) + 1 - \frac{1}{4(g-x)}$. At this value of d, $n-y-d = (g-x) - 1 + \frac{1}{4(g-x)} < (g-x)$ since $(g-x)$ is an integer. Thus the left hand side of (1) is bounded by

$$(2x-1)\sqrt{y}\sqrt{g-x}\sqrt{g} + (2g-2x-1)\sqrt{n-y-d}\sqrt{x}\sqrt{g} + d\sqrt{x}\sqrt{g-x}\sqrt{g}$$

$$< \sqrt{g-x}\,[(2x-1)\sqrt{y}\sqrt{g} + (2g-2x-1)\sqrt{x}\sqrt{g} + d\sqrt{x}\sqrt{g}] \tag{2}$$

$$\leq \sqrt{g-x}\,[(2x-1)\sqrt{y}\sqrt{g} + (2g-2x-1)\sqrt{x}\sqrt{g}$$

$$+ ((n-y) - (g-x) + 1 - 1/(4(g-x)))\sqrt{x}\sqrt{g}] \tag{3}$$

Next we find the maximum value of (3) as a function of y: let $f(y) = (2x-1)\sqrt{y}\sqrt{g} + (n-y)\sqrt{x}\sqrt{g}$. Then the maximum value of $f(y)$ occurs at $y = x - 1 + \frac{1}{4x} < x$ since x is an integer. Thus (2) is bounded by

$$\sqrt{g-x}\,[(2x-1)\sqrt{x}\sqrt{g} + (2g-2x-1)\sqrt{x}\sqrt{g} + d\sqrt{x}\sqrt{g}]$$

$$\leq \sqrt{g-x}\,[(2g-2)\sqrt{x}\sqrt{g} + \sqrt{n}\sqrt{x}] \quad (\text{since } d \leq \sqrt{n/g})$$

$$< \sqrt{x}\sqrt{g-x}\,[(2g-1)\sqrt{n}] \quad (\text{since } g < n).$$

This last line is the desired right hand side of line (1). ■

3. The main result

We begin by looking for a $O(\sqrt{n/g})$ noncontractible cycle.
Given any simple cycle C we perform the following operation and
analysis to determine whether C is contractible or not,
separating or not. We can imagine "cutting" the surface along C,
then "sewing" in two discs, keeping a copy of C on the boundary
of each disc. Call the resulting graph G(C); it may no longer be a
triangulation.

Suppose one component $G_1(C)$ of G(C) has n' vertices, e' edges
and f' faces. Set g' = $\frac{1}{2}(2 - n' + e' - f')$, the genus of the surface
on which $G_1(C)$ is embedded. If g' = 0 or g, the cycle C was
contractible. If g' = g - 1 and G(C) is connected, then C was
noncontractible and nonseparating. G(C) is embedded on a surface
of genus g - 1, and a planarizing set for G(C) together with the
vertices of C forms a planarizing set for G. Finally if 0 < g' < g
and G(C) is not connected, then C was noncontractible and
separating. The component $G_1(C)$ is embedded on a surface of genus
g' and $G(C)\backslash G_1(C)$ is embedded on a surface of genus g - g'. A
planarizing set for G will consist of a planarizing set for each
component of G(C) together with the vertices of C; see Figure 2.

Theorem 1. If G is an n-vertex graph embedded on a surface of
genus g > 0, then G has a planarizing set of size at most
$26\sqrt{gn} - 13\sqrt{n/g}$.

Proof: We may assume that G is a triangulation since adding
edges to triangulate each face can only increase the size of the
planarizing set. The proof is by induction on g. In [9] it was
shown that a graph has a planarizing set of at most

$6\sqrt{gn}\log g + 6\sqrt{gn}$ vertices. Thus we may assume that $g > 2$, for $g \leq 2$ implies $6\sqrt{gn}\log g + 6\sqrt{gn} < 13\sqrt{gn} \leq 26\sqrt{gn} - 13\sqrt{n/g}$ for all positive g and n.

We may also assume that $\sqrt{n/g} > (26 - \frac{13}{3}) = 21.667$, for otherwise $n \leq (26 - \frac{13}{3})\sqrt{gn} \leq 26\sqrt{gn} - 13\sqrt{n/g}$ for $g \geq 3$, and all n vertices would form a planarizing set. Thus for future reference we assume

$$1 < .046\sqrt{n/g} \tag{4}$$

$$= .046\frac{1}{g}\sqrt{gn} \leq .015\sqrt{gn} \text{ for } g \geq 3. \tag{5}$$

We begin by finding a breadth first spanning tree T with levels $L_0, L_1, \ldots, L_r$ where L_i consists of all vertices at distance i from the root t and where r is the radius of T. Let $|L_i|$ denote the number of vertices in L_i, and set $F_i \subseteq L_i$ equal to those vertices of L_i adjacent to a vertex of L_{i+1}; we call F_i the frontier of L_i. We also define the level of an edge {u,v} (or of a triangle {a,b,c}) to be the maximum level of a vertex in the edge (or triangle).

Lemma 9. For $0 \leq i < r$, F_i induces a subgraph that consists of edge-disjoint cycles.

Sketch of proof: If F_i induces a subgraph of edge-disjoint cycles, then the modulo two sum of all edges of triangles at level $i+1$ with the edges of the cycles of F_i is clearly an edge-disjoint union of cycles and can be shown to equal F_{i+1}. (A similar result can be found in [13].) ∎

We note however that this decomposition into cycles may not be unique.

Suppose the graph G contains a noncontractible cycle C of length at most $13\sqrt{n/g}$; because this parameter arises so often we define $K = 13\sqrt{n/g}$. We perform the surface cutting construction described at the beginning of this section, but in addition we delete the two copies of C and all incident edges and we triangulate the resulting, nontriangular faces. Suppose C is nonseparating and noncontractible. By induction the remaining graph has a planarizing set P of size at most $26\sqrt{(g-1)n} - 13\sqrt{n/(g-1)}$. Then $P \cup C$ forms a planarizing set for G and by Lemma 7 has size at most $26\sqrt{gn} - 13\sqrt{n/g}$. Suppose C is separating and noncontractible. Then the remaining graph consists of two graphs, say $G_1(C)$ and $G_2(C)$ with y and $n - y - |C|$ vertices, respectively and of genus x and $g - x$, respectively where $0 < x < g$. By induction $G_1(C)$ has a planarizing set P_1 of size at most $26\sqrt{xy} - 13\sqrt{y/x}$, and $G_2(C)$ has a planarizing set P_2 of size at most $26\sqrt{(g-x)(n-y-d)} - 13\sqrt{(n-y-d)/(g-x)}$. Then $P_1 \cup P_2 \cup C$ forms a planarizing set for G and by Lemma 8 (with $|C| = d$) is of size at most $26\sqrt{gn} - 13\sqrt{n/g}$.

Otherwise every noncontractible cycle in G is larger than K. For $i = 1,2,\ldots,r$ let S_i be the region of the surface formed from all triangles and their boundaries with labels at most i; cycles of F_i form the boundary between S_i and $S(g) \backslash S_i$. We set $S_0 = F_0 = \{t\}$. Suppose we cut the surface $S(g)$ along the cycles of F_i, leaving a graph embedded on S_i with v_i vertices, e_i edges and f_i faces. Then the Euler characteristic of S_i is given by

$$E_i = v_i - e_i + f_i.$$

S_i is a subset of the sphere if and only if $E_i = 2$. See Figure 3.

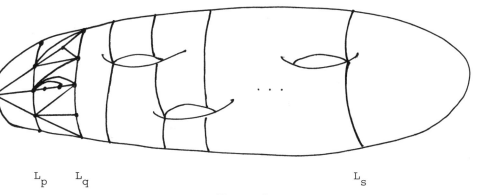

$$L_p \qquad L_q \qquad\qquad\qquad\qquad L_s$$

Figure 3.

Let q be the least integer such that either F_{q+1} contains a noncontractible cycle or $E_{q+1} < 2$. Figure 3 contains an example in which F_{q+1} contains noncontractible cycles. Let $p \leq q$ be the largest integer such that $|L_p| \leq K$; thus F_p contains only contractible cycles. Note that one cycle of F_p, call it c_p, separates the surface into a contractible region containing the root t and the noncontractible region. Finally let s be the greatest integer such that $E_{s-1} < g$, but $E_s = g$. Thus the region $S(g) \backslash S_g$ is a subset of the sphere and contains all vertices on levels s+1 and higher.

If s > p+1, then $|L_i| > K$ for $p < i < s$ by the definition of p and since $L_{q+1}, \ldots, L_{s-1}$ all contain noncontractible cycles of length greater than K. Let $G_{p,s}$ be the graph obtained from G by contracting all vertices on levels $L_0, L_1, \ldots, L_{p-1}$ to a new root t* and by deleting all vertices on levels $L_{s+1}, \ldots, L_r$. If $G_{p,s}$ has radius at most $5\sqrt{n/g}$, then by Lemma 4 and line (5), $G_{p,s}$ has a planarizing set P of size at most

$$4 \cdot 5 g\sqrt{n/g} + 1 \le 21.667 \sqrt{gn} \le 26 \sqrt{gn} - 13 \sqrt{n/g}$$

for $g > 2$. Note that since $L_0 \cup \ldots \cup L_{p-1}$ is embedded in a contractible region as is $L_{s+1} \cup \ldots \cup L_r$, then P forms a planarizing set for G as well as for $G_{p,s}$.

If the radius is larger than $5\sqrt{n/g}$, we divide $G_{p,s}$ up into b "bands" of radius $r' = \lceil \sqrt{n/g} \rceil$ where $b = \lceil (s-p)/r' \rceil$. For $i = 1, \ldots, b-1$ we let

$$B_i = L_{p+(i-1)r'+1} \cup \ldots \cup L_{p+ir'}, \text{ and}$$

$$B_b = L_{p+(b-1)r'+1} \cup \ldots \cup L_s.$$

Let $|B_i| = n_i$ and for $i = 1, \ldots, b$ let L_i^* be the smallest level in B_i. Then $|L_i^*| \le n_i/r'$. For future reference we set $t = \lceil 2\sqrt{n/g} \rceil$ and note that

$$n_1 \ge Kr' \qquad \text{since all levels have size } \ge K$$

$$\ge 6tr' \qquad \text{since } 6t \le 12\sqrt{n/g} + 6 < K \quad \text{by (4).} \qquad (6)$$

Consider a frontier $F_i^* \subseteq L_i^*$; by Lemma 9 it consists of edge-disjoint cycles. Each component of F_i^* that contains fewer than K vertices contains only contractible cycles; for each such contractible cycle C_i we delete all vertices in its (contractible) interior. We redefine F_i^* to be $F_i^* \setminus C_i$. (In other words the vertices of C_i are no longer considered to be in the frontier.) We have thrown away only a part of the graph that lies in a contractible region. Every component of (the remaining) F_i^* has at least K vertices, and by Corollary 6 these components can each be covered by at most $\lfloor n_i/(t+1) + n_i/K \rfloor$ trees of radius at most t. For $i = 2, \ldots, b-1$, let these components be covered by trees $T_1, T_2, \ldots, T_u$.

Instead of using F_1^*, we use $F_p \subseteq L_p$ and treat it in a slightly different way. Recall that $|F_p| \le |L_p| \le K$, and that F_p

contains a distinguished contractible cycle, c_p. We delete all

other cycles of F_p and their contractible interiors. We cover c_p

with at most $\lceil c_p/(2t+1) \rceil \leq \lceil 13\sqrt{n/g}/(4\sqrt{n/g}) \rceil = 4$ trees of radius

t (i.e., by paths of 2t edges). Call these trees $P_1, \ldots, P_w$.

From these pieces we construct the desired spanning forest F

of (the remainder of) $G_{p,s}$. First we cover c_p, $F_2^*, F_3^*, \ldots,$ and

F_{b-1}^* with the trees $P_1, \ldots, P_w, T_1, \ldots, T_u$. Then we use the portion

of the original tree T that extends from c_p up to and including

vertices in $L_2^* \setminus F_2^*$ (but not including F_2^*), for i = 2 to b-2

from F_i^* up to and including $L_{i+1}^* \setminus F_{i+1}^*$, and from F_{b-1}^* up

through L_s. F is a spanning forest of the remaining graph since a

vertex in the level above L_p or L_i^* is either contained in a

short contractible cycle and so is deleted or is adjacent only to

vertices in c_p or in (the remaining) F_i^*. Each portion from the

original tree T involves at most 2r' levels and so the resulting

trees in F have radius at most $t + 2r' \leq 4\sqrt{n/g} + 3 \leq 4.138\sqrt{n/g}$ by

(4).

Next we count the number of components of F. On levels L_2^*

and up we have at most

$$\sum_{i=2}^{b-1} (|L_i^*|/t + |L_i^*|/K) \leq \sum_{i=2}^{b-1} (n_i/tr' + n_i/r'K)$$

$$\leq n/tr' + n/r'K - n_1/tr' - n_1/r'K$$

$$\leq n/tr' + n/r'K - 7 \qquad\qquad\qquad \text{from (6).}$$

The cycle c_p is covered by at most 4 trees of radius t and so in

total F contains at most $d = n/tr' + n/r'K - 3$ components and

$(d-1) < n/tr' + n/r'K$. By Lemma 4, $G_{p,s}$ has a planarizing set of

size at most

$$4gr + (d-1)(2r+1) + 1 < 4g(t+2r') + (n/tr' + n/r'K)(2t + 4r'+1) + 1$$

$$\leq 4g(4.138\sqrt{n/g}) + (n/(2(n/g)) + n/(13(n/g)))(8\sqrt{n/g} + 7) + 1$$

$$\leq 16.55\sqrt{gn} + ((1/2)g + (1/13)g)(8.32\sqrt{n/g}) + 1 \qquad \text{by (4)}$$

$$\leq 16.55\sqrt{gn} + 4.8\sqrt{gn} + .015\sqrt{gn} \qquad \text{by (5)}$$

$$= 21.365\sqrt{gn} < 21.667\sqrt{gn}$$

$$\leq 26\sqrt{gn} - 13\sqrt{n/g} \quad \text{for } g \geq 3.$$

Thus F forms the desired planarizing set for $G_{p,s}$ and for G. ∎

4. Conclusion.

In [1] a stronger result was obtained, namely that in every triangulation of a surface of genus g with n vertices there is a nonseparating noncontractible cycle of length at most $\sqrt{2n}$. We conjecture that if $g \leq n$ there is always a $O(\sqrt{n/g})$ noncontractible cycle. This would imply Theorem 1: removing such a cycle and applying the conjecture repeatedly to graphs of smaller genus would produce a $O(\sqrt{gn})$ planarizing set. In [10] the following is established.

Theorem. If G is a triangulation of a surface of genus g with n vertices, then

a) if $g \leq n$, there is a $O(\sqrt{n/g}\log g)$ noncontractible cycle, and

b) if $g > n$, there is a $O(\log g) = O(\log n)$ noncontractible cycle.

In a subsequent paper we shall provide $O(e)$-time algorithms to find the planarizing set of Theorem 1 and the noncontractible cycle of the latter theorem.

Acknowledgements. The authors would like to thank Stan Wagon for many helpful conversations.

References

1. M. O. Albertson and J. P. Hutchinson, On the independence ratio of a graph, J. Graph Theory 2 (1978), 1-8.

2. J. A. Bondy and U. S. R. Murty, Graph Theory with Applications, American Elsevier Publishing Co., Inc., N.Y., 1976.

3. H. N. Djidjev, Genus reduction in nonplanar graphs, preprint.

4. ------, On the problem of partitioning planar graphs, SIAM J. Algebraic Discrete Methods 3 (1982), 229-240.

5. -------, A separator theorem, Comptes rendus de l'Académie bulgare des Sciences 34 (1981), 643-645.

6. -------, personal communication.

7. I. S. Filotti and J. N. Mayer, A polynomial-time algorithm for determining the isomorphism of graphs of fixed genus, Proceedings 12th ACM Symp. Th. Comp. (1980) 236-243.

8. I. S. Filotti, G. L. Miller and J. Reif, On determining the genus of a graph in $O(V^{O(g)})$ steps, Proceedings 11th ACM Symp. Th. Comp. (1979) 27-37.

9. J. R. Gilbert, J. P. Hutchinson and R. E. Tarjan, A separator theorem for graphs of bounded genus, J. Algorithms 5 (1984) 391-407.

10. J. P. Hutchinson, On small noncontractible cycles in embedded graphs, (to appear).

11. R. J. Lipton and R. E. Tarjan, A separator theorem for planar graphs, SIAM J. Appl. Math. 36 (1979), 177-189.

12. G. L. Miller, Isomorphism testing for graphs of bounded genus, Proceedings 12th ACM Symp. Th. Comp. (1980) 225-235.

13. G. L. Miller, Finding small simple cycle separators for 2-connected planar graphs, University of S. California Technical Report #85-336.

14. N. Robertson and P. D. Seymour, Generalizing Kuratowski's Theorem, Congressus Numerantium 45 (1984) 129-138.

15. A. T. White, Graphs, Groups and Surfaces, North-Holland, Amsterdam, 1973.

Algorithms for Routing around a Rectangle

(Extended Abstract)

Hitoshi Suzuki
Takao Nishizeki
and
Nobuji Saito

Department of Electrical Communications
Faculty of Engineering, Tohoku University
Sendai 980, Japan

Abstract. Efficient algorithms are given for the routing problems around a rectangle. These algorithms find a routing with two or three layers for two-terminal nets specified on the sides of a rectangle. The minimum area routing problem is also solved.

1. Introduction

In this paper we give three efficient algorithms for the routing problems around a rectangle. The routing region of our problem is modeled by a plane grid having exactly one rectangular hole. Each net consists of two terminals specified on the sides of the rectangular hole. In our routing the paths connecting terminals are pairwise edge-disjoint and are wired in two or three layers using the knock-knee mode.

The first algorithm finds a routing using three layers in a given region having an arbitrary perimeter. The time complexity is linear in the perimeter of the grid.

The second algorithm finds a routing using two layers in a given region having a rectangular perimeter. It runs in time linear in the number of terminals if they are initially sorted.

The third algorithm finds an outer rectangle of minimum area such that there is a routing using two layers in the region bounded by the outer rectangle and a given inner one. The algorithm has the same complexity as the second, and is faster than the known ones [GL,LaP]. Furthermore the area of the minimum outer rectangle can be explicitly expressed in terms of *"density of terminals"*.

In the algorithms we reduce the routing problems to the edge-disjoint path problem for a cycle graph with multiple edges.

2. Edge-disjoint paths

A *grid* is a subgraph of a plane integer grid. A *grid network* $N=(G,E)$ is defined as follows (see Fig. 1).

(1) $G=(V,E)$ is a connected grid having exactly one rectangular hole, where V is the set of vertices of G and E the set of edges. If B is the boundary of the hole and B' is the outer boundary of G, then all the vertices of G except those on B and B' have degree four.

(2) P is a set of 2-terminal nets (t_i,t_i'), $1 \le i \le k$. All the terminals lie on B, no terminal lies on the four corners c_1, c_2, c_3 and c_4 of B, and at most one terminal lies on each vertex of B except these corners.

One may assume that the corners c_1, c_2, c_3 and c_4 of B have coordinates $(0,0)$, $(0,h)$, (w,h) and $(0,w)$, respectively. The coordinates of vertex $v \in V$ are denoted by $(x(v),y(v))$. We assume that the set of terminals are initially sorted. The sorting can be done in $O(\text{MIN}\{b,k \log k\})$ time, where b denotes the number of vertices on B and k the number of nets. A grid network is *rectangular* if the outer boundary B' is rectangular (see Fig. 2). Let Q_i be a path connecting terminals t_i and t_i' on G. A set of k paths $\{Q_1,Q_2,...,Q_k\}$ are called *edge-disjoint paths* if $E(Q_i) \cap E(Q_j)=\varnothing$ for all i and j, $1 \le i < j \le k$, where $E(Q_i)$ denotes the set of edges in path Q_i. Edge-disjoint paths are drawn by thick lines in Figs. 1 and 2.

The subgraph of G corresponding to B is also denoted by B. We now construct a cycle (multi)graph G_C from the subgraph B as follows. First trim away the four corners of B: delete the four vertices c_1, c_2, c_3 and c_4 from B; and add four new edges $e_1=[(1,0),(0,1)]$, $e_2=[(0,h-1),(1,h)]$, $e_3=[(w-1,h),(w,h-1)]$ and $e_4=[(w,1),(w-1,0)]$. Next replace each edge of the trimed B by multiple edges. The multiplicity of edge $e \ne e_1, e_2, e_3, e_4$ equals the minimum number of edges in G parallel to e whose deletion channels the outer face B' and the hole B. On the other hand, the multiplicity of corner edge e_1 equals the number of edges in a minimum cutset crossing B and B' in the subgraph of G induced by vertices $\{v \in V | x(v) \le 1 \text{ and } y(v) \le 1\}$. The multiplicity of e_2, e_3 and e_4 is similarly defined. (See Fig. 3.) The resulting (multi)graph is called the *cycle graph G_C*. The network $N_C = (G_c, P)$ is called the *cycle network induced from N*. Then we have the next theorem.

Theorem 1. A grid network N has edge-disjoint paths if and only if the cycle network N_c has. $\square$

Clearly the cycle network N_c is constructed from N in $O(b')$ time, where b' denotes the number of vertices on B'. Edge-disjoint paths in a cycle network N_c can be found in $O(b)$ time [SNS1]. Furthermore edge-disjoint paths of a grid network N can be constructed from edge-disjoint paths in N_c in $O(k)$ time [SNS1,SNS2]. Thus edge-disjoint paths in a grid network N can be found in $O(b')$ time. Especially for a rectangular grid network edge-disjoint paths can be found in $O(k)$ time.

3. Routing

Routing using the knock-knee mode is defined as follows. A conducting layer is a graph isomorphic with the grid G. Assume that $l \geq 2$ layers $L_1, L_2, ..., L_l$ are available. These layers are stacked on top of each other, with L_1 on the bottom, L_2 next, ..., and L_l on the top. A *routing* of a network $N = (G, P)$ is the doublet of edge-disjoint paths $\{Q_1, Q_2, ..., Q_k\}$ in N and the assignment of a single layer to each edge of path Q_i, $1 \leq i \leq k$. If Q_i changes from L_g to L_h at a vertex, then a via is established between layers L_g and L_h at the vertex. If a via connects layers L_g and L_h $(g < h)$ at a vertex, then layers L_j, $g < j < h$, cannot be used at that vertex by another path. We have the following theorem.

Theorem 2. If a grid network has edge-disjoint paths, then it also has a routing with three layers. Especially if a rectangular grid network has edge-disjoint paths, then it has a routing with two layers. (See Figs. 4 and 5.) $\square$

The routing of a grid network N guaranteed by Theorem 2 can be found in $O(k)$ time from edge-disjoint paths in the cycle network N_c [SNS1,SNS2].

4. Minimum area routing

Given B and P, we wish to find a minimum rectangular grid network $N = (G, P)$ having a routing with two layers. Let B_T, B_B, B_L, and B_R be the sets of edges on the top, bottom, left and right sides of B, respectively. Let c_i', $1 \leq i \leq 4$, be the corner of the outer rectangle B' corresponding to c_i, as depicted in Fig. 2. We define the area A of a rectangular grid network N by

$$A = \{x(c_4') - x(c_1')\} \times \{y(c_2') - y(c_1')\}.$$

Let $h_T = y(c_2') - y(c_2) + 1$. Similarly define h_B, w_L, and w_R, as illustrated in Fig. 2. Then

$$A = (h - 2 + h_T + h_B) \times (w - 2 + w_L + w_R).$$

Since the height $h = |B_L|$ and width $w = |B_T|$ of the hole are constant, we shall minimize $h_T + h_B$ and $w_L + w_R$ in order to minimize the area A. For two edges e and e' in B we denote by $d(e,e')$ the number of nets such that one terminal lies in one of the components of $B - \{e,e'\}$ and the other in the other component. For $S, S' \in \{T, B, L, R\}$, let

$$d_{SS'} = \text{MAX}\{d(e,e') | \, e \in B_S, \, e' \in B_{S'}\}.$$

By Theorems 1 and 2 network N_c must satisfy the *"cut condition"* if N has a routing with two layers. Therefore the following lower bounds hold: $h_T + h_B \geq d_{TB}; \, w_L + w_R \geq d_{LR}.$

The sizes h_T, h_B, w_L, and w_R of the minimum network can be expressed in terms of $d_{SS'}$. Let

$$a_T = \{d_{TL} + d_{TR} - (d_{BL} + d_{BR}) + 2d_{TB}\}/4,$$
$$a_B = \{d_{BL} + d_{BR} - (d_{TL} + d_{TR}) + 2d_{TB}\}/4,$$
$$a_L = \{d_{TL} + d_{BL} - (d_{TR} + d_{BR}) + 2d_{LR}\}/4,$$

and

$$a_R = \{d_{TR} + d_{BR} - (d_{TL} + d_{BL}) + 2d_{LR}\}/4.$$

Note that $a_T + a_B = d_{TB}$ and $a_L + a_R = d_{LR}$. For $S, S' \in \{T, B, L, R\}$, define

$$D_{SS'} := \{e \in B_S | \text{ there is } e' \in B_{S'} \text{ with } d(e,e') = a_S + a_{S'}\}.$$

The set $D_{SS'}$ is *even* if each component of $B - \{e_1, e_2\}$ contains an even number of terminals for all pairs of edges $e_1, e_2 \in D_{SS'}$. Then we have the following theorem.

Theorem 3. Suppose that an inner rectangular boundary B together with a set P of nets on B are given. Then there is a rectangular grid network N which has a routing with two layers and whose sizes satisfy

  (a) $|h_T - a_T|, |h_B - a_B|, |w_L - a_L|, |w_R - a_R| \leq 1$;
  (b) if D_{TB} is even, $h_T + h_B = d_{TB}$; otherwise $h_T + h_B = d_{TB} + 1$;
  (c) if D_{LR} is even, $w_L + w_R = d_{LR}$; otherwise $w_L + w_R = d_{LR} + 1$.

Moreover no network smaller than N has a routing with two layers. □

We can compute $d_{SS'}$ and $D_{SS'}$ for all pairs of sides S and S' in $O(k)$ time. This fact together with Theorem 3 imply that a rectangular grid network of minimum area can be found in $O(k)$ time.

Remark: Independently of us   A. Frank and É. Tardos have obtained algorithms which are partly similar to ours. A joint paper is being prepared.

References

[GL]   T. F. Gonzalez and S. L. Lee, An optimal algorithm for optimal routing around a rectangle, *Proc. 20th Allerton Conference on Communication, Control, and Computing* (Oct. 1982), pp.636-645.

[LaP]   A. S. LaPough, A polynomial time algorithm for optimal routing around a rectangle, *Proc. 21st Symp. on Foundations of Computer Science* (1980), pp.282-293.

[SNS1] H. Suzuki, T. Nishizeki, and N. Saito, An algorithm for finding edge disjoint paths around a rectangle, *Tech. Rept. CAS85-133*, Inst. Elect. and Commun. Eng. of Japan (1986), pp.9-16 (*in Japanese*).

[SNS2] H. Suzuki, T. Nishizeki, and N. Saito, Routing around a rectangle, *Tech. Rept. AL85-27*, Inst. Elect. and Commun. Eng. of Japan (1985), pp.1-12 (*in Japanese*).

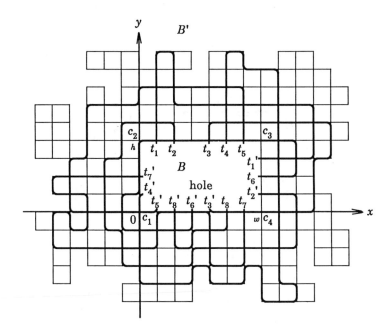

Fig. 1 A grid network.

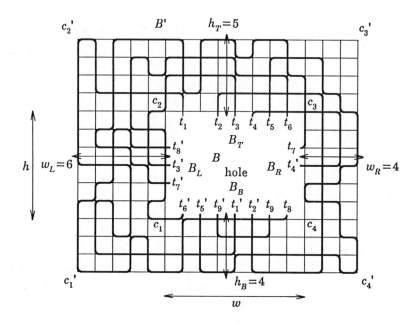

Fig. 2 A rectangular grid network.

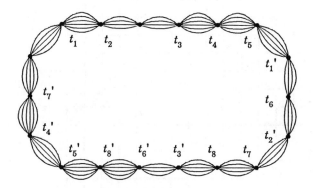

Fig. 3 The cycle network N_c induced from the grid
network N in Fig. 1.

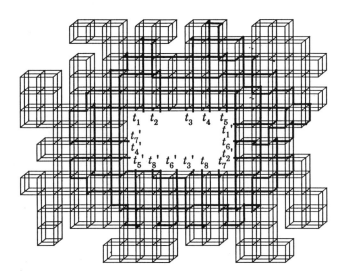

Fig. 4 A routing with three layers of the network in Fig. 1.

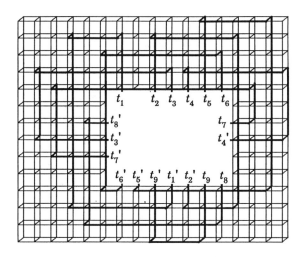

Fig. 5 A routing with two layers of the network in Fig. 2.

A Remark on the Complexity of the Knapsack Problem

Hajime Machida

Department of Computer Science

University of Electro-Communications

Chofu-shi, Tokyo 182, Japan

Abstract. The knapsack problem can be solved in $O(2^{n/2})$ steps by a method called the basic algorithm (or two list algorithm). In this paper, (i) it is shown that for some restricted class of inputs a modification of the basic algorithm is possible to run in $O(2^{\gamma n})$ steps ($0 < \gamma < 1/2$), and, on the other hand, (ii) it is indicated that for the full class of inputs an improvement over the basic algorithm seems quite difficult. The latter is derived from considering a lower bound on the complexity of the three list problem.

DISCRETE ALGORITHMS AND
COMPLEXITY

107

1. Introduction

A simple version of the *knapsack problem*, which is sometimes called the *subset sum problem* ([1]), is to decide if there exists a subset $S \subseteq \{1, 2, \ldots, n\}$ for which

$$b = \sum_{i \in S} a_i$$

holds when n+1 positive integers $a_1, a_2, \ldots, a_n$ and b are given as an input. This is a well-known NP-complete problem, and has been extensively studied in various fields such as operations research and cryptography.

This paper tries to give an observation on the computational complexity of this problem. Throughout the paper, complexity is measured as the number of arithmetic and comparison operations performed.

Obviously, the knapsack problem can be solved in $O(2^n)$ steps by composing every partial sum (subset sum) of $a_1, a_2, \ldots, a_n$ and checking if it is equal to b. On the other hand, since the problem is NP-complete, it is not expected to find a solution in polynomial number of steps.

An interesting question, therefore, is to find how much we can reduce the number of steps (in the worst case) from $O(2^n)$. This and related questions have been the subject of many authors including Horowitz and Sahni [2], Schroeppel and Shamir [4], and Karnin [3]. By exploiting one simple and clever method, which appears in all three papers mentioned above and will be described in §2, it is shown that the knapsack problem can be solved in $O(2^{n/2})$ steps. After [4], we call this method the *basic algorithm*. (This is also called *two list algorithm* in [3].)

At first sight, modifications of the basic algorithm in various ways might look plausible to obtain better bounds. In fact, as we will see in the following section, it can be slightly modified to run in less than $O(2^{n/2})$ steps for some restricted class of inputs. However, for the full class of inputs, improvement seems quite difficult, no matter whether it is based on the basic algorithm or on some totally different method. Up to now, no algorithm is known to overcome this $O(2^{n/2})$ bound.

In §3, we give an indication that an improvement does not seem to be possible as far as it is based on the basic algorithm. For this purpose, we introduce a new problem, which we call the *three list problem*, and by considering a lower bound on the complexity of this problem we derive somewhat informally the difficulty (if not the impossibility) of an improvement through the basic algorithm.

Note that upper bounds of this kind for other NP-complete problems are investigated in Tarjan and Trojanowski [6]. There, $O(2^{n/3})$ upper bound is given for the maximum independent set problem (or, equivalently, the clique problem).

2. The Basic Algorithm and a Restricted Modification

First we present the basic algorithm.

Basic Algorithm:

1) Divide a_1, a_2, $\cdots$, a_n into two groups

$$A_1 = (a_1, a_2, \cdots , a_{\lfloor n/2 \rfloor})$$

and

$$A_2 = (a_{\lfloor n/2 \rfloor + 1}, \cdots , a_{n-1}, a_n).$$

2-1) Compute all subset sums x_i ($1 \leq i \leq 2^{\lfloor n/2 \rfloor}$) of A_1 and sort them into an *ascending* order to make a list

$$L_1 = (x_1, x_2, \cdots, x_{2^{\lfloor n/2 \rfloor}}).$$

2-2) Compute all subset sums y_j $(1 \le j \le 2^{\lceil n/2 \rceil})$ of A_2 and sort them
into a *descending* order to make a list

$$L_2 = (y_1, y_2, \ldots, y_{2^{\lceil n/2 \rceil}}).$$

3) Initialize $i \leftarrow 1$ and $j \leftarrow 1$.
Repeat the following until $i > 2^{\lfloor n/2 \rfloor}$ or $j > 2^{\lceil n/2 \rceil}$:

  <u>if</u> $x_i + y_j < b$ <u>then</u> $i \leftarrow i+1$;

  <u>if</u> $x_i + y_j > b$ <u>then</u> $j \leftarrow j+1$;

  <u>if</u> $x_i + y_j = b$ <u>then</u> answer "yes" and halt.

<u>if</u> i (or j) exceeds $2^{\lfloor n/2 \rfloor}$ (or $2^{\lceil n/2 \rceil}$), <u>then</u> answer "no" and halt.

Actually, the term "basic algorithm" is often used to indicate only
the essential part of the algorithm, namely, the last halves of steps
2-1) and 2-2) and step 3). In such case, lengths of lists L_1 and L_2 may
not be identical.

It is easy to see that the algorithm is correct and that it
terminates in $O(2^{n/2})$ steps in the worst case.

<u>N.B.</u> Strictly speaking, this bound should be stated as $O(n2^{n/2})$
rather than $O(2^{n/2})$, because sorting $2^{n/2}$ elements requires $O(n2^{n/2})$
steps. However, we follow the tradition to ignore polynomial factors in
O-notation when dominant factors are exponential functions.

In order to illustrate the algorithm, we give a simple example.

<u>Example.</u> Suppose n=6, and a_1=2, a_2=21, a_3=25, a_4=3, a_5=10, a_6=18,
and b=50. For this input, A_1 = (2, 21, 25) and A_2 = (3, 10, 18), and the
sorted lists L_1 and L_2 of subset sums are

$$L_1 = (0, 2, 21, 23, 25, 27, 46, 48)$$

and

$$L_2 = (31, 28, 21, 18, 13, 10, 3, 0).$$

In step 3), computation proceeds making pairs from left to right in the diagram below.

L_1:   0   2   21   23   25   27   46   48

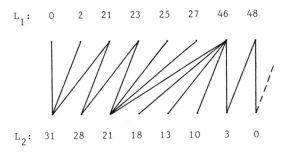

L_2:   31   28   21   18   13   10   3   0

Since the list L_1 is exhausted before the desired sum (= 50) is found, the algorithm answers "no" to this input and halts.

As stated in the introduction, various modifications over the basic algorithm are conceivable, but so far none of them turned out to be successful in reducing the complexity. An improvement by some new techniques is, of course, quite welcome. But, this seems even more difficult.

In the following proposition, we show that there is an $O(2^{\gamma n})$ - algorithm for the knapsack problem if the class of inputs is restricted as stated below, where $0 < \gamma < 1/2$ is a constant depending on the restriction. This is accomplished by consecutive applications of the basic algorithm with different b's in inputs.

Proposition 1. Let δ and ϵ be constants satisfying $0 < 2\delta < \epsilon < 1/2$. Let $I(\delta, \epsilon)$ be the class of inputs $(a_1, a_2, \ldots, a_n; b)$ to the knapsack problem for which there is an i $(1 \leq i \leq n-\epsilon n)$ such that the difference between the i-th largest element and the (i+ϵn)-th largest element among $a_1, a_2, \ldots, a_n$ is no more than $2^{\delta n}$. Then, the knapsack problem with the input set $I(\delta, \epsilon)$ can be solved in $O(2^{\gamma n})$ steps, where 0

$< \gamma < 1/2$ is a constant depending only on δ and ϵ.

Proof. Let $(a_1, a_2, \ldots, a_n; b)$ be in $I(\delta, \epsilon)$ and, w.l.o.g., assume that $a_1 \leq a_2 \leq \cdots \leq a_{\epsilon n}$ and $a_{\epsilon n} - a_1 \leq 2^{\delta n}$. Set $A_0 = \{a_1, a_2, \ldots, a_{\epsilon n}\}$.

The algorithm is as follows: Compute all subset sums of A_0. For each *distinct* value of subset sum x of A_0, if $x < b$ then apply the basic algorithm with the input $(a_{\epsilon n+1}, a_{\epsilon n+2}, \ldots, a_n; b-x)$. If $x=b$, a solution is found without using any element outside A_0. And, if $x > b$, just throw this x away.

The correctness of the algorithm is obvious. The amount of work done is, in essence, the sum of the following: i) $O(2^{\epsilon n})$ to compute subset sums of A_0 and ii) $O(2^{(n-\epsilon n)/2})$, for one application of the basic algorithm, multiplied by the number of times the basic algorithm is applied. The last quantity is the number of mutually distinct values in all subset sums of A_0. In order to obtain an upper bound on this, partition every a_i $(1 \leq i \leq \epsilon n)$ into two parts: $a_i = a_1 + r_i$. By assumption, $0 \leq r_i \leq 2^{\delta n}$. Then, a subset sum can be decomposed into several a_1's and a value obtained as a sum of r_i's, which ranges from 0 to $(\epsilon n-1)2^{\delta n}$. Thus, the number of distinct values of subset sums of A_0 is bounded above by the possible number of contributions of a_1 in a sum $(= \epsilon n)$ times the possible number of values represented as a sum of r_i's $(\leq (\epsilon n-1)2^{\delta n}+1)$, which is $O(n^2 2^{\delta n})$. Part ii), therefore, is $O(2^{(1-\epsilon+2\delta)n/2})$. Finally, the desired γ is obtained if we put $\gamma = \max\{\epsilon, (1-\epsilon+2\delta)/2\}$. □

3. The Three List Problem and its Relation to the Knapsack Problem

a) The Three List Problem

The algorithm shown in Proposition 1 may be characterized as one constructing three lists of numbers and checking if an element from the first list and an element from the second list sums to an element of the third list. Other attempts to improve the basic algorithm often results in the similar situation. All this inspires us to consider the following problem.

Three List Problem: Given three lists of positive integers $(a_1, a_2, \ldots, a_p)$, $(b_1, b_2, \ldots, b_q)$ and $(c_1, c_2, \ldots, c_r)$ where each list is sorted into an ascending order, determine if there exist i, j and k such that

$$a_i + b_j = c_k.$$

This simple problem has a straightforward algorithm: For every c_k ($1 \leq k \leq r$), apply the similar procedure as Step 3) of the basic algorithm with $(a_1, a_2, \ldots, a_p)$ as L_1, $(b_1, b_2, \ldots, b_q)$ as L_2 in the reverse order and c_k as b.

It is easy to see that this algorithm runs in $O((p+q)r)$ steps. So, an upper bound on the complexity of the three list problem is $O((p+q)r)$.

However, what we are interested in is not an upper bound but a lower bound. In fact, suppose we are able to show a lower bound of the same order as the upper bound above, then the implication would be the following: Any algorithm which solves the knapsack problem relying heavily on the basic algorithm must encounter, in an intermediate stage of the computation, with a situation where two lists $(a_1, a_2, \ldots, a_p)$ and $(b_1, b_2, \ldots, b_q)$ are prepared and sums $a_i + b_j$ are to be matched with entries in $(c_1, c_2, \ldots, c_r)$, though the last list may not explicitly be given as a list. This is identical to the three list problem. It is natural to assume $p \sim 2^u$, $q \sim 2^v$ and $r \sim 2^w$ where $n = u+v+w$. But, then, the assumption of $\Omega((p+q)r)$ lower bound to the three list problem implies

$\Omega((2^u+2^v)2^w)$ lower bound to the knapsack problem, which is no less than $\Omega(2^{n/2})$. This is by no means a rigorous argument. However, it tells us, to some extent, the insufficiency of the basic algorithm.

b) A Lower Bound

Now we consider a lower bound on the complexity of the three list problem. As the reader will see, we actually give a lower bound on the number of comparison operations performed.

First comes the definition of $\mu(p, q; r)$ which plays the central role in the following discussion.

Definition. Let p, q and r be positive integers. Consider the p×q lattice in the plane as shown in the diagram. Assosiate to each intervel (i-1, i) in the x-axis a positive integer a_i and to each interval (j-1, j) in the y-axis a positive integer b_j, where $1 \le i \le p$ and $1 \le j \le q$, such that $a_1 \le a_2 \le \cdots \le a_p$ and $b_1 \ge b_2 \ge \cdots \ge b_q$ hold. Call $\alpha = ((a_1, a_2, \cdots, a_p), (b_1, b_2, \cdots, b_q))$ an assignment of weights to unit intervals. A weight of an (open) unit square in the p×q lattice corresponding to an interval (i-1, i) in x-axis and to an interval (j-1, j) in y-axis is defined to be the sum of a_i and b_j. A step function on the lattice connecting the origin (0, 0) and the point (p, q) is called a contour if a weight of any unit square below it is (strictly) greater

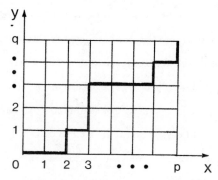

than a weight of any unit square above it. We define $\mu_\alpha(p, q; r)$ to be the number of ways in which r contours in the p×q lattice are chosen (repetition permitted) under an assignment α, and $\mu(p, q; r)$ to be the maximum of $\mu_\alpha(p, q; r)$ where α ranges over all assignments α. (In other words, $\mu_\alpha(p, q; r)$ is the number of arrangements of r contours in the p×q lattice under assignment α.)

Note that a contour is necessarily a monotone function and that two contours never cross over each other.

Proposition 2. Let t(p, q; r) be the number of steps necessary to solve the three list problem in the worst case where p, q and r are lengths of each list in an input. Then

$$t(p, q; r) \geq \log_2 \mu(p, q; r).$$

Proof. Suppose that lists $(a_1, a_2, \ldots, a_p)$, $(b_1, b_2, \ldots, b_q)$ and $(c_1, c_2, \ldots, c_r)$ are given as an input to the three list problem. Let $\alpha = ((a_1, a_2, \ldots, a_p), (b_1, b_2, \ldots, b_q))$ be an assignment to intervals of the p×q lattice. In the lattice, each c_k $(1 \leq k \leq r)$ uniquely determines a contour in an obvious way if c_k is not represented as a sum of a_i and b_j $(1 \leq i \leq p, 1 \leq j \leq q)$. If $c_k = a_i + b_j$ for some i and j, on the other hand, a contour is not uniquely determined by c_k.

We claim the following:

(i) After a series of comparison operations performed, the answer "no" can be issued only if we know every $c_k (1 \leq k \leq r)$ determines a unique contour. In other words, for some unit square if the knowledge obtained so far is not sufficient to decide uniquely a contour corresponding to c_k passes above it or below it, it is possible that the weight of the square is c_k and the answer to the input may be "yes".

(ii) Assume that ℓ comparisons are done and the number of placements of r contours in the lattice that are consistent with all outcomes (e.g., $\leq$ or $>$) of ℓ comparisons is μ. Suppose another comparison is performed. Then, at least $\mu/2$ of placements of r contours must have the same outcome under the $\ell+1$th comparison, that is, at least $\mu/2$ of placements of r contours are consistent with all $\ell+1$ comparisons.

Now, by claims (i) and (ii), it is clear that we need no less than $\log_2 \mu_\alpha$ (p, q; r) comparisons in order to extract exactly one placement of r contours from μ_α(p, q; r) placements. Thus we have the desired inequality. □

At present we do not know the exact value of μ(p, q; r). (See Remark at the end of the paper.) However, we have the following.

Lemma. i) $\mu(p, q; r) \leq (_{p+q}C_p)^r$,

ii) $\mu(p, q; r) \geq \max \{(_{(p/r)+q}C_q)^r, (_{p+(q/r)}C_p)^r\}$.

Proof. i): Clear, since $_{p+q}C_p$ is the number of monotone step functions going up and right from (0,0) to (p,q). ii): Divide the interval [0,p] in the x-axis into r equal parts, each subsection having the length p/r. Consider r monotone step functions such that the k-th function stays 0 in the first k-1 subsections, goes up only in the k-th subsection, and stays q in the rest of subsections. These step functions are contours for some assignment of weights to unit intervals. The number of placements of r such contours is $(_{(p/r)+q}C_q)^r$, which gives a lower bound for μ(p, q; r). Another lower bound is similarly obtained by dividing the interval in the y-axis. □

The following is an immediate consequence of Proposition 2 and ii) in Lemma.

   Corollary. Let $t(p, q; r)$ be as in Proposition 2.

   $t(p, q; r) \gtrsim \max \{r(p \log(1+q/pr)+(q/r)\log(1+pr/q)),$

   $\qquad\qquad\qquad r(q \log(1+p/qr)+(p/r)\log(1+qr/p))\}.$

To conclude, we remark again an implication of the above argument to the knapsack problem. *Assume* that, in the process of solving the knapsack problem with an input of size n, we encounter with the three list problem whose input consists of three lists of length 2^u, 2^v and 2^w where $n = u+v+w$. Then, according to Corollary,

   complexity of the knapsack problem (under the above assumption)

   $\geq$ complexity of the three list problem

   $\gtrsim 2^w(2^u \log(1+2^{-u+v-w}) + 2^{v-w}\log(1+2^{u-v+w}))$

   $\sim 2^{n-v}+2^v$

   $= \Omega(2^{n/2}).$

This tells us the difficulty of improving $O(2^{n/2})$ upper bound of the knapsack problem through superficial modification of the basic algorithm. However, as a matter of course, it does not exclude any possibility of improvement by deeper considerations and subtle treatment of the problem.

Remark. Related to $\mu(p, q; r)$ is the number of ways in which r monotone step functions are chosen in the pxq lattice such that no two cross over each other. As pointed out by Richard Stanley, this is identical to the number of "plane partitions" with p rows, q columns and the largest entry $\leq$ r. The exact value is known for this number. The subject of plane partition is thoroughly studied in Stanley [5].

   The author is grateful to Ronald Graham and Richard Stanley for kindly introducing him into the beautiful theory of plane partitions.

References

[1] Garey, M.R., and Johnson, D.S., *Computers and Intractability*, Freeman and Company, San Francisco, 1979.

[2] Horowitz, E., and Sahni, S., Computing partitions with applications to the knapsack problem, *J. Ass. Comput. Mach.*, 21, 2 (1974), 277-292.

[3] Karnin, E.D., A parallel algorithm for the knapsack problem, *IEEE Trans. on Comput.*, C-33, 5 (1984), 404-408.

[4] Schroeppel, R., and Shamir, A., A $TS^2 = O(2^n)$ time/space trade-off for certain NP-complete problems, in *Proc. 20th IEEE Symp. on Foundations of Comput. Sci.*, 1979, 328-336.

[5] Stanley, R.P., Theory and application of plane partitions, Parts 1 and 2, *Studies in Applied Math.*, 50 (1971), 167-188, 259-279.

[6] Tarjan, R.E., and Trojanowski, A.E., Finding a maximum independent set, *SIAM J. on Comput.*, 6, 3 (1977), 537-546.

Fast, Rigorous Factorization

and

Discrete Logarithm Algorithms

Carl Pomerance*

Department of Mathematics

The University of Georgia

Athens, Georgia   30602, USA

§1.   Introduction.

The last decade has seen an exponential increase in activity
concerning the related algorithmic problems of factoring integers and
computing discrete logarithms in finite fields. Since an "answer" to an
instance of one of these problems can be very easily verified, it is
possible to profitably employ an efficient algorithm that has not been
rigorously analyzed. In fact every practical factorization or discrete
logarithm algorithm that purports to be sub-exponential in its worst case
has only heuristic analyses.

In factoring, the fastest known algorithms all share a heuristic
worst case running time of $L(N)^{1+o(1)}$ to factor N , where

$$L(N) = \exp(\sqrt{\log N \, \log\log N})$$

and log denotes the natural logarithm; see Coppersmith, Odlyzko,
Schroeppel [7], Lenstra [12], Pomerance [16], and Schnorr, Lenstra [17].
The fastest rigorously proved factoring algorithm has expected running
time $L(N)^{\sqrt{5/2} \, + \, o(1)}$, see Pomerance [16].

---

*Supported in part by an NSF grant.

DISCRETE ALGORITHMS AND
COMPLEXITY

For discrete logarithms in $GF(q)$ (the finite field with q elements), the fastest known algorithms to compute a discrete logarithm from scratch have heuristic running time $L(q)^{1+o(1)}$ if q is prime and heuristic running time $\exp\{O((\log q)^{1/3}(\log\log q)^{2/3})\}$ if q is a power of 2; see Coppersmith [6], Coppersmith, Odlyzko, Schroeppel [7], and Odlyzko [15]. For the case of q prime, Adleman [1] has sketched a rigorous argument that discrete logarithms may be computed in time $L(q)^c$ for some constant c. Although this exponent c was not computed, using the tools cited in Adleman's paper, an upper bound of $2\sqrt{2} + o(1)$ may be inferred. Using the tools in Pomerance [16], a value of $c = \sqrt{5/2} + o(1)$ may be obtained. For $GF(q)$ with q a power of 2, Hellman, Reyneri [21] have given a rigorous treatment similar to Adleman's obtaining an upper bound of $L(q)^{\sqrt{12} + o(1)}$. (Thanks are due to K. McCurley for this reference.)

The case when $q = p^n$ is a non-trivial power of an odd prime has been less well studied. For p relatively small, the techniques for $GF(2^n)$ carry over essentially intact. For $n = 2$ we have the recent work of ElGamal [9]. Odlyzko [15] points out that this method can be extended to the case n bounded. I do not consider these fields here.

In this paper, I shall present and rigorously analyze two similar random algorithms, one for factoring and one for computing discrete logarithms in $GF(q)$ where q is prime or a power of 2. The factoring algorithm will have expected worst case running time $L(N)^{\sqrt{2} + o(1)}$ and the discrete logarithm algorithm will have expected worst case running time $L(q)^{\sqrt{2} + o(1)}$ for a preprocessing stage and expected worst case running time $L(q)^{\sqrt{1/2} + o(1)}$ for the actual discrete logarithm calculation.

Both methods are quite similar to previously considered algorithms. In particular, the factoring algorithm is a variant of Dixon's random squares method [8], which itself is based on ideas of Morrison, Brillhart

[14] and earlier writers. Here the random squares method is augmented with Lenstra's elliptic curve factoring method [12] and Wiedemann's coordinate recurrence method [20] for solving a sparse system of linear equations over a finite field. The discrete logarithm algorithm is based on the index calculus method of Western, Miller [19] (see [15] for further references). Again, the new ingredients are the elliptic curve method (in the case q prime) and the coordinate recurrence method.

It is perhaps paradoxical that the elliptic curve factoring method can be used as a subroutine in a rigorously analyzed algorithm while it itself has not been completely rigorously analyzed. The point is that the algorithms described here are random, so a subroutine need not work on all inputs. What will be shown is that a somewhat weakened form of the elliptic curve method works fairly rapidly for most inputs. The argument uses a new result of Friedlander, Lagarias [10] in analytic number theory.

That it might be possible to rigorously employ his elliptic curve method as a subroutine in the random squares algorithm was suggested by Lenstra [12]. This method has already been used in the heuristic analyses of some discrete logarithm algorithms, see Coppersmith, Odlyzko, Schroeppel [7].

In [18], Seysen describes a random factoring algorithm that under the sole assumption of the Extended Riemann Hypothesis (ERH) can be proved to have expected running time $L(N)^{\sqrt{5/4} + o(1)}$. It is likely that by using some of the methods of this paper that the expected running time for Seysen's algorithm can be reduced to $L(N)^{1 + o(1)}$, still under the assumption of the ERH.

§2.   A rigorous version of the elliptic curve factoring method.

If $v,w \geq 2$, let

$$k(v,w) = \prod_{j=2}^{[w]} j^{e_j}$$

where e_j is the largest integer with $j^{e_j} \leq v + 2\sqrt{v} + 1$. One iteration
of the elliptic curve method to factor N with parameters v,w is as
follows (cf. Lenstra [12], paragraph (2.4)).

Step 1.   Choose a, x_0, y_0 at random in $\mathbb{Z}/N$ and let

$b = y_0^2 - x_0^3 - ax_0$.   Then $P := (x_0, y_0)$

is on the curve $E : y^2 = x^3 + ax + b$.

Step 2.   Attempt to compute $k(v,w)P$ mod N on E by the addition

procedure described in [12].

The addition procedure mimics addition of points on elliptic curves modulo
a prime. Since N is presumably not prime, the procedure of Step 2 may
break down. But this is good, for as shown in [12], if the addition
procedure breaks down, a non-trivial divisor of N is necessarily
revealed.

If Step 2 is completed, then the algorithm has been unsuccessful in
factoring N . However, one then can go back to Step 1 and repeat the
procedure gaining a new chance to factor N. If $n, w \geq 2$, let

$$\psi_0(n,w) = \#\{m \in (n-\sqrt{n}, n+\sqrt{n}) : \text{no prime factor of } m \text{ exceeds } w\}.$$

The following result is Corollary (2.8) in [12].

THEOREM A (Lenstra).   *There is an effectively computable constant*

$1 > c_1 > 0$ *with the following property. Let* N, v *be integers*

exceeding 1   *such that* N *has at least two distinct prime factors and*

such that the smallest prime factor p *of* N *satisfies* $3 < p \leq v$. *If* w

is such that $\psi_0(p,w) \geq 3$, *then the success probability of obtaining a*

non-trivial factorization of N *with at most* h *iterations of the*

elliptic curve method with parameters v,w *is at least*

$$1 - (1-c_1)^{h\psi_0(p,w)/(\sqrt{p} \log v)} .$$

Thus if h is a large constant times $\sqrt{p}$ $(\log v)/\psi_0(p,w)$ we will

expect success with at most h iterations. Since the running time for

one iteration is of order $w \log v$ arithmetic operations mod N, to

choose an optimal w we essentially wish to minimize the expression

$\sqrt{p}$ $w/\psi_0(p,w)$ (ignoring the factor $\log^2 v$).

Let

$\psi(x,w) = \#\{m \leq x:$ no prime factor of m exceeds $w\}$.

If one conjectures that $\sqrt{p}/\psi_0(p,w)$ is about the same as $p/\psi(p,w)$, it

is easy to choose an optimal w . Indeed, it is known that the expression

$pw/\psi(p,w)$ for a fixed number $p > 3$ is minimized for $w = L(p)^{\sqrt{1/2} + o(1)}$

and the value of the fraction for this w is $L(p)^{\sqrt{2} + o(1)}$. That is,

from the conjecture that $\sqrt{p}/\psi_0(p,w)$ is about the same as $p/\psi(p,w)$

one can deduce that the elliptic curve method is expected to factor N in

time $L(p)^{\sqrt{2} + o(1)}$ if N is divisible by at least 2 distinct primes and

its least prime p exceeds 3. (Of course, one does not know p in

advance. The protocol for implementing this optimized version of the

elliptic curve method involves a gradually increasing value of the

parameter v in later iterations, always choosing $w = L(v)^{\sqrt{1/2}}$. When

the prime p is finally trapped, we find that we probably have spent time

$L(p)^{\sqrt{2} + o(1)}$ doing so.)

Although this optimized version of the elliptic curve method is based

on an unproved hypothesis, Theorem A is just that, a theorem. Although

the unproved hypothesis seems very difficult and is far from resolution,

we do have theorems that point in this direction. The following result is

a special case of Theorem 6 in [10].

THEOREM B (Friedlander-Lagarias). *For any fixed* $\varepsilon > 0$ *there is a*

positive constant $c(\varepsilon)$ *such that uniformly for all* $x \geq 2$, y *with*

$y \geq \exp\{(\log x)^{5/6 + \varepsilon}\}$, *the exceptional set of integers* $m \leq x$ *for which*

$$\psi(m + \frac{1}{2}\sqrt{x}, y) - \psi(m - \frac{1}{2}\sqrt{x}, y) > \frac{1}{16} \rho\left(\frac{\log x}{\log y}\right)\sqrt{x} \qquad (2.1)$$

fails has cardinality at most $c(\varepsilon)x \cdot \exp\{-\frac{1}{2}(\log x)^{1/6}\}$.

Remarks. Here ρ denotes Dickman's function, the continuous solution on $[0,\infty)$ of the differential-delay equation

$$u\rho'(u) = -\rho(u-1), \quad \rho(u) = 1 \quad \text{for} \quad 0 \le u \le 1.$$

It is known (de Bruijn [4]) that

$$\rho(u) = \exp\{-(1 + o(1))u \log u\}. \qquad (2.2)$$

Theorem B does indeed point towards the unproved hypothesis mentioned above, since from de Bruijn [6], we have $\psi(x,y) \sim \rho\left(\frac{\log x}{\log y}\right) x$ for x,y satisfying the hypotheses of the theorem.

We shall apply Theorem B with $y = \exp\{(\log(x/4))^{6/7}\}$ and for m running through primes in $(x/4, x]$. Let $S(x)$ denote the set of primes $3 < p \le x$ for which

$$\frac{1}{\sqrt{p}} \psi_0(p, \exp\{(\log p)^{6/7}\}) > \exp\{-\frac{1}{6}(\log x)^{1/7} \log\log x\}. \qquad (2.3)$$

THEOREM B'. *If* $\pi(x)$ *denotes the number of primes* $p \le x$, *then*

$$\pi(x) - \#S(x) = O(x \cdot \exp\{-\frac{1}{2}(\log x)^{1/6}\}).$$

Proof. Let $N_1(x)$ denote the number of primes $p \in (x/4, x]$ for which (2.3) fails. For p in this range, we have

$$\sqrt{p} > \frac{1}{2}\sqrt{x}, \quad \exp\{(\log p)^{6/7}\} > \exp\{(\log(x/4))^{6/7}\}.$$

In light of (2.2), if x is large enough, then the right side of (2.3) is smaller than the right side of (2.1) with $y = \exp\{(\log(x/4))^{6/7}\}$. Thus, for large x, if p is counted by $N_1(x)$, then p does not satisfy (2.1). Thus

$$N_1(x) \le c_2 x \cdot \exp\{-\frac{1}{2}(\log x)^{1/6}\}$$

for some absolute constant c_2 and for all large x.

Next, we let $N_2(x)$ denote the number of primes $p \in (x/16, x/4]$ for which (2.3) fails. Then $N_2(x) \le N_1(x/4)$, so that

$$N_2(x) \le c_2 \frac{x}{4} \exp\{ - \frac{1}{2} (\log \frac{x}{4})^{1/6}\},$$

if x is large. In general let $N_i(x)$ denote the number of primes $p \in (x/4^i, x/4^{i-1}]$ for which (2.3) fails where i is any integer with $4^i < \sqrt{x}$. For large x we have

$$N_i(x) \le c_2 \frac{x}{4^i} \exp\{- \frac{1}{2} \left(\log \frac{x}{4^i}\right)^{1/6} \}$$

for all such i . Now

$$\pi(x) - \#S(x) = \sum_i N_i(x) + O(\sqrt{x}) ,$$

and so a simple calculation gives our result.

We are now in a position to prove the major result of this section.

THEOREM 2.1. *There is a random algorithm which on input of an integer*

$N \ge 2$ *and a parameter* $v \ge 2$ *will produce integers* F, R *with* $N = FR$

and the complete prime factorization of F *. Moreover, with probability*

at least $1 - (\log N)/N$ *no prime in* $S(v)$ *divides* R *. The running time*

is $O((\log N)^4 \exp\{2(\log v)^{6/7}\})$.

Proof. By dividing out any factors 2, 3 from N, we may assume

$(6,N) = 1$. This can be accomplished in at most $O(\log N)$ arithmetic

operations, that is, in time $O((\log N)^3)$.

Let

$$w = \exp\{(\log v)^{6/7}\}, \quad h = 1 + [\frac{1}{c_1} (\log v)(\log N)\exp\{\frac{1}{6}(\log v)^{1/7}\log\log v\}]$$

where c_1 is as in Theorem A. We apply the elliptic curve method with

parameters v,w to N repeatedly until either we obtain a non-trivial

factorization of N or we have done h iterations, whichever comes

first. This can be accomplished in at most $O(hw \log v)$ arithmetic

operations mod N, that is, in time

$$O((\log N)^3 \exp\{2(\log v)^{6/7}\}).$$

If N is not a prime power and has a prime factor p in $S(v)$, then

the probability that the above procedure produces a non-trivial factorization of N is at least

$$1 - (1-c_1)^{h\psi_0(p,w)/(\sqrt{p}\ \log v)} > 1 - \frac{1}{N}\ .$$

Indeed, by Theorem A, the probability is at least the first expression and since $p \in S(v)$, we have

$$\frac{h\psi_0(p,w)}{\sqrt{p}\ \log v} \geq \frac{1}{c_1}\ \log N\ ,$$

so that

$$1 - (1-c_1)^{h\psi_0(p,w)/(\sqrt{p}\ \log v)} \geq 1 - (1-c_1)^{\frac{1}{c_1}\log N} > 1 - \frac{1}{N}\ .$$

If N has been factored, we apply the same procedure to the factors. If in turn, one of them factors, we again repeat the procedure on its factors, and so on. Since N is the product of at most $\log N$ primes, the time for all of these applications of the elliptic curve method is at most

$$O((\log N)^4\ \exp\{2(\log v)^{6/7}\}).$$

With probability at least $1 - (\log N)/N$, each factor m of N which the above procedure does not factor is either a power of a prime in $S(v)$ or is not divisible by any prime in $S(v)$. For each such m write m in the form k^a where k,a are integers and a is maximal. This can be accomplished in time $O((\log N)^4)$. If $k > v$, then stop working on the factor m of N. If $k \leq v$, apply the primality test in [2] to k, taking time at most

$$O((\log v)^{c_3 \log\log\log(10v)})$$

for some constant c_3. Let F denote the product of all such k^a for which k has been proved prime and let $R = N/F$. Then with probability at least $1 - (\log N)/N$ no prime in $S(v)$ divides R.

§3.   Factoring with random squares.

It has long been known that if N is divisible by at least 2

distinct odd primes, then factoring N is random polynomial time

equivalent to producing random solutions to the congruence $x^2 \equiv y^2$ mod N.

Indeed, if $x^2 \equiv y^2$ mod N is a random solution, then (x-y,N) is a

non-trivial factor of N with probability at least 1/2. Conversely, if

the complete prime factorization of N is known and y is a random

residue mod N, then it is a simple matter using the elementary theory of

congruences to make a random choice in the set of x mod N with

$x^2 \equiv y^2$ mod N.

This concept is exploited successfully in several of the practical

factoring algorithms, principally the continued fraction method [14] and

the quadratic sieve [16]. However, these practical algorithms suffer two

theoretical deficiencies. One, we cannot prove the congruences

$x^2 \equiv y^2$ mod N that are produced are truly random. Two, we cannot prove

the methods are likely even to produce any congruences $x^2 \equiv y^2$ mod N,

random or not. It should be stressed, however, that these deficiencies

probably lie in our current methods of proof or in our ingenuity, not

in the algorithms themselves which almost certainly work as claimed.

The random squares factoring method of Dixon [8] is a particularly

simple and randomized version of the continued fraction method (from which

the continued fraction has been removed!) that is amenable to rigorous

analysis. By trading the practical advantages of the continued fraction

method or the quadratic sieve for rigor, the true value of the random

squares method lies in the theoretical analysis of the complexity of

factoring, not in actually doing so.

The random squares method with parameter v to factor N may be

described briefly as follows. Let Q(A) denote the least non-negative

residue of A mod N. In stage 1, one continues to choose random integers

A until $\pi(v) + 1$ values of $Q(A)$ are found which completely factor with
the primes up to v. In stage 2, a non-empty subset $Q(A_1), \ldots, Q(A_k)$ of
the stage 1 successes is found whose product is a square, say x^2. If
$y \equiv A_1 \ldots A_k$ mod N, then clearly $x^2 \equiv y^2$ mod N.

It is not hard to show that if N is divisible by at least 2
distinct odd primes and if each $(A_i, N) = 1$, then $(x-y, N)$ is a
non-trivial factor of N with probability at least 1/2 (see Lemma 3 in
[8]). Indeed, among the various residues A mod N for which
$Q(A) = Q(A_1)$ at least half of these choices give a value of y mod N
(when substituted for A_1 in the definition of y) which lead to a
non-trivial factorization of N. Since the algorithm is "indifferent" to
which value of A gave the quadratic residue $Q(A_1)$ in stage 1, at least
half of the instances of the algorithm which use $Q(A_1)$ in stage 2 lead
to a non-trivial factorization of N.

To further specify the random squares method one must also describe
the subroutines used to accomplish the main tasks of stage 1 and stage 2.
That is, in stage 1 we must specify which method is used to recognize
which values of $Q(A)$ produced factor completely with the primes up to v.
Further, in stage 2 we must specify which method is to be used to find the
non-empty subset. Once these subroutines are specified, the parameter v
is then chosen so as to minimize the running time.

In [14] it was shown that the problem of finding the non-empty subset
in stage 2 is really a problem in linear algebra. Indeed if

$$Q(A) = \prod_{i=1}^{\pi(v)} p_i^{a_i}$$

is the prime factorization of a stage 1 success, where p_i denotes the
i-th prime and the exponents a_i are non-negative integers, then a linear
dependency among the vectors $(a_1, \ldots, a_{\pi(v)})$ mod 2 corresponds to a
non-empty subset of the numbers $Q(A)$ whose product is a square. Since
we have $\pi(v) + 1$ such vectors, a linear dependency must exist.

In [8], Dixon used trial division by the primes up to v as the subroutine in stage 1 and Gaussian elimination as the subroutine in stage 2 and was able to show that with v chosen appropriately the running time is $\leq L(N)^{3\sqrt{2} + o(1)}$. In [16] it was shown that with these subroutines the optimal choice of v is $L(N)^{1/2 + o(1)}$ and the running time is exactly $L(N)^{2 + o(1)}$. Furthermore, in [16] it was shown that if the Pollard-Strassen factorization method with the early abort strategy is used in stage 1 and the Coppersmith-Winograd elimination method is used in stage 2, then the optimal choice of v is $L(N)^{\sqrt{2/5} + o(1)}$ and the running time is exactly $L(N)^{\sqrt{5/2} + o(1)}$.

In this section we shall show that if the algorithm of Theorem 2.1 is used in stage 1 and a new elimination method of Wiedemann [20] is used in stage two, then the optimal choice of v is $L(N)^{\sqrt{1/2} + o(1)}$ and the running time is exactly $L(N)^{\sqrt{2} + o(1)}$.

Towards this end, we begin as follows. Let $\psi_1(x,y,z)$ denote the number of integers $n \leq x$ divisible solely by primes p such that if $p > z$, then $p \in S(y)$.

LEMMA 3.1. *If* $y = L(x)^a$ *with* $a > 0$ *fixed and* $z = \exp\{64(\log\log x)^6\}$, *we have*

$$\psi_1(x,y,z) \sim \psi(x,y) \sim \rho\left(\frac{1}{a}\sqrt{\frac{\log x}{\log\log x}}\right) x = x \cdot L(x)^{-\frac{1}{2a} + o(1)} .$$

Proof. The equality follows from (2.2) and the latter asymptotic relation follows either from the main result in Hildebrand [11] or from Maier [13]. It remains to show the first asymptotic relation. Let

$u = (\log x)/\log y = \frac{1}{a}\sqrt{\frac{\log x}{\log\log x}}$. First note that

$$0 \leq \psi(x,y) - \psi_1(x,y,z) \leq \sum_{p\in(z,y],\, p\notin S(y)} \psi(\frac{x}{p}, y)$$

$$= x \sum_{p\in(z,y],\, p\notin S(y)} \left(\frac{1}{p}\rho\left(u - \frac{\log p}{\log y}\right)\right)\left(1 + o\left(\frac{u\log u}{\log x}\right)\right)$$

$$\leq \rho(u-1) \ x \ \left(1 + O\!\left(\frac{u \ \log \ u}{\log \ x}\right)\right) \sum_{p\in(z,y],\,p\notin S(y)} \frac{1}{p} \qquad (3.1)$$

where again we use the papers [11], [13].

Using partial summation and Theorem B' we have

$$\sum_{p\in(z,y],\,p\notin S(y)} \frac{1}{p} = \frac{1}{y}(\sum_{p\in(z,y],\,p\notin S(y)} 1) + \int_z^y \frac{1}{t^2}(\sum_{p\in(z,t],\,p\notin S(y)} 1)dt$$

$$\leq \frac{1}{y}(\sum_{p\leq y,\,p\notin(y)} 1) + \int_z^y \frac{1}{t^2}(\sum_{p\leq t,\,p\notin S(y)} 1)dt$$

$$= O(\exp\{-\tfrac{1}{2}(\log y)^{1/6}\}) + O(\int_z^y \frac{1}{t}\exp\{-\tfrac{1}{2}(\log t)^{1/6}\}dt)$$

$$= O((\log z)^{5/6}\exp\{-\tfrac{1}{2}(\log z)^{1/6}\})$$

$$= O\!\left(\frac{(\log\log x)^5}{\log x}\right) . \qquad (3.2)$$

Further from Lemma 3 in Alladi [3] it follows that

$$\rho(u-1) \sim \rho(u)u \log u \quad \text{as} \quad u \to \infty .$$

Putting this estimate and (3.2) into (3.1) it follows that

$$\psi_1(x,y,z) = \psi(x,y) + O\left(\rho(u) \ x \ \frac{u \ (\log \ u)(\log\log x)^5}{\log \ x}\right)$$

$$= \psi(x,y)\left(1 + O\!\left(\frac{(\log\log \ x)^{11/2}}{(\log \ x)^{1/2}}\right)\right) ,$$

which proves the first asymptotic relation of the lemma.

Let $\omega(N)$ denote the number of distinct prime factors of N and let $\tau(N)$ denote the number of natural divisors of N .

Lemma 3.2. *Let* $x \geq 1$, *let* S *be an arbitrary set of primes, let* $N > 1$ *be an integer not divisible by any prime in* S, *let* $T(x)$ *denote the set of integers* $m \leq x$ *not divisible by any prime outside of* S , *and let*

$$T_N(x) = \{m \in [1,N]: \ Q(m) = m^2 \bmod N \in T(x)\} .$$

Then

$$2^{\omega(N)} \cdot \#T(x) \geq \#T_N(x) \geq (\#T(\sqrt{x}))^4(\sum_{t\in T(\sqrt{x})} \tau(t))^{-2} .$$

Proof. This result is a mild generalization of Lemma 3.1 in [16] where the set S consists of all the primes in an interval. That lemma is itself a generalization of Lemma 2 in Dixon [8]. The proof of the lemma at hand follows from the same argument.

Theorem 3.3. *Let* $a > 0$ *be fixed. If* $N > 1$ *is an integer not divisible by any prime up to* $L(N)^a$ *and* S *is the set of primes* $p \le L(N)^a$ *in* $S(L(N)^a)$ *together with all of the primes up to* $\exp\{64(\log\log N)^6\}$, *then*

$$\# \, T_N(N) = N \cdot L(N)^{-\frac{1}{2a} + o(1)},$$

using the notation of Lemma 3.2.

Proof. From Lemma 3.1 we have

$$\# \, T(N) = N \cdot L(N)^{-\frac{1}{2a} + o(1)}, \quad \# \, T(\sqrt{N}) = \sqrt{N} \cdot L(N)^{-\frac{1}{4a} + o(1)}.$$

Thus our result will follow from Lemma 3.2 if we show

$$2^{\omega(N)} = L(N)^{o(1)}, \quad \sum_{t \in T(\sqrt{N})} \tau(t) = \sqrt{N} \cdot L(N)^{-\frac{1}{4a} + o(1)}. \tag{3.3}$$

From the hypothesis that N has no prime factor up to $L(N)^a$, it follows that

$$\omega(N) \le \frac{1}{a} \sqrt{\frac{\log N}{\log\log N}},$$

so that the first equality in (3.3) is immediate.

Since

$$\sum_{t \in T(\sqrt{N})} \tau(t) \ge \# \, T(\sqrt{N}) = \sqrt{N} \cdot L(N)^{-\frac{1}{4a} + o(1)}$$

from Lemma 3.1, we have half of the second equality in (3.3). To complete the proof it is sufficient to cite Lemma 3.2 in [16], where a quantity greater than or equal to $\sum_{t \in T(\sqrt{N})} \tau(t)$ is majorized by the expression $\sqrt{N} \cdot L(N)^{-\frac{1}{4a} + o(1)}$.

The following algorithm is the main goal of this section. The letter "R" stands for the random squares method, "E" stands for the elliptic curve method, and "C" the coordinate recurrence method.

Algorithm REC

Let $a > 0$ be fixed. On input of an integer $N > 1$, first use trial division to test N for prime factors up to $v = L(N)^a$. If this procedure produces a non-trivial factorization of N, then stop. Otherwise, let $z = \max\{3, \exp\{64(\log\log N)^6\}\}$. We iterate the following procedure until we have $\pi(v) + 1$ successes. The procedure is to choose a random integer $A \in [1, N-1]$, remove any prime factors up to z from $Q(A) = A^2 \bmod N$ by trial division, and if the unfactored portion exceeds 1, apply the algorithm of Theorem 2.1 with parameter $v = L(N)^a$ to this unfactored portion of $Q(A)$. A "success" is defined as a pair $A, Q(A)$ for which this procedure outputs the complete prime factorization of $Q(A)$ and none of these primes exceeds v.

For each of the $\pi(v) + 1$ successes $A, Q(A)$, let $\vec{v}(A)$ denote the vector $(a_1,\ldots,a_{\pi(v)}) \bmod 2$ where $Q(A) = \prod_{i=1}^{\pi(v)} p_i^{a_i}$ and p_i denotes the i-th prime. Use the coordinate recurrence method of Wiedemann [20] (Algorithm 1) to find a subset $\vec{v}(A_1),\ldots,\vec{v}(A_k)$ of the $\pi(v) + 1$ vectors with $\vec{v}(A_1) + \ldots + \vec{v}(A_k) = \vec{0}$. Let x be an integer with $x^2 = Q(A_1) \ldots Q(A_k)$ and let $y = A_1 \ldots A_k \bmod N$. Compute $(x-y, N)$. If this is a non-trivial factor of N, the algorithm has been successful.

From Theorems 2.1 and 3.3 we see that we shall expect to iterate the procedure with the random A's precisely $L(N)^{a + \frac{1}{2a} + o(1)}$ times to achieve the requisite number of successes. Since each iteration of this procedure has running time $L(N)^{o(1)}$, the expected time for the collection of all of the factored $Q(A)$'s is $L(N)^{a + \frac{1}{2a} + o(1)}$. Thus a choice of $a = \sqrt{1/2}$ will minimize the expected running time of this stage of the algorithm - it is $L(N)^{\sqrt{2} + o(1)}$.

The second stage of the algorithm involving the coordinate recurrence method is also probabilistic. Since each vector $\vec{v}(A)$ has at most $O((\log N)/\log\log N) = L(N)^{o(1)}$ non-zero entries, the running time for this stage will be $L(N)^{2a+o(1)} = L(N)^{\sqrt{2} + o(1)}$ with $a = \sqrt{1/2}$. Note that Algorithm 1 in [20] involves solving $A\vec{x} = \vec{b}$ where A is a non-singular square matrix. If this procedure is applied when A is possibly singular, then the algorithm will either solve the equation for $\vec{x}$ or find a non-trivial solution to $A\vec{x} = \vec{0}$. We use this algorithm as follows. Take the first $\pi(v)$ vectors and from the matrix A by writing these vectors as columns. Let $\vec{b}$ be the $\pi(v) + 1-$ st vector written as a column. Thus we shall either find a linear dependency involving the $\pi(v) + 1 - $ st vector or we shall find a linear dependency among just the first $\pi(v)$ vectors. In either case, we have found the requisite linear dependency.

The integer x may be as large as $L(N)^{aL(N)^a}$. However, it is only necessary to compute x mod N. This can be done in time $L(N)^{a + o(1)}$ by first finding the prime factorization of x and then computing x mod N. An alternative is to follow the algorithm described in [14].

The coordinate recurrence method (Algorithm 1 of [20]) is probabilistic. According to Proposition 3 in [20], the expected number of iterations of Algorithm 1 before a linear dependency is found is of order $\log \pi(v) = L(N)^{o(1)}$. Note that we might use Algorithm 2 in [20]. This has deterministic running time $L(N)^{2a + o(1)}$, but requires more space - $L(N)^{2a + o(1)}$ against $L(N)^{a + o(1)}$ for Algorithm 1.

Assuming we successfully find the linear dependency, the probability Algorithm REC will produce a non-trivial factor of N is at least $1/2$, provided N is divisible by at least 2 distinct odd primes - see the discussion earlier in this section.

Summing up we have the following analysis of Algorithm REC.

Theorem 3.4. *With* $a = \sqrt{1/2}$, *the expected running time of*
Algorithm REC is $L(N)^{\sqrt{2} + o(1)}$ *and the space required is*
$L(N)^{\sqrt{1/2} + o(1)}$. *If* N *is divisible by at least 2 distinct odd*
primes, the probability that Algorithm REC will produce a non-trivial
factor of N *is at least* $1/2$.

§4. Discrete logarithms in GF(p).

Let p denote a fixed prime exceeding 3. In this section we shall
see how a certain natural analog of Algorithm REC from section 3 can be
used to compute discrete logarithms in GF(p). The general idea is as
follows (cf. Adleman [1], Western-Miller [19]). Suppose g is a
primitive element in GF(p), $x \in GF(p)*$, and we wish to compute $\log_g x$,
that is, some number y mod (p-1) with $g^y = x$. Let $v \geq 2$ be a
parameter. Suppose the least positive residue of g^e in GF(p) factors
completely over the primes up to v :

$$g^e \equiv \prod_{i=1}^{\pi(v)} p_i^{a_i} \mod p.$$

Taking the $\log_g$ of both sides we obtain

$$e \equiv \sum_{i=1}^{\pi(v)} a_i \log_g p_i \mod(p-1). \tag{4.1}$$

Stage one is to choose random exponents $e \in \{1,\ldots,p-1\}$ until so many
values are found with g^e mod p factoring completely with the primes up
to v that the corresponding system of equations of the form (4.1) for
the unknown quantities $\log_g p_i$ mod(p-1) for $i = 1,\ldots,\pi(v)$ has full
rank. (What it means for a system of linear equations over $\mathbb{Z}/(p-1)$ to
have full rank is that when considered over $\mathbb{Z}/q$, the system has full
rank for each prime factor q of p-1.)

Stage two is to solve the system of equations of the form (4.1) for
the quantities $\log_g p_i$ mod(p-1) for $i = 1,\ldots,\pi(v)$.

If x is one of the primes up to v , or more generally, if x

factors completely with the primes up to v , then it is an easy matter to

write $\log_g x \mod(p-1)$ as a linear combination of the now known quantities

$\log_g p_i \mod(p-1)$ and so compute it. Probably, though, x will not be in

this form in which case we enter stage three of the algorithm. This

involves choosing random exponents e until one is found with the least

positive residue of $g^e x$ factoring completely with the primes up to v :

$$g^e x \equiv \prod_{i=1}^{\pi(v)} p_i^{b_i} \mod p \ .$$

Thus

$$\log_g x \equiv -e + \sum_{i=1}^{\pi(v)} b_i \log_g p_i$$

and we are done.

Stages one and two comprise a precomputation part of the algorithm.

If we next want to compute $\log_g x'$ for some other $x' \in GF(p)$, we

need only stage 3 for x' since we already know the logarithms of the small

primes.

This general algorithm is known as the index calculus algorithm (the

word index is synonymous with discrete logarithm). As with the random

squares method, the version of the index calculus algorithm presented here

will use the elliptic curve method and the coordinate recurrence method as

subroutines. The only difficulty in the analysis will concern showing

when the system of equations of the form (4.1) is expected to have full

rank. To solve this problem, we shall amend the index calculus algorithm

slightly by also considering values of $g^e p_i \mod p$ for random exponents

e and for the various p_i. We begin with the following simple lemma, the

main idea of which appears in [1].

LEMMA 4.1. *Let* V *be a vector space over a field* F *with* $\dim V = k$ *and* $0 < k < \infty$. *Let* S *be a finite set of vectors in* V *and let* $b_1, \ldots, b_k$ *be a basis of* V. *Let* $\ell = [2 \log_2 k] + 3$ *where* $\log_2$ *refers to the binary logarithm. With the uniform distribution over* S, *say we make* $2k\ell$ *independent choices of elements from* S *(with replacement), labeling the chosen vectors* $v_1, \ldots, v_{k\ell}, w_1, \ldots, w_{k\ell}$. *Let* V' *be the subspace of* V *spanned by* $v_1, \ldots, v_{k\ell}$ *and the vectors* $b_j + w_{(j-1)\ell+i}$ *for* $j = 1, \ldots, k$ *and* $i = 1, \ldots, \ell$. *Then with probability at least* $1 - 1/(2k)$, $V' = V$.

Proof. Let $V_0 = \{0\}$ and for $j = 1, \ldots, k$, let V_j denote the subspace of V spanned by $v_1, \ldots, v_{j\ell}$. Then the probability that

$$\#(S \cap V_k) \geq \frac{1}{2} \cdot \#S \tag{4.2}$$

is at least $1 - k \cdot 2^{-\ell}$. Indeed, if (4.2) fails, then for any fixed $j = 0, \ldots, k-1$, the probability that each of $v_{j\ell+1}, \ldots, v_{(j+1)\ell}$ is in V_j is less than $2^{-\ell}$. But if one of these vectors is not in V_j, then $\dim V_{j+1} > \dim V_j$. Thus, if (4.2) fails, then with probability at least $1 - k \cdot 2^{-\ell}$ we have $0 < \dim V_1 < \ldots < \dim V_k$, so that $V_k = V$. But if $V_k = V$, then (4.2) obviously holds. This proves our assertion about the probability that (4.2) holds.

Assume now that (4.2) holds. Let W_j be the subspace of V spanned by V_k and the vectors $b_j + w_{(j-1)\ell+i}$ for $i = 1, \ldots, \ell$. Fix any $j = 1, \ldots, k$. Then with probability at least $1 - 2^{-\ell}$ we have $b_j \in W_j$. Indeed, if $w_{(j-1)\ell+i} \in V_k$, then

$$b_j \in \mathrm{span}(V_k, b_j + w_{(j-1)\ell+i}) \subseteq W_j .$$

Further, from (4.2) the probability that at least one of $w_{(j-1)\ell+i} \in V_k$ for $i = 1, \ldots, \ell$ is at least $1 - 2^{-\ell}$. Thus our assertion follows.

Thus with probability at least $1 - 2k \cdot 2^{-\ell}$ we have both (4.2) and $b_j \in W_j$ for each $j = 1, \ldots, k$. In this case V' contains the basis

$b_1,\ldots,b_k$, so $V' = V$. It remains to note that

$$1 - 2k \cdot 2^{-\ell} > 1 - 1/(2k).$$

Remark. It should be clear from the proof that if we allow repeated elements in S so that S is now a multi-set the same result holds. More generally the same result holds if we replace the uniform distribution on S with an arbitrary distribution.

We are now in a position to consider the following algorithm. The letter "I" stands for the index calculus algorithm, "E" stands for the elliptic curve method, and "C" the coordinate recurrence method.

ALGORITHM IEC

On input of a prime $p > 3$, a primitive element $g \bmod p$, a non-zero residue $x \bmod p$, and a parameter $v = L(p)^a$ where $a > 0$ is fixed, do the following. Let $z = \max\{3, \exp\{64(\log\log p)^6\}\}$, let $k = \pi(v)$, and let $\ell = [2 \log_2 k] + 3$. Iterate the following procedure until we have $k\ell$ successes. The procedure is to choose a random integer $e \in \{1,\ldots,p-1\}$, form $g^e \bmod p$, remove any prime factors up to z by trial division, and if the unfactored portion exceeds 1, continue with the algorithm of Theorem 2.1 with parameter v. A "success" is defined as a pair e, $g^e \bmod p$ where this procedure outputs the complete prime factorization of $g^e \bmod p$ and no prime involved exceeds v. Next, for $j = 1,\ldots,k$ continue with the same procedure applied to $(p_j g^e) \bmod p$ for random choices of e until we have ℓ successes for each j. Here, p_j denotes the j-th prime. This concludes stage one of the algorithm.

Next, let $y_j = \log p_j \bmod(p-1)$. Each success among the first $k\ell$ is of the form

$$g^e \equiv \prod_{i=1}^{k} p_i^{a_i} \bmod p$$

and each success among the latter $k\ell$ is of the form

$$p_j g^e \equiv \prod_{i=1}^{k} p_i^{b_i} \bmod p.$$

The former relations lead to equations of the form

$$e \equiv \sum_{i=1}^{k} a_i y_i \mod(p-1)$$

while the latter relations lead to equations of the form

$$e \equiv -y_j + \sum_{i=1}^{k} b_i y_i \mod(p-1) \ .$$

We use the coordinate recurrence method [20] to solve these equations for $y_1,\ldots,y_k$. This concludes stage two of the algorithm.

Finally, choose random exponents e until one is found (using the same procedure as in stage one) with $(xg^e)\mod p$ factoring completely with the primes up to v . If

$$xg^e \equiv \prod_{i=1}^{k} p_i^{c_i} \mod p,$$

then $\log_g x \equiv -e + \sum_{i=1}^{k} c_i y_i \mod(p-1)$. This concludes the third and final stage of the algorithm.

Remarks. If e is a random variable with uniform distribution in $\{1,\ldots,p-1\}$ then so is $xg^e \mod p$ for any fixed $x \not\equiv 0 \mod p$. Thus from Therorem 2.1 and Lemma 3.1, the probability that the procedure just described will produce the complete prime factorization of $(xg^e)\mod p$ with no prime involved exceeding v is $L(p)^{-\frac{1}{2a} + o(1)}$. Thus the expected running time of stage 1 is $L(p)^{a + \frac{1}{2a} + o(1)}$ and the expected running time of stage 3 is $L(p)^{\frac{1}{2a} + o(1)}$.

Some comment is needed for stage two. First, from Lemma 4.1, the system of equations has full rank with probability at least $1 - 1/(2k)$. Second, the coordinate recurrence method must be applied in a finite field and $Z/(p-1)$ is not one. There are two exits from this dilemma. One is to apply algorithm REC from section 3 to p-1, completely factoring it in expected time $L(p)^{\sqrt{2} + o(1)}$. Next, for each prime q that divides $p-1$ we apply the coordinate recurrence method to the system of equations considered over $\mathbb{Z}/q$. If $q^2|p-1$ then we use a Hensel lifting argument to solve the system of equations over $\mathbb{Z}/q^2$ (again by the coordinate recurrence method over $\mathbb{Z}/q$), and so on if a higher power of q divides $p-1$. Solutions over the various $\mathbb{Z}/q^a$ are then glued together with the Chinese Remainder Theorem to form the solution over $\mathbb{Z}/(p-1)$.

The other way to solve the system via the coordinate recurrence method does not involve trying especially hard to factor $p-1$. If this method is applied to a system over a non-field it could well break down when it tried to invert a non-invertible element. In our case this would just produce a non-trivial factorization of the modulus. The coordinate recurrence method can then be begun again for the various factors of $p-1$. If the method does not break down with a particular modulus, it is expected to produce the required solution.

Since the system of equations is sparse, the expected running time to solve the system of equations is $L(p)^{2a+o(1)}$ and the space is $L(p)^{a+o(1)}$.

It is clear that to minimize the time for stage one we should choose $a = \sqrt{1/2}$. This leads to a running time of $L(p)^{\sqrt{2} + o(1)}$ for stage one and the same running time for stage two. We sum up our results in the following theorem.

THEOREM 4.2. *Suppose* $p > 3$ *is prime. Algorithm IEC with parameter* $L(p)^{\sqrt{1/2}}$ *is expected to complete preprocessing for the discrete logarithm problem over* $GF(p)$ *in time* $L(p)^{\sqrt{2} + o(1)}$ *and in space* $L(p)^{\sqrt{1/2} + o(1)}$. *After the preprocessing stage has been completed, any discrete logarithm in* $GF(p)$ *may be computed in expected time and space* $L(p)^{\sqrt{1/2} + o(1)}$.

§5. DISCRETE LOGARITHMS OVER $GF(2^n)$.

In the last section we represented elements of $GF(p) = \mathbf{Z}/p$ by
their least positive residue. Since this is an integer it made sense to
talk about an element of $GF(p)$ factoring into small primes. We would
like to have a similar situation in $GF(2^n)$. Recall that if
$f(x) \in (\mathbf{Z}/2)[x]$ is irreducible of degree n then
$GF(2^n) = (\mathbf{Z}/2)[x]/(f(x))$. Since each coset in this quotient structure
has a unique representative with degree $< n$, we may represent $GF(2^n)$ by
the polynomials in $(\mathbf{Z}/2)[x]$ with degree $< n$. Since $(\mathbf{Z}/2)[x]$ is
a unique factorization domain, it thus makes sense to talk about an
element of $GF(2^n)$ factoring into small primes (low degree irreducibles).

In fact, the situation for $GF(2^n)$ is somewhat easier than with
$GF(p)$. While we do not have an analog of the elliptic curve method, we do
have random polynomial time algorithms to factor polynomials in
$(\mathbf{Z}/2)[x]$ (see references on p.235 of [15]). Thus on presentation of a
polynomial $h(x) \in (\mathbf{Z}/2)[x]$ of degree $< n$, we can determine a
complete factorization of $h(x)$ into irreducibles in expected time less
than $(\log n)^c$ for some absolute constant $c > 0$.

The only other difference with $GF(p)$ is that we need an analogy to
Lemma 3.1 which gives the proportion of polynomials in $(\mathbf{Z}/2)[x]$ up to
a certain degree all of whose irreducible factors have small degrees.
Such a result may be found in Odlyzko [15].

LEMMA 5.1 (Odlyzko). *Suppose* $m^{1/100} \leq d \leq m^{99/100}$. *The proportion of
polynomials in* $(\mathbf{Z}/2)[x]$ *of degree* $\leq m$ *all of whose irreducible
factors have degrees* $\leq d$ *among all polynomials in* $(\mathbf{Z}/2)[x]$ *with
degree* $\leq m$ *is* $\exp\{-(1+o(1))u \log u\}$ *where* $u = m/d$.

If we choose $v = [\log_2(L(2^n)^a)]$ for a fixed $a > 0$, then the number
of irreducible polynomials in $(\mathbf{Z}/2)[x]$ with degree $\leq v$ is
$2^{(1+o(1))v} = L(2^n)^{a+o(1)}$ (cf. Odlyzko [15]). Further, from Lemma

5.1, the number of members of $GF(2^n)$ whose principal representative is
a product of irreducible factors of degree $\leq v$ is $2^n \cdot L(2^n)^{-\frac{1}{2a} + o(1)}$.
Thus the expected time to complete stage one is $L(2^n)^{a + \frac{1}{2a} + o(1)}$.

The value $a = \sqrt{1/2}$ minimizes this expression, giving the running time of
$L(2^n)^{\sqrt{2} + o(1)}$.

Finally, the coordinate recurrence method may still be used in stage
two. The discrete logarithms are integers defined $\mod(2^n-1)$. If
2^n-1 is composite, the same devices as discussed in section 4 may be
used to get around this problem. Summing up we have the following.

THEOREM 5.2. *Algorithm IEC of section 4 with the changes discussed
above is expected to complete preprocessing for the discrete logarithm
problem in* $GF(2^n)$ *in time* $L(2^n)^{\sqrt{2} + o(1)}$ *and in space*
$L(2^n)^{\sqrt{1/2} + o(1)}$ *. After preprocessing, any discrete logarithm may be
computed in expected time and space* $L(2^n)^{\sqrt{1/2} + o(1)}$ *.*

Remark. While the algorithms of sections 3 and 4 are in a sense near to
the best we know of, even allowing heuristic - empirical algorithms, the
algorithm of this section is far from the best discrete logarithm
algorithm over $GF(2^n)$. As mentioned in the introduction, the algorithm
of Coppersmith [6] has a heuristic running time of
$\exp\{O(n^{1/3}(\log n)^{2/3})\}$. Nevertheless, the algorithm of this section is
the fastest we know of now with a rigorous analysis.

REFERENCES

1. L. M. Adleman, A subexponential algorithm for the discrete logarithm
    problem with applications to cryptography, Proc. 20th IEEE Found. Comp.
    Sci. Symp. (1979), 55-60.

2. L. M. Adleman, C. Pomerance, and R. S. Rumely, On distinguishing
    prime numbers from composite numbers, Annals Math. 117(1983), 173-206.

3. K. Alladi, The Turán-Kubilius inequality for integers without large
    prime factors, J. Reine Angew. Math. 335 (1982), 180-196.

4. N. G. de Bruijn, The asymptotic behaviour of a function occurring in
    the theory of primes, J. Indian Math. Soc. (N.S.) 15(1951), 25-32.

5. N. G. de Bruijn, On the number of positive integers $\leq$ x and free of
    prime factors $>$ y, Nederl. Akad. Wetensch. Proc. Ser. A 54(1951),
    50-60.

6. D. Coppersmith, Fast evaluation of logarithms in fields of
    characteristic two, IEEE Trans. Inform. Theory IT-30(1984), 587-594.

7. D. Coppersmith, A. M. Odlyzko, R. Schroeppel, Discrete logarithms in
    GF(p), Algorithmica 1(1986), 1-15.

8. J. D. Dixon, Asymptotically fast factorization of integers, Math.
    Comp. 36(1981), 255-260.

9. T. ElGamal, A subexponential-time algorithm for computing discrete
    logarithms over GF(p^2), IEEE Trans. Inform. Theory, to appear.

10. J. B. Friedlander and J. C. Lagarias, On the distribution in short
    intervals of integers having no large prime factor, J. Number Theory, to
    appear.

11. A. Hildebrand, On the number of positive integers $\leq$ x and free of
    prime factors $>$ y, J. Number Theory 22(1986), 289-307.

12. H. W. Lenstra, Jr., Factoring integers with elliptic curves,
    preprint.

13. H. Maier, On integers free of large prime factors, unpublished manuscript.

14. M. A. Morrison and J. Brillhart, A method of factoring and the factorization of F_7, Math. Comp. 29(1975), 183-205.

15. A. M. Odlyzko, Discrete logarithms in finite fields and their cryptographic significance, in "Advances in Cryptology" (Pro. Eurocrypt '84), Springer Lecture Notes in Computer Science 209(1985), 224-314.

16. C. Pomerance, Analysis and comparison of some integer factoring algorithms, in "Computational Methods in Number Theory: Part I", H. W. Lenstra, Jr. and R. Tijdeman, eds., Math. Centre Tract 154(1982), 89-139.

17. C. P. Schnorr and H. W. Lenstra, Jr., A Monte Carlo factoring algorithm with linear storage, Math. Comp. 43(1984), 289-311.

18. M. Seysen, A probabilistic factorisation algorithm with quadratic forms of negative discriminant, Math. Comp., to appear.

19. A. E. Western and J. C. P. Miller, "Tables of Indices and Primitive Roots", Royal Society Mathematical Tables, vol. 9, Cambridge Univ. Press, 1968.

20. D. Wiedemann, Solving sparse linear equations over finite fields, IEEE Trans. Inform. Theory IT-32(1986), 54-62.

21. M. E. Hellman and J. M. Reyneri, Fast computation of discrete logarithms in GF(q), in "Advances in Cryptography: Proceedings of CRYPTO '82, D. Chaum, R. Rivest, and A. Sherman, eds., pp. 3-13, Plenum Press, 1983.

Redundant Coding for Local Computability

Hiroto Yasuura, Naofumi Takagi and Shuzo Yajima

Department of Information Science
Faculty of Engineering
Kyoto University
Kyoto, 606, Japan

Abstract   We introduce a concept of *local computability* for designing high-speed parallel algorithms on fan-in restricted models.   A function $F:\Sigma^n \to \Sigma^m$ is k-locally computable if each subfunction $f_i:\Sigma^n \to \Sigma$ of $F=(f_1, f_2, \cdots, f_m)$ depends on only at most k input variables.   If k is a constant independent of n, the number of input variables, we can construct an $O(1)$ time parallel algorithm for F on a fan-in restricted computation model.   In order to realize the local computability,   we use a redundant coding scheme.   We show that a binary operation of any finite Abelian group is k-locally computable under a redundant coding scheme, where k is a constant independent of the order of the group.   We also show that we can design a redundant coding scheme for a residue ring Z_m of integers under which addition and multiplication can be performed in $O(1)$ and $O(\log \log \log m)$ time, respectively, in parallel, when m is the product of the smallest r primes.

1. Introduction

Discovery of a good coding scheme or data structure is a key to development of efficient algorithms.   Many famous efficient algorithms for sequential computation owe to discovery of good coding schemes or data structures.[1]   In parallel computation, coding schemes also seems to play an important role in design of efficient algorithms.

In the beginning of '60s,   Avizienis pointed out the advantage of a *redundant coding scheme* in design of high-speed arithmetic circuits.[2]   In recent years,   we have been designing several parallel algorithms for arithmetic operations suitable for VLSI implementation using

DISCRETE ALGORITHMS AND
COMPLEXITY

145

redundant coding techniques.[7,9]   These results suggest that we can also apply the redundant coding techniques for design of high-speed parallel algorithms in various areas other than arithmetic operations.   Actually, design of efficient pipeline algorithms is closely related with the redundant coding.

In a redundant binary coding, we can construct a carry-propagation-free adder as a combinational logic circuit.   Namely, we can compute each digit of the sum from only each three digits of the addend and augend.   Thus addition of two numbers can be done by a constant depth circuit independent of the length of the operands, if we assume that the number of fan-in for each gate is restricted.   It is clearly impossible to make such a fast addition algorithm when we use the ordinary binary representation.   In the ordinary binary   notation, since the most significant digit of the sum depends on all digit of two operands, the depth of an adder should be $\Omega(\log n)$ where n is the length of the binary notation of operands.   Winograd showed that it is impossible to construct a constant depth adder unless we use redundant coding schemes.[5]

Our inevitable question, which is mainly discussed in this paper, is for what kind of operations or functions we can construct efficient parallel algorithms using redundant coding. We will introduce a concept of *local computability*.   The local computability is defined by the maximum number of digits of operands required to determine each digit of a result.   When every digit of the result depends on at most k digits of operands, we say the operation is *k-locally computable* under the coding scheme.   If k is small, we can design a small depth circuit for the operation, because each digit of the result is a function of at most k input variables.   We are particularly interested in the case that k is a constant independent of the size of domain on which the operation is defined.   Therefore, our question is reduced to what kinds of operations have coding schemes under which these operations are k-locally computable for some constant k independent of the size of the domain of operations.

We show that a binary operation of any Abelian group is 14-locally computable under a redundant coding scheme on an alphabet with three elements.   Thus we can construct a constant depth combinational circuit computing the operation.   We also show that there exists a redundant coding for a residue ring Z_m of integers under which addition is $O(1)$-locally computable and multiplication is $O(\log \log m)$-locally computable, when m is the product of the smallest r primes.   Using the redundant coding, we can compute addition and multiplication on Z_m in time $O(1)$ and $O(\log \log \log m)$, respectively.

In section 2, we define terms related with redundant coding and local computability.   A constant time parallel algorithm for addition on a residue group Z_m of integers is presented in section 3.   The main results are given in section 4, and applications are discussed in section 5.

2. Coding and Local Computability

2.1 Coding Scheme

Let S be a finite set. We denote the number of elements in S by $|S|$. Let an alphabet Σ be a finite set of symbols used for coding. We assume that $|\Sigma| > 1$. Σ^n represents a set of strings on Σ with length n. We encode elements in S into strings in Σ^n. Here, we only consider fixed-length codes.

Definition 1. A mapping C is a coding scheme for S on an alphabet Σ with length n, if the following two conditions are satisfied.

(1) $C : \Sigma^n \rightarrow S \cup \{\bot\}$, where $\bot \notin S$.

(2) For any element s in S, there is at least one element x in Σ^n such that $C(x) = s$. x is called a *code* of s.

Since a coding scheme is defined as a mapping from a coding space Σ^n to the set $S \cup \{\bot\}$, we can specify a redundant coding scheme. A coding scheme C is *redundant* if there is an element in S which has two or more codes (See Fig.1). We define *efficiency* of the coding scheme C by $(\log_{|\Sigma|} |S|)/n$.

Consider a binary operation $\circ$ defined on S. Assume that S is closed under the operation $\circ$. We define a binary operation $*$ on Σ^n such that

$$C(x * y) = C(x) \circ C(y) \qquad \cdots (1)$$

if both $C(x)$ and $C(y)$ are in S. Namely, $(S, \circ)$ is homomorphic to $(\{x \mid x \in \Sigma^n$ such that $C(x) \in S \}$, $*$). We say operation $*$ *corresponds* to operation $\circ$. $*$ is specified by a function $F: \Sigma^{2n} \rightarrow \Sigma^n$. If a coding scheme C is redundant, F is not uniquely determined, because there are two or more candidates of $x * y$ in Σ^n such that $C(x * y) = C(x) \circ C(y)$.

2.2 Computation Model and Local Computability

We use a *combinational circuit* on Σ with fan-in restriction as a model of parallel computation. The combinational circuit is composed of computation elements and wires. Each computation element in the circuit computes a function $f: \Sigma^i \rightarrow \Sigma$, where f is a member of a finite set B called a basis. Mathematically, a combinational circuit is defined as a labeled acyclic graph. Each vertex corresponds to an input port or a computation element. Edges correspond to wires connecting ports and computation elements. A vertex with indegree 0 is an input port and an input variable is assigned to it as its label. A vertex with indegree i ($i \geq 1$) is a computation element computing an i-variable function f in B. The label of the computation vertex is the i-variable function f. Since B is assumed to be finite, indegree of each vertex (i,e, fanin of a computation element) is bounded by a constant. We do not assume any restrictions on fanout of vertices.

Σ^n $S \cup \{\perp\}$

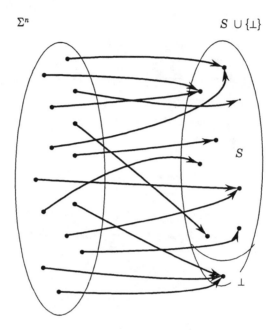

Fig. 1   A Redundant Coding Scheme C

The *size* of a combinational circuit is the number of computation elements included in the circuit. The *depth* of the circuit is the longest path in the circuit. Size is a measure of the number of resources used in a parallel algorithm. Depth corresponds to computation time of the algorithm if we assume that all elements has the same delay and no delay exists on wires. In the theory of combinational circuit complexity, the lower and upper bounds of size of circuits that compute functions depending on exact n variables are $\Omega(n)$ and $O(2^n/n)$, respectively [6]. Depth is also bounded by $\Omega(\log n)$ and $O(n)$.

Here, we will define local computability. Let $F = (f_1, f_2, \cdots, f_m)$ be a function from Σ^n to Σ^m and $f_i : \Sigma^n \to \Sigma$ be a subfunction of F. F is called a k-locally computable function if each subfunction f_i depends on only at most k input variables.

Definition 2.   Let S, $\circ$ and C be a finite set, a binary operation defined on S and a coding scheme for S on Σ with length n, respectively. The operation $\circ$ is said to be k-*locally computable under the coding scheme* C, if there is a k-locally computable function F specifying an operation $*$ on Σ^n corresponding to $\circ$.

If an operation ∘ is k-locally computable, we can construct a combinational circuit computing ∘ with depth $O(k)$ and size $O(2^k n/k)$. We are especially interested in k-locally computable operations such that k is a constant independent of the size of sets on which the operations are defined. The depth and size of circuits computing the operations are $O(1)$ and $O(n)$, respectively. We can say that we have constant time parallel algorithms for these operations.

3. Addition on Residue Class

In this section, we construct a coding scheme for the residue class modulo m, denoted by Z_m, in the set of integers. The basic technique used in this section is a redundant binary coding on an alphabet $\{0, 1, -1\}$.[2,7] Each integer in $Z_m = \{0, 1, 2, \cdots, m-1\}$ is represented by strings with length $n = \lceil \log_2 m \rceil$. Coding scheme C is defined as follows;

$$C : \{0, 1, -1\}^n \to Z_m \cup \{\bot\}$$

$$C(x_{n-1} x_{n-2} \cdots x_0) = \begin{cases} s & \text{if } 0 \leqq s < m, \\ m+s & \text{if } -m < s < 0, \\ \bot & \text{otherwise,} \end{cases}$$

where $s = \sum_{i=0}^{n-1} x_i 2^i$. The efficiency of C is

$$\lceil \log_3 m \rceil / n = \lceil \log_3 m \rceil / \lceil \log_2 m \rceil = O(1).$$

Now we will define a binary operation $\oplus$ on $\{0, 1, -1\}^n$ corresponding to addition $+_m$ on Z_m. Let $(m_n\ m_{n-1}\ m_{n-2} \cdots m_0)$ be an ordinary binary representation of m and $+$ be integer addition.

Algorithm $\oplus$ /Addition on Z_m under C/
Input $x = (x_{n-1} x_{n-2} \cdots x_0)$ and $y = (y_{n-1} y_{n-2} \cdots y_0)$, where $x_i, y_i \in \{0, 1, -1\}$.
Output $z = (z_{n-1} z_{n-2} \cdots z_0)$, where $z_i \in \{0, 1, -1\}$ and $C(z) = C(x) +_m C(y)$.
Method
> **begin**
> $u := \text{ADD}(x, y)$;
> **if** $m = 2^n$ **then** $z := (u_{n-1} u_{n-2} \cdots u_0)$;
> **else**
> **begin**
> > $-m := ((-m_n) (-m_{n-1}) \cdots (-m_0))$;
> > $2m := ((m_{n-1}) (m_{n-2}) \cdots (m_0)\ 0)$;
> > $-2m := ((-m_{n-1}) (-m_{n-2}) \cdots (-m_0)\ 0)$;
> > **case** (u_n, u_{n-1}) **of**
> > > $(0, 0): \quad z := (u_{n-1} u_{n-2} \cdots u_0)$;

$(0, 1), (1, -1), (1, 0)$:

    begin

        if $(1 -1)$ **then** $(u_n, u_{n-1}) := (0, 1)$;

        $v := \text{ADD1}(u, -m)$;

        $z := (v_{n-1} v_{n-2} \cdots v_0)$;

    end;

$(0, -1), (-1, 1), (-1, 0)$:

    begin

        if $(-1\ 1)$ **then** $(u_n, u_{n-1}) := (0, -1)$;

        $v := \text{ADD2}(u, m)$;

        $z := (v_{n-1} v_{n-2} \cdots v_0)$;

    end;

$(1, 1)$:

    begin

        $v := \text{ADD1}(u, -2m)$;

        $z := (v_{n-1} v_{n-2} \cdots v_0)$;

    end;

$(-1, -1)$

    begin

        $v := \text{ADD2}(u, 2m)$;

        $z := (v_{n-1} v_{n-2} \cdots v_0)$;

    end;

    end;

  end;

end;

procedure $\text{ADD}(p, q)$:

begin

for $i := 0$ **to** $n - 1$ **do**

    According to Table 1, generate t_i and c_{i+1}; /We assume that both p_{-1} and q_{-1} are 0./

for $i := 0$ **to** n **do**

    According to Table 2, generate $s_i = t_i + c_i$; /We assume that $t_n = c_0 = 0$./

return $(s_n, s_{n-1}, \cdots, s_0)$;

end;

procedure $\text{ADD1}(p, q)$:

begin

for $i := 0$ **to** n **do**

    According to Table 3, generate t_i and c_{i+1};

for $i := 0$ **to** $n + 1$ **do**

    According to Table 2, generate $s_i = t_i + c_i$; /We assume that $t_{n+1} = c_0 = 0$./

p_i	q_i	p_{i-1} q_{i-1}	c_{i+1}	t_i
1	1	- -	1	0
1	0	contain 1	1	-1
0	1	not contain 1	0	1
0	0			
1	-1	- -	0	0
-1	1			
-1	0	contain -1	-1	1
0	-1	not contain -1	0	-1
-1	-1	- -	-1	0

Table 1. Rule of Addition I

t_i c_i	s_i
0 0	0
0 1	1
1 0	1
0 -1	-1
-1 0	-1
-1 1	0
1 -1	0
1 1	never occur
-1 -1	never occur

Table 2. Rule of Addition II

p_i q_i	c_{i+1} t_i
-1 0	-1 1
0 0	0 0
1 0	0 1
-1 -1	-1 0
0 -1	-1 1
1 -1	0 0

Table 3. Rule for ADD1

return $(s_{n+1}, s_n, \cdots, s_0)$;

end;

procedure ADD2(p, q):

begin

for $i := 0$ **to** n **do**

According to Table 4, generate t_i and c_{i+1};

for $i := 0$ **to** $n + 1$ **do**

According to Table 2, generate $s_i = t_i + c_i$; /We assume that $t_{n+1} = c_0 = 0$./

return $(s_{n+1}, s_n, \cdots, s_0)$;

end;

p_i q_i	c_{i+1} t_i
-1 0	0 -1
0 0	0 0
1 0	1 -1
-1 1	0 0
0 1	1 -1
1 1	1 0

Table 4. Rule for ADD2

We will show that Algorithm $\oplus$ corresponds to $+_m$ and its local computability.

Lemma 1. ADD is addition for redundant binary integers and 6-locally computable.

Proof. From the rule in Table 1,

$$p_i + q_i = 2c_{i+1} + t_i.$$

Since we suppose $t_n = c_0 = 0$,

$$\sum_{i=0}^{n-1} p_i 2^i + \sum_{i=0}^{n-1} q_i 2^i = \sum_{i=0}^{n-1} (p_i + q_i) 2^i = \sum_{i=0}^{n-1} (2c_{i+1} + t_i) 2^i = \sum_{i=0}^{n} c_i 2^i + \sum_{i=0}^{n} t_i 2^i = \sum_{i=0}^{n} s_i 2^i$$

s_i depends only on c_i and t_i. c_i is calculated from $p_{i-1}, q_{i-1}, p_{i-2}$ and q_{i-2}. t_i is computed from $p_i, q_i,$ p_{i-1} and q_{i-1}. Thus , s_i depends on $p_i, q_i, p_{i-1}, q_{i-1}, p_{i-2}$ and q_{i-2}. Q.E.D.

Lemma 2. The operation $\oplus$ defined by Algorithm $\oplus$ corresponds to addition $+_m$ on Z_m.

Proof. We will examine each case in the algorithm.

When $m = 2^n$, we can easily show that

$$C(x) +_m C(y) = C(z).$$

Let us examine the other cases.

Case 1. $(u_n, u_{n-1}) = (0, 0)$.

Since $-m < \sum_{i=0}^{n-1} u_i 2^i < m$, $C(x) +_m C(y) = C(z)$.

Case 2. $(u_n, u_{n-1}) = (0, 1), (1, -1),$ or $(1, 0)$.

Since $(-m_i)$ is 0 or -1, we can use the computation rule in Table 3. In ADD 1, s_i $(=v_i)$ can be computed by the rule in Table 2, because c_i is 0 or -1 and t_i is 0 or 1. Since $0 < u < 2m$, $-m < v < m$. When $(u_n, u_{n-1}) = (0, 1)$, $t_{n+1} = t_n = c_{n+1} = c_n = 0$, because $m_n = 0$ and $m_{n-1} = 1$. Thus we can conclude that both v_{n+1} and v_n are 0. When $(u_n, u_{n-1}) = (1, 0)$, both v_{n+1} and v_n are also 0, because $t_n = 1$, $c_n = -1$, and $t_{n+1} = c_{n+1} = 0$.

Case 3. $(u_n, u_{n-1}) = (0, -1), (-1, 1),$ or $(-1, 0)$.

The proof is similar to case 2.

Case 4. $(u_n, u_{n-1}) = (1, 1)$.

Since $2^n < u < 2m$, $2^n - 2m < u - 2m < 0$. We know $2m > 2^n > m$, so we have $-m < v < 0$. We also have $m_{n-1} = 1$, $m_{n-2} = 0$ or 1, and $u_n = u_{n-1} = 1$. Thus we can obtain $t_{n+1} = t_n = c_{n+1} = c_n = 0$. So finally we conclude that both v_{n+1} and v_n are 0.

Case 5. $(u_n, u_{n-1}) = (-1, -1)$.

The proof is similar to case 4.

Therefore we have shown that

$$C(x) +_m C(y) = C(z)$$

for all cases in the algorithm. Q.E.D.

Theorem 1. Addition on the residue class modulo m, Z_m, is 14-locally computable under a coding scheme on an alphabet with 3 elements.

Proof. From lemma 1, u_i depends on 6 digits of operands, x_i, y_i, x_{i-1}, y_{i-1}, x_{i-2}, and y_{i-2}. We can select each case examining only u_n and u_{n-1}. Since m is a constant, v_i depends on u_i, u_{i-1}, u_n and u_{n-1}. Thus each digit of the final result, z_i, depends on 14 digits of inputs, i.e., x_{n-1}, y_{n-1}, x_{n-2}, y_{n-2}, x_{n-3}, y_{n-3}, x_i, y_i, x_{i-1}, y_{i-1}, x_{i-2}, y_{i-2}, x_{i-3}, and y_{i-3}. Q.E.D.

When the size of an alphabet is large, we can generalize Algorithm $\oplus$ as follows. Let $N = |\Sigma| > 6$ and $r = N - 3$. We assume that $\Sigma = \{ -(r/2+1), \cdots, -1, 0, 1, \cdots, (r/2+1) \}$, when N is odd, and $\Sigma = \{ -(\lfloor r/2+1 \rfloor), \cdots, -1, 0, 1, \cdots, (\lfloor r/2+1 \rfloor) , X \}$, when N is even where we don't use X for coding. Let the length of codes be $n = \lceil \log_r m \rceil + 1$. The coding scheme is defined as;

$$C : \Sigma^n \to Z_m \cup \{\perp\}$$

$$C(x_{n-1}\ x_{n-2}\ \cdots\ x_0) = \begin{cases} s & \text{if } 0 \leq s < m, \\ m+s & \text{if } -m < s < 0, \\ \perp & \text{otherwise,} \end{cases}$$

where $s = \sum_{i=0}^{n-1} x_i r^i$. Efficiency of the coding is

$$\lceil \log_N m \rceil / n = \lceil \log_N m \rceil / (\lceil \log_{N-3} m \rceil + 1) = O(1).$$

We will specify an operation on Σ^n corresponding to $+_m$ by the following algorithm.

Algorithm $\oplus_r$ /Addition on Z_m for large alphabets /

Input $x = (x_{n-1}\ x_{n-2}\ \cdots\ x_0)$ and $y = (y_{n-1}\ y_{n-2}\ \cdots\ y_0)$, where $x_i, y_i \in \Sigma$ and $C(x), C(y) \in Z_m$.

Output $z = (z_{n-1}\ z_{n-2}\ \cdots\ z_0)$, where $z_i \in \Sigma$ and $C(z) = C(x) +_m C(y)$.

Method

> **begin**
>
> $u = (u_n, u_{n-1} \, u_{n-2} \, u_{n-3} \cdots u_0) := \text{ADD}r\,(x, y);$
>
> **if** $m = r^{n-1}$ **then** $z := (0 \, u_{n-2} \, u_{n-3} \cdots u_0);$
>
> **else**
>
> **begin**
>
>> **case** $2u_n + u_{n-1}$ **of**
>>
>> *zero* : $z := (u_{n-1} \, u_{n-2} \cdots u_0);$
>>
>> *positive*:
>>
>>> **begin**
>>>
>>> $v = (v_n \, v_{n-1} \cdots v_0) := \text{ADD}r(u, -m);$
>>>
>>> $z := (v_{n-1} \, v_{n-2} \cdots v_0);$
>>>
>>> **end;**
>>
>> *negative* :
>>
>>> $v = (v_n \, v_{n-1} \cdots v_0) := \text{ADD}r(u, m);$
>>>
>>> $z := (v_{n-1} \, v_{n-2} \cdots v_0);$
>>>
>>> **end;**
>>
>> **end;**
>
> **end;**
>
> **procedure** $\text{ADD}r(p, q)$:
>
> **begin**
>
> **for** $i := 0$ **to** $n - 1$ **do**
>
>> **if** $p_i + q_i > r/2$ **then** $(c_{i+1}, t_i) := (1, \, p_i + q_i - r);$
>>
>> **else if** $p_i + q_i < -r/2$ **then** $(c_{i+1}, t_i) := (-1, \, p_i + q_i + r);$
>>
>> **else** $(c_{i+1}, t_i) := (0, \, p_i + q_i);$
>
> **end;**
>
> **for** $i := 0$ **to** n **do**
>
>> $s_i = t_i + c_i;$
>
> **end;**
>
> **return** $(s_n, s_{n-1}, \cdots, s_0);$
>
> **end;**

ADDr is addition on the redundant r-ary representation [2], and 4-locally computable. It is easy to show that v_n is always 0. The adjustment is done by examining u_n and u_{n-1}. Then the i-th digit of the result is computable from 6 digits of each operands, i.e., x_{n-1}, y_{n-1}, x_{n-2}, y_{n-2}, x_{n-3}, y_{n-3}, x_i, y_i, x_{i-1}, y_{i-1}, x_{i-2}, and y_{i-2}.

Theorem 2. For addition $+_m$ on Z_m, there is a coding scheme on any alphabet with $O(1)$ efficiency under which $+_m$ is $O(1)$-locally computable.

Proof. As shown above, when the size of alphabet is 3 or more than 7, we can construct a coding scheme under which $+_m$ is 14- or 12-locally computable. When $|\Sigma| = 2$, we can make a coding schme under which the operation is at most 28-locally computable, because each element in {0, 1, -1} can be coded by 2-bits. For the case of 4, 5, and 6, we can easily construct coding schemes only using three symbols in the alphabet and achieve 14-local computability. The efficiency of these codings is bounded by a constant independent of m and $|\Sigma|$.   Q.E.D.

4. High-speed Parallel Computation of Operations on Finite Abelian Group

In the previous section, we showed that addition on Z_m can be $O(1)$-locally computable under redundant coding schemes. In this section, we will show that an operation on any finite Abelian (commutative) group is also k-locally computable under a redundant coding scheme, where k is a constant independent of the order (the number of elements) of the group. Using the redundant coding, we can construct a constant time parallel algorithm for the operation. We also discuss high-speed computation on a finite ring including two operations.

Since Z_m is isomorphic to a cyclic group of order m, we can immediately derive the following lemma from Theorem 2.

Lemma 3. For any finite cyclic group $(G, \circ)$ and alphabet Σ, there is a redundant coding scheme on Σ of efficiency $O(1)$ under which $\circ$ is $O(1)$-locally computable.

It is well known in group theory that any Abelian (commutative) group can be decomposed into a direct product of cyclic groups.

Theorem 3. For any finite Abelian group $(G, \circ)$ and alphabet Σ, there is a redundant coding scheme C on Σ such that $\circ$ is $O(1)$-locally computable under C and efficiency of C is $O(1)$

Proof. Suppose that G is decomposable into cyclic groups $G_1, G_2, \cdots, G_l$. An element in G can be represented by a vector $(x_1, x_2, \cdots, x_l)$ where x_i is an element in G_i. A binary operation on G can be computed by elementwise operations on the representation. Namely,

$$(x_1, x_2, \cdots, x_l) \circ (y_1, y_2, \cdots, y_l) = (x_1 \circ y_1, \ x_2 \circ y_2, \cdots, x_l \circ y_l)$$

where $x_i \circ y_i$ is a binary operation on G_i. If we encode each element in G_i by a redundant coding in Lemma 3, we can achieve $O(1)$-local computability for the operation on G. The efficiency of the code is also bouded by a constant independent of the order of G, the number of decomposed cyclic groups l and the size of alphabet.   Q.E.D.

Using the redundant coding C in Theorem 3, we can easily design a constant time parallel algorithm for the operation on G.

Corollary1. For any finite group $(G, \circ)$, , we can construct a combinational circuit on any alphabet Σ such that the depth is $O(1)$ and the size is $O(\log_{|\Sigma|}\|G|)$.

Next, we will consider a set with two or more operations such as rings and fields. Here, we show a redundant coding for the residue ring of integer modulo m, Z_m, under which addition and multiplication can be performed in high speed. The technique used here is a combination of residue arithmetic[1] and redundant coding. For simplicity, we assume that $|\Sigma| = 3$. We can easily derive the similar result for an arbitrary alphabet.

Theorem 4. Let q_1, q_2, $\cdots, q_s$ be a set of integers which are pairwise relatively prime. Let m be a product of q_i's ($i = 1, 2, \cdots, s$) and (Z_m, $+_m$, $\times_m$) be the residue ring modulo m. There is a redundant coding scheme such that $+_m$ is $O(1)$-locally computable and $\times_m$ is $O(\log_2 \max q_i)$-locally computable.

proof. In the residue arithmetic, an integer u in Z_m can be uniquely represented as a vecter form,

$$u = (u_1,\ u_2, \cdots, u_s),$$

where $u_i = u$ modulo q_i. Addition and multiplication on Z_m can be realized by elementwise additions and multiplications on Z_{q_i}, respectively. Namely, when $u = (u_1,\ u_2, \cdots, u_s)$, $v = (v_1, v_2, \cdots, v_s)$, and $w = (w_1,\ w_2, \cdots, w_s)$, $w_i = u_i + v_i \bmod q_i$ if $w = u +_m v$ and $w_i = u_i \times v_i \bmod q_i$ if $w = u \times_m v$. We encode each element in the residue representation using a redundant coding in the previous section. Then we achieve $O(1)$-local computability for addition. Since multiplication is also reduced to elementwise operations, $\times_m$ is $O(\log_2 \max q_i)$-locally computable under the coding scheme. The efficiency of the coding scheme is clearly $O(1)$. Q.E.D.

Corollary 2. Let m be the product of first smallest s primes, there is a redundant coding scheme C with efficiency $O(1)$ such that $+_m$ and $\times_m$ are respectively $O(1)$- and $O(\log_2 \log_2 m)$-locally computable under C. Moreover, we can construct an adder with size $O(\log_2 m)$ and depth $O(1)$, and a multiplier with size $O((\log_2 m)^2)$ and depth $O(\log_2 \log_2 \log_2 m)$ under C.

Proof According to the theory of integers, the magnitude of the s-th smallest prime is $O(\log_2 m)$, when m is the product of first s primes.[5] The length of the code is,

$$\sum_{i=1}^{s} \lceil \log_2 p_i \rceil \ =\ O\left(\log_2 \prod_{i=1}^{s} p_i\right) \ =\ O(\log_2 m).$$

Addition can be realized by a circuit with depth $O(1)$, and size $O(\log_2 p_i)$. Thus the total size of the adder is $O(\log_2 m)$. Multiplication can be done by the following method. First, we compute $w_i = u_i \times v_i$ in the ring of integers. This multiplication can be performed by a binary tree of adders which realize procedure ADD in Algorithm $\oplus$. The circuit includes $\lceil \log_2 p_i \rceil - 1$ adder elements and the hight of the tree is $\lceil \log_2 \lceil \log_2 p_i \rceil \rceil$. Since the length of the binary representation grows one digit per one addition, the internal product w_i is represented by $2\lceil \log_2 p_i \rceil + \lceil \log_2 \lceil \log_2 p_i \rceil \rceil - 1$ digits. Next we compute $z_i = w_i \bmod p_i$. For all j between $\lceil \log_2 p_i \rceil$ and $2\lceil \log_2 p_i \rceil + \lceil \log_2 \lceil \log_2 p_i \rceil \rceil - 1$, we beforehand compute $x_{ij} = 2^j \bmod p_i$. We add x_{ij} or 0 or $-x_{ij}$ accordingly as the digit of 2^j is 1 or 0 or -1. The addition of this stage must be computed in Z_{p_i}. This addition can be done by a binary tree form circuit of adders which realize Algorithm $\oplus$. The number of the adders is $\lceil \log_2 p_i \rceil + \lceil \log_2 \lceil \log_2 p_i \rceil \rceil$. Since all addition can be done in constant time independent of the length of operands, the depth of the multiplier is

$$O(\log_2 \log_2 p_s) = O(\log_2 \log_2 \log_2 m).$$

The number of gates included in the multiplier is $O((\log_2 m)^2)$, because

$$\sum_{i=1}^{s} (\log_2 p_i)^2 \ \leq \ (\sum_{i=1}^{s} \log_2 p_i)^2 \ = \ O(\,(\log_2 \prod_{i=1}^{s} p_i)^2) \ = \ O((\log_2 m)^2). \qquad \text{Q.E.D.}$$

5. Applications

The redundant coding technique for achieving local compuatbility is useful for design of high-speed arithmetic circuits. We have already designed several high-speed circuits computing multiplication, division, logarithmic and trigonometric functions internally using the redundant binary coding.[7,9] As shown in this paper, there is possibility to use the redundant coding for achieving local computability, i.e. high-speed computation, in design of various logic circuits. We will show several examples of applications of redundant coding techniques for high-speed and highly reliable computation.

The clock rate of a sequential circuit is determined from the computation time of the combinational part of the circuit. If we can design the combinational part operating fast, we can reduce the clock period of the circuit. The computation time of the combinational part depends on the state assignment. If we find a good satete assignment in which the next value of each state variable depends on a small number of present state variables, we can reduce the computation time. In order to achieve the local computability, we may use the redundant coding techniques. A shift-register realization of sequential circuits is a good example of realization of local computability using a redundant coding. More general examples are circuits with pipelined architecture. In a pipelined circuit, the state and output of each cell (stage) are determined from the previous state of the cell and the outputs of the neighbor cells. It realizes the local computation based on some kind of redundant coding. Establishing a systematic method to design redundant coding for local computability, we can design highly efficient piplined circuits.

The redundant coding can be also applied to special combinational circuit design, such as parallel prefix circuits (PPC). In PPC, the basic cell should realize an operation on a semigroup. If the operation is locally computable under a redundant coding scheme, we can design a high-speed and small size PPC.

For the local computable function, we can construct an easily testable circuit. Locally exhaustive testing is the test providing exhaustive test patterns for all sets of inputs that drive an output.[4] If the function is locally computable, the number of inputs driving each output is very small. So the exhaustive test pattern for each output is relatively short. For example, the circuit computing ADD in section 3, since each output depends on only 6 inputs, the length of the test patterns for each output is only $3^6 = 729$. Considering the corelations among outputs, we can conclude that the circuit can be tested by the 729 patterns independent of the number of input variables.

By the theory of parallel computational complexity, the computation time on parallel computation models is closely related with the memory space of sequential computation.[3,6,9] Borodin et. al. showed a small space sequential computation using redundant coding.[3] Our results will also applicable to the small space computation on Turing machine and a random access machine.

6. Conclusion

We proposed a method to achieve the local computability using redundant coding schemes. Using the method, we can compute in parallel an operation on any finite Abelian group in constant time independent of the order of the group. We also showed a ring in which addition and multiplication can be performed fast. The proposed method is effective to design not only high-speed logic circuits but easily testable circuits and small space sequential algorithms.

In this paper we mainly described the redundant coding for finite groups. Further work should be done for more general algebraic scheme, such as semigroups and sets including more than two operations including unary operations.

Acknowledgement

The authors express their appreciation to T. Asada, Y. Okabe and N. Ishiura of Kyoto University for their discussions and comments . This work is supported in part by a grant in aid for scientific research of Ministry of Education of Japan, 60460113.

References

1)   A. Aho, J. Hopcroft and J. Ullman, *The Design and Analysis of Computer Algorithms* , Addison-Wesley, 1974.

2)   A. Avizienis, "Signed-digit number representations for fast parallel arithmetic", *IRE Trans. Elec, Comp.*, vol. EC-10, no. 3, pp.389-400, September 1961.

3)   A. Borodin, S. Cook and N. Pippenger, "Parallel computation for well-endowed rings and space-bounded probabilistic machine", *Information and Control*, vol.58, pp.113-136, 1983.

4)   E. J. McCluskey, "Verification Testing", *IEEE Trans. Comput.*, vol.C-33, no.6, pp. 541-546, June, 1984.

5) H. Riesel, *Prime Numbers and Computer Methods for Factorization, Progress in Mathematics*, Birkhäuser, 1985.

6) J. Savage, *The Complexity of Computing*, John Wiley and Sons, 1976.

7) N. Takagi, H.Yasuura and S.Yajima, "High-speed VLSI multiplication algorithm with a redundant binary addition tree", *IEEE Trans. Comput.*, vol.C-34, no.9, pp.789-796, September, 1985.

8) S. Winograd, "On the time required to perform addition", *Journal of the ACM*, vol. 12, no. 2, pp.277-285, April 1965.

9) H.Yasuura, "Design and analysis of hardware algorithms", *Design Methodologies* (Edited by S.Goto), *Advances in CAD for VLSI*, vol.6, pp.185-214, North-Holland, 1986.

SOME PROPERTIES OF
THE PARALLEL BUBBLING AND
PARALLEL SORTS ON A
MESH—CONNECTED PROCESSOR ARRAY

Kazuhiro SADO
Yoshihide IGARASHI

Department of Computer Science
Gunma University
Kiryu 376, Japan

Abstract   By investigating the property of the parallel bubbling, we evaluate the exact number of operations necessary to move each item to its final position by the parallel bubble sort.   This evaluation is useful for designing efficient parallel sorts on a mesh—connected processor array and for analyzing their time efficiency.   Two parallel sorts on the mesh—connected model are shown.   We also discuss lower bounds on computing time for the class of iterative merge sorts and the class of iterative pseudo-merge sorts.   It is shown that $4.5\sqrt{N} - 3\log_2\sqrt{N} - 2$ steps and $3.5\sqrt{N} - \log_2\sqrt{N} - 3$ steps are lower bounds for these classes, where N is the number of items to be sorted.

1. Introduction

Recently parallel sorting algorithms and their implementations on VLSI models have been intensively studied[2, 4, 5, 7-9, 11-17].   Although some of parallel sorting algorithms can be executed in $O(\log N)$ steps for N items[1, 4, 10], the structure of such algorithms are complicated and their

161

realization is extremely difficult. A mesh–connected processor array is widely accepted as a realistic model of a parallel computer. Any implementation for sorting N items on the model cannot be faster than $O(\sqrt{N})$ steps. A number of implementations of Batcher's algorithms (i.e., the odd–even merge sort and the bitonic sort[3]) on the model have been reported[7, 11, 16, 17]. However, they are rather complex in their control structures. A parallel sorting algorithm by lang et al.[9] is based on merging four subfiles in the mesh–connected processor array. Its control structure is much simpler than those of the implementations of Batcher's algorithms. The computing time of their algorithm is $7\sqrt{N} - 7$ steps.

In this paper we examine the property of the parallel bubbling. Through this paper, the logarithm base is always 2. We introduce an interesting function POTENTIAL defined on the set of pairs of items and contents of a linear processor array. We show that the function value of POTENTIAL(α, A) is the exact number of steps necessary to move item α to its final position by the parallel bubble sort starting with contents A of the linear array. This function is a useful tool for designing and for analyzing some parallel sorting algorithms on the mesh–connected processor array. We give two parallel sorts on the mesh–connected model. The computing times of these algorithms are $6.5\sqrt{N} + 2\log\sqrt{N} - 5$ steps and $6\sqrt{N} + 4\log\sqrt{N} - 13$ steps. We show how function POTENTIAL is used to prove the correctness of the algorithms and analyze their computing times.

We also discuss time lower bounds of two classes of parallel sorts on the mesh–connected model. Algorithms of these classes are called iterative merge sorts and iterative pseudo–merge sorts. We show that $4.5\sqrt{N} - 3\log\sqrt{N} - 2$ steps and $3.5\sqrt{N} - \log\sqrt{N} - 3$ steps are time lower bounds of iterative merge sorts and iterative pseudo–merge sorts, respectively.

2. Properties of the parallel bubbling

We suppose that N items are initially stored in array $A[1..N]$. For clarity of explanation we assume that each item can be distinguished from other items by some identification. The key value of item α is denoted by $\alpha.key$. The key value of the item in $A[i]$ may be denoted by $A[i].key$. The parallel partial bubble sort is defined by the following procedure:

```
    procedure BUBBLE(A[i .. j], k);
    begin
1.    for s := 1 to k do
2.      if odd(s) then begin
3.        for all t:= ⌈(i+1)/2⌉ .. ⌊j/2⌋ do in parallel
4.          if A[2t-1].key > A[2t].key then
5.            exchange A[2t-1], A[2t]
          end
        else
6.        for all t := ⌈i/2⌉ .. ⌊(j-1)/2⌋ do in parallel
7.          if A[2t].key > A[2t+1].key then
8.            exchange A[2t], A[2t+1]
    end.
```

The parallel bubble sort of N items is, therefore, defined as BUBBLE($A[1..N]$, N). In the above procedure we consider that the computation from line 2 to line 8 takes one time unit. This time unit is called one step. We should note that the contents of array A at the end of step s is the same as the contents of array A at the beginning of step $s+1$. Where there is no confusion, the contents of array A is also denoted by A. When BUBBLE($A[1..n]$, k) is executed, $A^{(s)}$ denotes the contents of array A at the beginning of step s of the computation (or equivalently at the end of step $s-1$).

Definition 1. Assume that A denotes a configuration of N items in array $A[1..N]$. For an item α in A and a position p ($1 \leq p \leq N$) in the array,

(1) POS(α, A) is the position of item α in the array,

(2) ORDERED(α, p, A) is the number of positions j such that $p \leq j$ < POS(α, A) and $A[j].key \leq \alpha.key$, or such that POS(α, A) < $j \leq p$ and $\alpha.key \leq A[j].key$,

(3) NOTORDER(α, p, A) is the number of positions j such that $p \leq j$ < POS(α, A) and $\alpha.key < A[j].key$, or such that POS(α, A) < $j \leq p$ and $A[j].key < \alpha.key$,

(4) MAXLT(α, A) = max({0} ∪ {ORDERED(α, j, A) - NOTORDER(α, j, A) + 1| 1 ≤ j < POS(α, A) and $\alpha.key < A[j].key$}), and

(5) MAXGT(α, A) = max({0} ∪ {ORDERED(α, j, A) - NOTORDER(α, j, A) + 1| POS(α, A) < $j \leq N$ and $A[j].key < \alpha.key$}).

The following three lemmas are immediate from the above definition.

Lemma 1. For any item α in A and position p ($1 \leq p \leq N$), $0 \leq$ MAXLT(α, A) $\leq N-2$ and $0 \leq$ MAXGT(α, A) $\leq N-2$.

Lemma 2. Suppose that BUBBLE($A[1..N]$, k) is executed. Let s be a step such that $2 \leq s \leq k$. If no two items in A are exchanged at step

s, then all the items in A are already sorted in nondecreasing order of the key values at the beginning of step s.

Lemma 3. Suppose that BUBBLE($A[1 .. N]$, N) is executed. Let α be an item in A and s be a step of the computation. If $i \leq \text{POS}(\alpha, A^{(s)}) \leq j$, and if for any $1 \leq p < i$ and $j < q \leq N$ $A^{(s)}[p].key \leq \alpha.key \leq A^{(s)}[q].key$, then α reaches its final position not later than the end of step $s + j - i$ and remains at the final position after that step.

We now introduce an interesting function POTENTIAL which is defined on pairs of items and array configurations.

Definition 2. For an item α in A, POTENTIAL(α, A) is defined as follows:
(1) When NOTORDER(α, 1, A) = 0,
   POTENTIAL(α, A) = NOTORDER(α, N, A) + MAXGT(α, A).
(2) When NOTORDER(α, N, A) = 0,
   POTENTIAL(α, A) = NOTORDER(α, 1, A) + MAXLT(α, A).
(3) When NOTORDER(α, 1, A) $\neq$ 0 and NOTORDER(α, N, A) $\neq$ 0,
   POTENTIAL(α, A) = NOTORDER(α, 1, A) + NOTORDER(α, N, A) +
   max{1, MAXLT(α, A), MAXGT(α, A)}.

Note that if NOTORDER(α, 1, A) = 0 and NOTORDER(α, N, A) = 0, then POTENTIAL(α, A) = 0 is from any of (1) and (2) of the above definition. Therefore, Definition 2 is well defined. Since POTENTIAL(α, A) = 0 if and only if NOTORDER(α, 1, A) = 0 and NOTORDER(α, N, A) = 0, the next lemma is immediate.

Lemma 4. Suppose that BUBBLE($A[1 .. N]$, k) is executed. If POTENTIAL(α, $A^{(s)}$) = 0, then α does not move from the beginning of step s to the end of the computation of BUBBLE($A[1 .. N]$, k).

The next theorem is the main result in this section. It can be proved by a careful case analysis. The reader may find the details of the proof in [13].

Theorem 1. Suppose that BUBBLE($A[1 .. N]$, k) is executed. If $2 \leq s \leq k$ and POTENTIAL(α, $A^{(s)}$) > 0, then POTENTIAL(α, $A^{(s+1)}$) = POTENTIAL(α, $A^{(s)}$) $- 1$.

The next theorem can be proved in a similar way to that of the proof of Theorem 1.

Theorem 2. Suppose that BUBBLE($A[1 .. N]$, N) is executed. Then for any item α in A

(1) $0 \leq \text{POTENTIAL}(\alpha, A^{(1)}) \leq N$,

(2) $\text{POTENTIAL}(\alpha, A^{(2)}) = \text{POTENTIAL}(\alpha, A^{(1)}) - 1$ or $\text{POTENTIAL}(\alpha, A^{(2)}) = \text{POTENTIAL}(\alpha, A^{(1)})$, and

(3) if $\text{POTENTIAL}(\alpha, A^{(1)}) = N$ then $\text{POTENTIAL}(\alpha, A^{(2)}) = \text{POTENTIAL}(\alpha, A^{(1)}) - 1 = N - 1$.

The next two corollaries are immediate from Theorem 1 and Theorem 2.

Corollary 1. Suppose that BUBBLE($A[1..N]$, N) is executed. Then for any item α in A and any step s ($2 \leq s \leq N$), $\text{POS}(\alpha, A^{(s+\text{POTENTIAL}(\alpha, A^{(s)}))})$ is the final position of α in the computation, and α does not move after the end of step $s + \text{POTENTIAL}(\alpha, A^{(s)}) - 1$.

Corollary 2. Suppose that BUBBLE($A[1..N]$, N) is executed. Then for any item α in A, α reaches its final position at the end of the $\text{POTENTIAL}(\alpha, A^{(1)})$th step or at the end of the $\text{POTENTIAL}(\alpha, A^{(1)}) + 1$ st step, and does not move after that step.

Example 1. Suppose that BUBBLE($A[1..5]$, 5) is executed for the inversely ordered initial configuration of A. That is, at the beginning of the computation for each i ($1 \leq i \leq 5$) $A[i].key = 6 - i$. For simplicity item α such that $\alpha.key = i$ is denoted by i. Then $\text{POTENTIAL}(1, A^{(1)}) = \text{POTENTIAL}(5, A^{(1)}) = 4$, $\text{POTENTIAL}(2, A^{(1)}) = \text{POTENTIAL}(3, A^{(1)}) = \text{POTENTIAL}(4, A^{(1)}) = 5$, $\text{POTENTIAL}(1, A^{(2)}) = \text{POTENTIAL}(2, A^{(2)}) = \text{POTENTIAL}(3, A^{(2)}) = \text{POTENTIAL}(4, A^{(2)}) = 4$ and $\text{POTENTIAL}(5, A^{(2)}) = 3$. The sorting process of BUBBLE($A[1..5]$, 5) is as follows:

At the beginning of step i	Contents of array A
$i = 1$	5, 4, 3, 2, 1
2	4, 5, 2, 3, 1
3	4, 2, 5, 1, 3
4	2, 4, 1, 5, 3
5	2, 1, 4, 3, 5
6	1, 2, 3, 4, 5

The purpose behind introducing the concepts of function POTENTIAL is now clear. As shown in Theorem 1, Theorem 2, Corollary 1 and Corollary 2, $\text{POTENTIAL}(\alpha, A^{(s)})$ is an interesting characteristic of the key value of item α at step s of the computation of BUBBLE($A[1..N]$, N). For $s \geq 2$, it indicates the exact number of steps required to move α to its final position. This characteristic will be a powerful tool for designing some efficient parallel sorts and for analyzing their time efficiency.

We will use the following well known result called the zero-one principle to simplify the proofs of the correctness of sorting algorithms.

Theorem 3 (zero-one principle[6]).   If a network with N input lines sorts all 2^N sequences of 0's and 1's, it will sort any arbitrary sequence of N key values.

When the key value of any item in array A is 0 or 1, the contents of A is said to be a 0-1 pattern.   The next lemma will be useful when we discuss sorting of 0-1 patterns.

Lemma 5.   Let the contents of A be a 0-1 pattern $0^s(1\,0)^t1^r$.   Then $\max\{\text{POTENTIAL}(\alpha, A) \mid \alpha$ is an item in $A\} = t$.

Let $\overline{\text{BUBBLE}}$ be a procedure obtained from BUBBLE by reversing the direction of the inequalities at line 4 and line 7.   Thus $\overline{\text{BUBBLE}}(A[1..N]$, $N)$ is the parallel bubble sort in nonincreasing order of key values for N input items.

3. Sorting on a mesh-connected processor array
3.1 Horizontal and vertical sorting

We consider a two-dimensional processor array $A[1..n, 1..m]$. Processor $A[i, j]$ is directly connected to its neighbors $A[i, j-1]$, $A[i-1, j]$, $A[i+1, j]$ and $A[i, j+1]$, provided they exist.   This model is called a mesh-connected processor array.   The processors are indexed by a one-to-one mapping from $\{1, ..., n\} \times \{1, ..., m\}$ onto $\{1, ..., nm\}$.   The row-major indexing and the snake-like row-major indexing are commonly

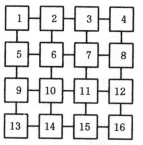
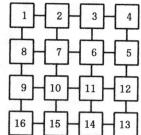

(a) Row-major indexing   (b) Snake-like row-major indexing

Fig. 1   Processor array indexing schemes

accepted ways to order a rectangle array (see Fig. 1). With respect to a rectangle array, sorting is defined as a process of moving the items in the array into an order specified by an index mapping. The ith row and the jth column of $A[1..n, 1..m]$ are denoted by $A[i, 1..m]$ and $A[1.. n, j]$, respectively. A sub-rectangle array (or subarray for short) consisting of processors $A[i, j]$ such that $1 \le p \le i \le q \le n$ and $1 \le r \le j \le t \le m$ is denoted by $A[p..q, r..t]$.

We show two parallel sorting algorithms on the mesh-connected model. Our algorithms are faster than the algorithm by Lang et al.[9] They are as simple as the algorithm by Lang et al. in their control structures. The basic operation of our algorithms is just the parallel bubbling whereas the algorithm by Lang et al. and the algorithm by Saga et al.[14] use the parallel bubbling and the simple parallel exchange as their basic operations. We now define the following two procedures:

  procedure HBUBBLE($A[p..q, r..t]$, g, k);
  begin
1. **if** $g = 1$ **then return**
2. **for all** $i := p .. q$ **do in parallel**
3. **for all** $j := 1 .. \lceil (t-r+1)/g \rceil$ **do in parallel**
4.   **if** odd(i) **then**
5.   BUBBLE($A[i, g(j-1)+r..gj+r-1]$, k)
    else
6. $\overline{\text{BUBBLE}}$($A[i, g(j-1)+r..gj+r-1]$, k)
  end.

  procedure VBUBBLE($A[p..q, r..t]$, g, k);
  begin
1. **if** $g = 1$ **then return**
2. **for all** $i := r .. t$ **do in parallel**
3. **for all** $j := 1 .. \lceil (q-p+1)/g \rceil$ **do in parallel**
4.   BUBBLE($A[g(j-1)+p..gj+p-1, i]$, k)
  end.

Example 2. HBUBBLE($A[1..8, 1..8]$, 4, 4) sorts the items of each of the following groups in nondecreasing order independently:

  $\langle A[1, 1], A[1, 2], A[1, 3], A[1, 4] \rangle$
  $\langle A[1, 5], A[1, 6], A[1, 7], A[1, 8] \rangle$
  $\langle A[2, 4], A[2, 3], A[2, 2], A[2, 1] \rangle$
       .
       .
       .
  $\langle A[8, 8], A[8, 7], A[8, 6], A[8, 5] \rangle$

Example 3. VBUBBLE($A[1..8, 1..8]$, 4, 4) sorts the items of each of the following groups in nondecreasing order independently:

  $\langle A[1, 1], A[2, 1], A[3, 1], A[4, 1] \rangle$
  $\langle A[5, 1], A[6, 1], A[7, 1], A[8, 1] \rangle$

.
.
.

$\langle A[5,\ 8],\ A[6,\ 8],\ A[7,\ 8],\ A[8,\ 8]\rangle$

Definition 3. For a key value v, the unsorted v-row size of subarray $A[r_1..r_2,\ c_1..c_2]$ is denoted by $\mathrm{RSIZE}^{(v)}(A[r_1..r_2,\ c_1..c_2])$ and defined as follows:

$$\mathrm{RSIZE}^{(v)}(A[r_1..r_2,\ c_1..c_2]) = r_L - r_G + 1$$

where $r_L = \max(\{r_1-1\} \cup \{i \mid r_1 \le i \le r_2$ and for some k $(c_1 \le k \le c_2)$ $A[i, k] \le v\})$, and $r_G = \min(\{r_2+1\} \cup \{j \mid r_1 \le j \le r_2$ and for some h $(c_1 \le h \le c_2)$ $A[j, h] > v\})$.

Note that for any case $r_L - r_G + 1 \ge 0$ in the above definition.

Definition 4. The unsorted row size of subarray $A[r_1..r_2,\ c_1..c_2]$ is denoted by $\mathrm{RSIZE}(A[r_1..r_2,\ c_1..c_2])$ and defined as $\max\{\mathrm{RSIZE}^{(v)}(A[r_1..r_2,\ c_1..c_2]) \mid v$ is in the set of key values of items in $A[r_1..r_2,\ c_1..c_2]\}$.

If the unsorted row size of subarray $A[r_1..r_2,\ c_1..c_2]$ is less than or equal to 1, we refer it as 1-roughly sorted.

Definition 5. The pseudo-unsorted row size of subarray $A[r_1..r_2,\ c_1..c_2]$ is denoted by $\mathrm{PRSIZE}(A[r_1..r_2,\ c_1..c_2])$ and defined as $\mathrm{RSIZE}(\mathrm{VBUBBLE}(A[r_1..r_2,\ c_1..c_2]),\ r_2-r_1+1,\ r_2-r_1+1)$.

Example 4. Let the key value contents of $A[1..8,\ 1..8]$ be as shown in Fig. 2 (a). Then the key value contents of $\mathrm{VBUBBLE}(A[1..8,\ 1..8], 8, 8)$ is shown in Fig. 2 (b). In this case, the pseudo-unsorted row size of the initial configuration of $A[1..8,\ 1..8]$ is 2.

The following four lemmas are straightforward from Definition 3, Definition 4 and Definition 5.

```
0 0 0 0 0 0 1 0        0 0 0 0 0 0 0 0
0 0 0 1 0 0 0 0        0 0 0 0 0 0 0 0
1 1 0 0 1 1 0 0        0 0 0 0 0 0 0 0
0 0 1 1 1 1 1 0        0 0 0 1 0 0 0 0
0 0 1 0 0 1 1 1        0 0 0 1 1 0 1 0
0 1 1 1 1 0 0 0        1 1 1 1 1 1 1 1
1 0 0 1 0 0 1 1        1 1 1 1 1 1 1 1
1 1 0 1 1 0 0 1        1 1 1 1 1 1 1 1
```

(a) Pseudo unsorted row size 2   (b) Unsorted Row size 2

Fig. 2   A Pseudo-unsorted row size and an unsorted row size

Lemma 6. Suppose that the key value of each item in $A[r_1..r_2, c_1..c_2]$ is 0 or 1. Then $\text{RSIZE}(A[r_1..r_2, c_1..c_2]) = \text{RSIZE}^{(0)}(A[r_1..r_2, c_1..c_2])$.

Lemma 7. Suppose that $\text{RSIZE}(A[r_1..r_2, c_1..c_2]) \leq 1$. Then the following two statements hold:

    (1) $A[r_1..r_2, c_1..c_2]$ can be sorted in snake-like row-major nondecreasing order by $\text{HBUBBLE}(A[r_1..r_2, c_1..c_2], c_2-c_1+1, c_2-c_1+1)$.

    (2) $A[r_1..r_2, c_1..c_2]$ can be sorted in row-major nondecreasing order by the following computation:

    for all $i := r_1 .. r_2$ **do in parallel**
    $\text{BUBBLE}(A[i, c_1..c_2], c_2-c_1+1)$

Lemma 8. Suppose that $\text{PRSIZE}(A[r_1..r_2, c_1..c_2]) \leq 1$. Then the following two statements hold:

    (1) $A[r_1..r_2, c_1..c_2]$ can be sorted in snake-like row-major nondecreasing order by the following computation:

    $\text{VBUBBLE}(A[r_1..r_2, c_1..c_2], r_2-r_1+1, r_2-r_1+1)$;
    $\text{HBUBBLE}(A[r_1..r_2, c_1..c_2], c_2-c_1+1, c_2-c_1+1)$

        (2) $A[r_1..r_2, c_1..c_2]$ can be sorted in row-major nondecreasing order by the following computation:

    $\text{VBUBBLE}(A[r_1..r_2, c_1..c_2], r_2-r_1+1, r_2-r_1+1)$;
    for all $i := r_1 .. r_2$ **do in parallel**
    $\text{BUBBLE}(A[i, c_1..c_2], c_2-c_1+1)$

Lemma 9. If $\text{PRSIZE}(A[r_1..r_2, c_1..c_2]) = u_1$ and $\text{PRSIZE}(A[r_2+1..r_3, c_1..c_2]) = u_2$, then $\text{RSIZE}(\text{VBUBBLE}(A[r_1..r_3, c_1..c_2], r_3-r_1+1, r_3-r_1+1))$ is at most u_1+u_2.

We prove the next lemma by using function POTENTIAL.

Lemma 10. Suppose that $\text{RSIZE}(A[r_1 .. r_2, c_1 .. c_2]) = t$. Then $\text{PRSIZE}(\text{HBUBBLE}(A[r_1..r_2, c_1..c_2], c_2-c_1+1, c_2-c_1+1])) \leq \lceil t/2 \rceil$, and each column of $\text{HBUBBLE}(A[r_1..r_2, c_1..c_2], c_2-c_1+1, c_2-c_1+1])$ can be sorted by BUBBLE in at most t steps.

Proof. For clarity we proceed the proof for the case of 0-1 patterns. The proof of the lemma for general patterns is essentially the same as the proof for 0-1 patterns. Let $\overline{A}[r_1..r_2, c_1..c_2]$ be the contents of the subarray after executing $\text{HBUBBLE}(A[r_1..r_2, c_1..c_2], c_2-c_1+1, c_2-c_1+1)$. Suppose that for any key value between the r_1th row and the i_1+1st row of $\overline{A}[r_1..r_2, c_1..c_2]$ is 0 and that any key value between the j_1+1st row and the r_2th row is 1, where $j_1-i_1+1 = t$. Let $\overline{A}[i_1..j_1, c_m]$ be a column such that it has the maximum number of 1's among the columns of $\overline{A}[i_1..j_1, c_1..c_2]$. For any column $\overline{A}[i_1..j_1, c_a]$ $(c_a \neq c_m)$ the key value of $\overline{A}[r, c_a]$ $(i_1 \leq r \leq j_1)$ cannot be 0 unless at least one of the following three conditions is satisfied:

(1) $\overline{A}[r, c_m].key = 0$.

(2) $c_a < c_m$ and r is odd.

(3) $c_a > c_m$ and r is even.

The number of 0's in $\overline{A}[i_1..j_1, c_a]$, therefore, cannot be more than the number of 0's in $\overline{A}[i_1..j_1, c_m] + \lceil t/2 \rceil$. Hence, the first part of this lemma has been proved. For any item α in $\overline{A}[r_1..r_2, c]$ $(c_1 \leq c \leq c_2)$, POTENTIAL$(\alpha, \overline{A}[r_1..r_2, c])$ is at most t. Suppose that BUBBLE$(\overline{A}[r_1..r_2, c], t)$ is executed. When POTENTIAL$(\alpha, \overline{A}^{(1)}[r_1..r_2, c]) = t$, POTENTIAL$(\alpha, \overline{A}^{(2)}[r_1..r_2, c]) = $ POTENTIAL$(\alpha, \overline{A}^{(1)}[r_1..r_2, c]) - 1$. When POTENTIAL$(\alpha, \overline{A}^{(s)}[r_1..r_2, c]) \geq 1$ and $s \geq 2$, POTENTIAL$(\alpha, \overline{A}^{(s+1)}[r_1..r_2, c]) = $ POTENTIAL$(\alpha, \overline{A}^{(s)}[r_1..r_2, c]) - 1$. These facts are from Theorem 1 and Theorem 2. Therefore, from Corollary 1, each column of $\overline{A}[r_1..r_2, c_1..c_2]$ can be sorted by BUBBLE in at most t steps.   □

The next lemma can be derived from Lemma 5, Theorem 2 and Corollary 1.

Lemma 11. Suppose that each column of $A[r_1..r_2, c_1..c_2]$ is sorted in nondecreasing order and that RSIZE$(A[r_1..r_2, c_1..c_2]) = t$. Then each column of HBUBBLE$(A[r_1..r_2, c_1..c_2], c_2-c_1+1, c_2-c_1+1)$ can be sorted by BUBBLE in at most $\lfloor t/2 \rfloor + 1$ steps.

By a careful case analysis, the next lemma can be also derived from Lemma 5, Theorem 2 and Corollary 1.

Lemma 12. Suppose that RSIZE$(A[r_1..r_2, c_1..c_2]) \leq 1$ and RSIZE$(A[r_1..r_2, c_2+1..c_3]) \leq 1$, where $c_2-c_1+1 = c_3-c_2$. Let $\overline{A}[r_1..r_2, c_1..c_3]$ be the contents of subarray $A[r_1..r_2, c_1..c_3]$ after executing HBUBBLE$(A[r_1..r_2, c_1..c_3], c_3-c_1+1, c_3-c_1+1)$. Then the following two statements hold:

(1) PRSIZE$(\overline{A}[r_1..r_2, c_1..c_3]) \leq 1$.

(2) For any cth column $(c_1 \leq c \leq c_3)$ $\overline{A}[r_1..r_2, c]$ can be sorted by BUBBLE in at most $\lfloor (r_2-r_1+1)/2 \rfloor + 1$ steps.

3.2 A pseudo-merge sort algorithm

We describe a pseudo-merge sort algorithm, SPMSORT. When SPMSORT is applied to $A[1..n, 1..n]$, we assume that n is a power of 2.

```
procedure SPMSORT(A[1..n, 1..n]);
begin
1.   for i := 1 to log n do begin
2.       VBUBBLE(A[1..n, 1..n], 2^i, 2^i);
3.       HBUBBLE(A[1..n, 1..n], 2^{i-1}, 2^{i-1});
4.       VBUBBLE(A[1..n, 1..n], 2^i, 2);
5.       HBUBBLE(A[1..n, 1..n], 2^i, 2^i)
     end;
6.   VBUBBLE(A[1..n, 1..n], n, n/2);
7.   HBUBBLE(A[1..n, 1..n], n, n)
end.
```

Theorem 4. Let n be a power of 2. Then SPMSORT($A[1..n, 1..n]$) sorts the items in array A into snake-like row-major nondecreasing order.

Proof. Let ASS(k) be the following assertion (A1):

(A1)   PRSIZE($A[2^{k-1}r+1 .. 2^{k-1}(r+1), 2^{k-1}c+1 .. 2^{k-1}(c+1)]$) ≤ 1 for all r = 0, ..., $n/2^{k-1}-1$, and c = 0, ..., $n/2^{k-1}-1$.

We prove by induction on k that ASS(k) is true at the beginning of the kth loop of **for** statement of SPMSORT.

Induction basis: ASS(1) is obviously true.

Induction step: From the induction hypothesis, we assume that ASS(i) is true at the beginning of the ith loop of **for** statement $(1 \leq i \leq \log n)$. When VBUBBLE at line 2 has been executed, from Lemma 9 the unsorted row size of each subarray $A[2^i r+1 .. 2^i(r+1), 2^{i-1}c+1 .. 2^{i-1}(c+1)]$ is at most 2 (r = 0, .., $n/2^i-1$ and c = 0, ..., $n/2^{i-1}-1$). For simplicity, in the following we omit indicating the ranges of r and c. When the statements at line 3 and line 4 have been executed, from Lemma 10 the unsorted row size of each subarray $A[2^i r+1 .. 2^i(r+1), 2^{i-1}c+1 .. 2^{i-1}(c+1)]$ is at most 1, and from Lemma 11 each column of the subarrays is sorted in nondecreasing order. Thus, when the statement at line 5 has been executed, from (1) of Lemma 12 the pseudo-unsorted row size of each subarray $A[2^i r+1 .. 2^i(r+1), 2^i c+1 .. 2^i(c+1)]$ is at most 1. Hence, at the beginning of the (i+1)th loop of **for** statement ASS(i+1) is true.

When the computation of the **for** loop has terminated, the pseudo-unsorted row size of $A[1..n, 1..n]$ is at most 1 (i.e., ASS($\log n$ + 1) is true), and from Lemma 12 the key value pattern of each column of the array can be sorted by BUBBLE in $n/2$ steps. Therefore, when the statements at line 6 and line 7 have been executed, from Lemma 12 the items in $A[1..n, 1..n]$ are completely sorted in snake-like row-major nondecreasing order. $\square$

Theorem 5. Let n be a power of 2. Then the computing time of SPMSORT($A[1..n, 1..n]$) is $6.5n + 2\log n - 5$ steps.

Proof. The computing time of **for** statement at line 1 is $\sum\limits_{i=1}^{\log n}(2^i + 2^{i-1} + 2 + 2^i) = 5n + 2\log n - 5$ steps. The computing time of the statements at line 6 and line 7 is $n/2 + n$ steps. Therefore, the total computing time of SPMSORT($A[1..n, 1..n]$) is $6.5n + 2\log n - 5$ steps.   □

As an example, we show a computing process of SPMSORT($A[1..8, 1..8]$) in Fig. 3.

We can easily modify SPMSORT so that it can sort the items in a rectangle array. The modified algorithm is given by the next procedure.

    procedure RPMSORT($A[1..n, 1..m]$);
    begin
1.   **for** $i := \log\lceil n/m \rceil + 1$ **to** $\log n$ **do begin**
2.   VBUBBLE($A[1..n, 1..m]$, 2^i, 2^i);
3.   HBUBBLE($A[1..n, 1..m]$, $2^{i-1} \times m/n$, $2^{i-1} \times m/n$);
4.   VBUBBLE($A[1..n, 1..m]$, 2^i, 2);
5.   HBUBBLE($A[1..n, 1..m]$, $2^i \times m/n$, $2^i \times m/n$)
       end;
6.   VBUBBLE($A[1..n, 1..m]$, n, $n/2$);
7.   HBUBBLE($A[1..n, 1..m]$, m, m)
    end.

The next theorem can be proved in the same way as those of Theorem 4 and Theorem 5.

Theorem 6. Let n and m be powers of 2. Then RPMSORT($A[1..n, 1..m]$) sorts the items in A into snake-like row-major nondecreasing order. Its computing time is $2.5n + 4m + 2\log n - 2\lceil n/m \rceil - 3m/n\lceil n/m \rceil - 2\log\lceil n/m \rceil$ steps.

3.3 A pseudo-merge sort with preprocessing

We next design a faster algorithm than SPMSORT.

Definition 6. The number of items α in $A[r_1..r_2, c_1..c_2]$ such that $\alpha.key$ is less than v is denoted by $LESS^{(v)}(A[r_1..r_2, c_1..c_2])$.

Lemma 13. Suppose that RSIZE($A[r_1..r_2, c_1..c_2]$) ≤ 1 and RSIZE($A[r_1..r_2, c_2+1..c_3]$) ≤ 1, where $c_2 - c_1 + 1 = c_3 - c_2$. Let t be the minimum integer that satisfies $|LESS^{(v)}(A[r_1..r_2, c_1..c_2]) - LESS^{(v)}(A[r_1..r_2, c_2+1..c_3])| \leq t(c_2 - c_1 + 1)$ for all key values v. Let $\bar{A}[r_1..r_2, c_1..c_3]$ be the contents of subarray $A[r_1..r_2, c_1..c_3]$ after executing HBUBBLE($A[r_1..r_2, c_1..c_3]$, c_3-c_1+1, c_3-c_1+1). Then for any cth column ($c_1 \leq c \leq c_3$), $\bar{A}[r_1..r_2, c]$ can be sorted by BUBBLE in at most $\lfloor (t+1)/2 \rfloor + 1$ steps.

Proof. For clarity we proceed the proof for the case of 0-1 patterns.

47	7	28	44	41	51	48	36
45	30	55	2	13	37	9	61
32	56	40	43	11	64	16	1
46	33	27	14	38	31	54	59
29	50	63	52	12	49	5	35
42	58	21	15	23	4	24	6
62	10	8	26	22	20	57	60
34	18	25	19	53	17	39	3

(a) Initial configuration

45	7	28	2	13	37	9	36
47	30	55	44	41	51	48	61
32	33	27	14	11	31	16	1
46	56	40	43	38	64	54	59
29	50	21	15	12	4	5	6
42	58	63	52	23	49	24	35
34	10	8	19	22	17	39	3
62	18	25	26	53	20	57	60

(b) At the end of line 2 in the first loop

7	45	2	28	13	37	9	36
47	30	55	44	51	41	61	48
32	33	14	27	11	31	1	16
56	46	43	40	64	38	59	54
29	50	15	21	4	12	5	6
58	42	63	52	49	23	35	24
10	34	8	19	17	22	3	39
62	18	26	25	53	20	60	57

(c) At the end of line 5 in the first loop

7	30	2	27	11	31	1	16
32	33	14	28	13	37	9	36
47	45	43	40	51	38	59	48
56	46	55	44	64	41	61	54
10	18	8	19	4	12	3	6
29	34	15	21	17	20	5	24
58	42	26	25	49	22	35	39
62	50	63	52	53	23	60	57

(d) At the end of line 2 in the second loop

7	30	2	14	11	13	1	9
33	32	28	27	37	31	36	16
45	46	40	43	38	41	48	54
56	47	55	44	64	51	61	59
10	18	8	15	4	12	3	5
34	29	21	19	20	17	24	6
42	50	25	26	22	23	35	39
62	58	63	52	53	49	60	57

(e) At the end of line 4 in the 2nd loop

2	7	14	30	1	9	11	13
33	32	28	27	37	36	31	16
40	43	45	46	38	41	48	54
56	55	47	44	64	61	59	51
8	10	15	18	3	4	5	12
34	29	21	19	24	20	17	6
25	26	42	50	22	23	35	39
63	62	58	52	60	57	53	49

(f) At the end of line 5 in the 2nd loop

2	7	10	8	1	4	5	3
19	15	14	18	12	11	9	6
21	25	26	27	13	17	20	16
32	30	29	28	31	24	23	22
33	34	42	40	35	36	37	38
46	45	43	44	49	48	41	39
47	50	55	52	51	53	57	54
63	62	58	56	64	61	59	60

(g) At the end of line 2 in the 3rd loop

1	2	3	4	5	7	8	10
19	18	15	14	12	11	9	6
13	16	17	20	21	25	26	27
32	31	30	29	28	24	23	22
33	34	35	36	37	38	40	42
49	48	46	45	44	43	41	39
47	50	51	52	53	54	55	57
64	63	62	61	60	59	58	56

(h) At the end of **for** loop

1	2	3	4	5	6	7	8
16	15	14	13	12	11	10	9
17	18	19	20	21	22	23	24
32	31	30	29	28	27	26	25
33	34	35	36	37	38	39	40
48	47	46	45	44	43	42	41
49	50	51	52	53	54	55	56
64	63	62	61	60	59	58	57

(i) At the end of the sorting process

Fig. 3   A Sorting Process by SPMSORT

The proof of the lemma for general patterns is essentially the same as the proof for 0-1 patterns. As $| \text{LESS}^{(1)}(A[r_1..r_2, c_1..c_2]) - \text{LESS}^{(1)}(A[r_1..r_2, c_2+1..c_3])| \leq t(c_2-c_1+1)$, every column in $\bar{A}[r_1..r_2, c_1..c_3]$ is in the form $0^a(10)^b1^d$, where $b \leq \lfloor t/2 \rfloor$. In the same way of the proof of Lemma 11, we can show that such a pattern can be sorted by BUBBLE in at most $\lfloor (t+1)/2 \rfloor + 1$ steps. □

Lemma 14. Let $c_2-c_1+1 = c_3-c_2$. Let $\bar{A}[r_1..r_2, c_1..c_3]$ be the contents of subarray $A[r_1..r_2, c_1..c_3]$ after executing HBUBBLE(VBUBBLE($A[r_1..r_2, c_1..c_3]$, r_2-r_1+1, r_2-r_1+1), c_3-c_1+1, c_3-c_1+1). Then for any key value v, $| \text{LESS}^{(v)}(\bar{A}[r_1..r_2, c_1..c_2]) - \text{LESS}^{(v)}(\bar{A}[r_1..r_2, c_2+1..c_3])| \leq c_2-c_1+1$.

Proof. We also proceed the proof for the case of 0-1 patterns. For any i $(0 \leq i \leq c_2-c_1)$, let $A'[r_1..r_2, i]$ be the contents of the subarray as follows:

$A'[r, i] = \bar{A}[r, c_1+i]$ if r $(r_1 \leq r \leq r_2)$ is odd;

$A'[r, i] = \bar{A}[r, c_3-i]$ if r $(r_1 \leq r \leq r_2)$ is even.

Then both $A'[r_1..r_2, i]$ and $A'[r_1..r_2, c_3-i]$ are in the form $0..01..1$ patterns, because for any r $(r_1 \leq r < r_2)$ $\text{LESS}^{(1)}(\bar{A}[r, c_1..c_3]) \leq \text{LESS}^{(1)}(\bar{A}[r+1, c_1..c_3])$, any odd numbered row in $\bar{A}$ is in the form $0..01..1$ and any even numbered row in $\bar{A}$ is in the form $1..10..0$. Therefore, $|\text{LESS}^{(1)}(\bar{A}[r_1..r_2, c_1..c_2]) - \text{LESS}^{(1)}(\bar{A}[r_1..r_2, c_2+1..c_3])| \leq c_3-c_1+1$. □

The next algorithm is denoted by FPMSORT. When FPMSORT is applied to $A[1..n, 1..m]$, we assume that both n and m are powers of 2. The algorithm uses the split factor t which is also a power of 2.

```
      procedure FPMSORT(A[1..n, 1..m], t);
      begin
 1.   if n/t < m/2
 2.     then low := 1
 3.     else low := log(2×n/d/m) + 1;
 4.   for i := log n/t downto low do begin
 5.     if i = log n/t
 6.       then j := n/t
 7.       else j := 2^i + 1;
 8.     VBUBBLE(A[1..n, 1..m], n/t, j);
 9.     HBUBBLE(A[1..n, 1..m], m×2^(i-log n/t-1), m×2^(i-log n/t-1));
        end;
10.   VBUBBLE(A[1..n, 1..m], n, n);
11.   for i := 1 to log m do begin
12.     HBUBBLE(A[1..n, 1..m], 2^i, 2^i);
13.     if i = log m
14.       then j := n/2
15.       else j := t/2 + 1;
16.     VBUBBLE(A[1..n, 1..m], n, j)
        end;
17.   HBUBBLE(A[1..n, 1..m], m, m)
      end
```

Theorem 7. Let n, m and t be powers of 2. Then FPMSORT($A[1..n$, 1 $..m]$, t) sorts the items in A into snake-like row-major nondecreasing order.

Proof. Let ASS(x, y, z) be the following assertion (A2):

(A2)   For any r_1 ($r_1 = 1$, $z+1$, ..., $n-z+1$), any w ($w = x$, $2x$, $4x$, .., $m/4$) and any c_1 ($c_1 = 1$, $2w+1$, ..., $m-2w+1$), let $r_2 = r_1+z-1$, $c_2 = c_1+w-1$, and $c_3 = c_1+2w-1$. Then for any key value v | LESS$^{(v)}$($A[r_1..r_2$, $c_1..c_2]$) $-$ LESS$^{(v)}$($A[r_1..r_2$, $c_2+1..c_3]$)| $\leq y(c_2-c_1 +1) = yw$.

In the loop of the first **for** statement, for any r_1 ($r_1 = 1$, $t+1$, ..., $n-t+1$) and any c_1 ($c_1 = 1$, $k+1$, ..., $m-k+1$), let $r_2 = r_1+t-1$, $c_2 = c_1+k-1$, and $c_3 = c_1+2k-1$, where $k = m2^{i-\log n/t-1}$. At the beginning of line 5 of the first loop, ASS($m/2$, 1, t) is true and PRSIZE($A[r_1..r_2$, $c_1..c_3]$) $\leq r_2-r_1+1 = n/t$. We assume PRSIZE($A[r_1..r_2$, $c_1..c_3]$) $\leq m2^{i-\log n/t-1}$, and ASS($m2^{i-\log n/t-1}$, 1, t) is true at the beginning of line 6. From Lemma 11?, for any c ($1 \leq c \leq m$) 2^i+1 steps are sufficient to sort the contents of $A[r_1..r_2$, $c]$ by BUBBLE. As $2^i+1 > n/t$, n/t steps are sufficient to sort the items in $A[r_1 ..r_2$, $c]$ by BUBBLE. From Lemma 14, at the end of line 9 |LESS$^{(v)}$($A[r_1..r_2$, $c_1..c_2]$) $-$ LESS$^{(v)}$($A[r_1..r_2$, $c_2+1..c_3]$)| $\leq (c_2-c_1+1)/2$ is true. Therefore, ASS($m2^{i-\log n/t-2}$, 1, t) is true. at the end of line 9. From Lemma 10, the procedures at line 8 and line 9 decreases the pseudo-unsorted row size of $A[r_1..r_2$, $c_1..c_3]$ by at least half. Therefore, at the end of line 9 PRSIZE($A[r_1..r_2$, $c_1..c_2]$) $\leq m2^{i-\log n/t-2}$, PRSIZE($A[r_1..r_2$, $c_1..c_2]$) $\leq m2^{i-\log n/t-2}$, and ASS($m2^{i-\log n/t-2}$, 1, t) is true. In the case where $i = low$, $n/t \leq m/2$ and PRSIZE($A[r_1..r_2$, $c_1..c_2]$) ≤ 1, or $n/t > m/2$ and the size of the column of $A[r_1..r_2$, $c_1..c_2]$ is 1. Therefore, at the end of the first **for** statement, for any c ($1 \leq c \leq m$) PRSIZE($A[1..n$, $c]$) ≤ 1, and ASS(1, t, 1) is true.

For each column c ($1 \leq c \leq m$) VBUBBLE at line 10 sorts the items of $A[1 ..n$, $c]$. Thus RSIZE($A[1..n$, $c]$) ≤ 1 and ASS(1, t, 1) is true.

We assume for any c_1 ($c_1 = 1$, $2^{i-1}+1$, ..., $m-2^{i-1}+1$) and $c_2 = c_1+2^{i-1}-1$ RSIZE($A[1..n$, $c_1..c_2]$) ≤ 1, and ASS(1, t, 1) is true. If $i \neq \log m$, for all s (0 $\leq s < m/2^i$) the computation of the statements at line 12, line 15 and line 16 merges $A[1..n$, $s2^i+1..s2^i+2^{i-1}]$ and $A[1..n$, $s2^i+2^{i-1}+1..(s+1)2^i]$ into $A[1..n$, $s2^i+1..(s+1)2^i]$. Thus from Lemma 13, at the end of line 18 RSIZE($A[1..n$, $s2^i+1..(s+1)2^i]$) ≤ 1. If $i = \log m$, the computation of the statements at line 12, line 14 and line 16 merges $A[1..n$, $1..m/2]$ and $A[1..n$, $m/2+1..m]$ into $A[1..n$, $1..m]$. From Lemma 12, at the end of line 16 (i.e., at the end of the last **for** statement), RSIZE($A[1..n$, $1..m]$) ≤ 1. From (1) of Lemma 7,

HBUBBLE at line 17 sorts A in snake-like row-major nondecreasing order.

□

Theorem 8. Let n, m and t be powers of 2. Then the computing time of FPMSORT($A[1..n, 1..m]$, t) is

$(3/2+2/t)n + 4m + (t/2+1)\log m + \log n/t - t/2 - 5 - c$

where for $n/t \leq m/2$ $c = tm/n$, and for $n/t > m/2$ $c = 4n/tm - \log(2n/tm)$.

Proof. The computing time of the first **for** statement (i.e., the sum of the computing time at line 9 and 10) is for $n/t \leq m/2$

$$\sum_{i=1}^{\log n/t} (2^i + 1 + 2^{i+\log(mt/2/n)}),$$

and for $n/t > m/2$

$$\sum_{i=\log 2n/t/m +2}^{\log n/t} (2^i + 1 + 2^{i+\log(mt/2/n)}).$$

The computing time of the last **for** statement (i.e., the sum of the computing time at line 14 and line 15) is

$$\sum_{i=1}^{\log m} 2^i + \sum_{i=1}^{\log m -1} (t/2+1) + n/2.$$

The computing times of line 12 and line 19 are n and m, respectively. Therefore, the computing time of FPMSORT($A[1..n, 1..m]$, t) is, for $n/t \leq m/2$, $(3/2+2/t)n + 4m + (t/2+1)\log m + \log n/t - tm/n - t/2 - 5$, and for $n/t > m/2$, $(3/2+2/t)n + 4m + (t/2+1)\log m + \log n/t - 4n/tm - \log 2n/tm - t/2 - 5$. □

The next theorem is immediate from the previous theorem.

Theorem 9. Let n be a power of 2. Then the computing time of FPMSORT($A[1..n, 1..n]$, 4) is $6n + 4\log n - 13$ steps.

As an example, we show a computing process of FPMSORT($A[1..8, 1..8]$, 4) in Fig. 4. Both SPMSORT and FPMSORT use the parallel bubbling only as their basic operation. Procedure FPMSORT is not completely iterative, and its control structure is slightly more complicated than that of procedure SPMSORT. Saga et al.[14] has recently shown a similar parallel sorting algorithm on the mesh-connected model. Its control structure is as simple as that of SPMSORT, and its computing time for sorting n^2 items is $6n + 3\log n - 13$ steps. However, the algorithm uses both the bubbling and the simple exchange as its basic operations.

47	7	28	44	41	51	48	36
45	30	55	2	13	37	9	61
32	56	40	43	11	64	16	1
46	33	27	14	38	31	54	59
29	50	63	52	12	49	5	35
42	58	21	15	23	4	24	6
62	10	8	26	22	20	57	60
34	18	25	19	53	17	39	3

45	7	28	2	13	37	9	36
47	30	55	44	41	51	48	61
32	33	27	14	11	31	16	1
46	56	40	43	38	64	54	59
29	50	21	15	12	4	5	6
42	58	63	52	23	49	24	35
34	10	8	19	22	17	39	3
62	18	25	26	53	20	57	60

2	7	28	45	9	13	36	37
55	47	44	30	61	51	48	41
14	27	32	33	1	11	16	31
56	46	43	40	64	59	54	38
15	21	29	50	4	5	6	12
63	58	52	42	49	35	24	23
8	10	19	34	3	17	22	39
62	26	25	18	60	57	53	20

(a) Initial configuration

(b) At the end of line 8 in the 1st loop of the first **for** statement

(c) At the end of line 9 in the 1st **for** statement (i.e., at the end of the 1st **for** statement)

2	7	19	18	1	5	6	12
8	10	25	30	3	11	16	20
14	21	28	33	4	13	22	23
15	26	29	34	9	17	24	31
55	27	32	40	49	35	36	37
56	46	43	42	60	51	48	38
62	47	44	45	61	57	53	39
63	58	52	50	64	59	54	41

2	7	18	19	1	5	6	12
10	8	30	25	11	3	20	16
14	21	28	33	4	13	22	23
26	15	34	29	17	9	31	24
27	55	32	40	35	49	36	37
56	46	43	42	60	51	48	38
47	62	44	45	57	61	39	53
63	58	52	50	64	59	54	41

2	7	18	19	1	3	6	12
10	8	28	25	4	5	20	16
14	15	30	29	11	9	22	23
26	21	32	33	17	13	31	24
27	46	34	40	35	49	36	37
47	55	43	42	57	51	39	38
56	58	44	45	60	59	48	41
63	62	52	50	64	61	54	53

(d) At the end of line 10

(e) At the end of line 12 in the 1st loop of the last **for** statement

(f) At the end of line 16 in the 1st loop of the last **for** statement

2	7	10	8	1	3	5	4
14	15	18	19	9	11	6	12
27	25	26	21	20	16	17	13
28	32	29	30	31	24	22	23
33	34	40	42	35	36	37	38
44	45	43	46	41	48	39	49
55	47	52	50	57	51	54	53
63	62	56	58	64	61	59	60

1	2	3	4	5	7	8	6
13	16	15	14	12	11	9	10
19	18	17	20	21	24	23	22
32	31	30	29	28	25	26	27
33	34	35	36	37	38	40	39
47	48	46	45	44	43	41	42
49	50	51	52	53	54	55	56
64	63	62	61	60	59	58	57

1	2	3	4	5	6	7	8
16	15	14	13	12	11	10	9
17	18	19	20	21	22	23	24
32	31	30	29	28	27	26	25
33	34	35	36	37	38	39	40
48	47	46	45	44	43	42	41
49	50	51	52	53	54	55	56
64	63	62	61	60	59	58	57

(g) At the end of line 16 in the 2nd loop of the last **for** statement

(h) At the end of line 16 in the 3rd loop of the last **for** statement (i.e., at the end of the last **for** statement)

(i) At the end of the sorting process

Fig. 4   A Sorting Process by FPMSORT

4. Lower Bounds on Computing Times

In this section we discuss lower bounds on the computing time by iterative merge sorts and by iterative pseudo-merge sorts on the mesh-connected processor array. We assume that the size of the processor array is $n \times n$, where n is a power of 2. We also assume that only the simple exchange and the bubbling are allowed to be used as the basic operations of those algorithms. Throughout this section we consider the snake-like row-major nondecreasing order only. The simple exchange means that an item in the array is exchanged with one of its neighbor items. For example, both SPMSORT and FPMSORT use the bubbling only. In this section we consider the following two classes of parallel sorting algorithms which can be implemented on the mesh-connected processor array.

(1) Iterative merge sorts using the bubbling and the simple exchange only as their basic operations.

(2) Iterative pseudo-merge sorts using the bubbling and the simple exchange only as their basic operations.

An iterative merge sort and an iterative pseudo-merge sort on $A[1..2^r, 1..2^r]$ are sorting algorithms based on the following schemes (s1) and (s2), respectively.

(s1) **for** $i := 1..r$ **do**
    construct in parallel all $2^i \times 2^i$ sorted subarrays
    by merging their four $2^{i-1} \times s^{i-1}$ sorted subarrays.

(s2) **for** $i := 1..r$ **do**
    construct in parallel all $2^i \times 2^i$ 1-roughly sorted subarrays
    by merging their four $2^{i-1} \times 2^{i-1}$ 1-roughly sorted subarrays;
    sort each row.

An algorithm in class (1) and an algorithm in class (2) are called an iterative merge sort and an iterative pseudo-merge sort, respectively. The algorithm by Lang et al.[8] and their improved one[9] are iterative merge sorts. The algorithm by Saga et al.[14] and SPMSORT are iterative pseudo-merge sorts. However, FPMSORT does not belong to any of these two classes. For sorting algorithms on the $n \times n$ mesh-connected processor array, $2n - 2$ steps are an obvious lower bound on the computing times.

Schnorr and Shamir[15] have recently made a $3n - 2\sqrt{n} - 3$ lower bound on the time complexity of sorting n^2 items on a very general model of $n \times n$ mesh-connected MIMD processor array. We shall give lower bounds on the computing times of iterative merge sorts and iterative pseudo-merge sorts.

Lemma 15. There exists an initial pattern on the 2×2 mesh-connected processor array such that at least 3 steps are required to sort it by any algorithm with the bubbling and the simple exchange only as its basic operations.

Proof. Note that we only consider the snake-like row-major nondecreasing order. Suppose that the initial pattern of $A[1..2, 1..2]$ is as follows: $A[1, 1].key = 2, A[1, 2].key = 3, A[2, 1].key = 1, A[2, 2].key = 4$. If at the first step the contents of $A[1, 1]$ and $A[2, 1]$ are exchanged, then at least two more steps are required to move the item with key value 2 in $A[2, 1]$ to its final position $A[1, 2]$. Thus at least three steps are required in this case. We can similarly show that at least three steps are required in any case where at the first step the contents of $A[1, 1]$ and $A[1, 2]$, or the contents of $A[1, 2]$ and $A[2, 2]$, or the contents of $A[2, 1]$ and $A[2, 2]$ are exchanged. Hence, this lemma holds. □

The next lemma is immediate.

Lemma 16. There exists an algorithm on the 2×2 mesh-connected processor array such that it 1-roughly sorts the items on this model in 2 steps, and the algorithm in time optimal.

Lemma 17. There exists an initial pattern on the 4×4 mesh-connected processor array such that at least 10 steps are required to sort it by any merge sort.

Proof. We consider the following initial configuration of $A[1..4, 1..4]$:
Let α be the 3rd smallest item in $A[3..4, 1..2]$, and exactly 3 items in $A[1..2, 1..4]$ are smaller than α. Exactly p items in $A[3..4, 3..4]$ are smaller than any item in the other three subarrays and $4-p$ items in $A[3..4, 3..4]$ are greater than any item in the other three subarrays $(0 \leq p \leq 4)$.

After sorting each 2×2 subarray, α is located in $A[4, 2]$. The effect of the contents of $A[3..4, 3..4]$ to $A[1, 1]$ does not appear before the 4th step of the second merging process. Therefore, the item in $A[1, 1]$ just after the 3rd step of the merging process is the same for any initial configuration of $A[3..4, 3..4]$. The item in $A[1, 1]$ just after the 3rd step of the merging process cannot be the 6th smallest one among the items initially sorted in $A[1..2, 1..4]$ and $A[3..4, 1..2]$. Hence, for an appropriate value of p, at this stage the distance between $A[1, 1]$ and the final position of the item in $A[1, 1]$ is at least 4. Therefore, there exists an initial pattern that takes at least 10 steps. □

Theorem 10. It takes at least $4.5n - 3\log n - 2$ steps to sort n^2 items $(n \geq 4)$ on the $n \times n$ mesh-connected processor array by any iterative merge sort.

Proof. Let $T(m)$ be computing time for sorting m^2 items by an iterative merge sort on the $m \times m$ mesh-connected processor array. Let us consider a $2k \times 2k$ array $A[1..2k, 1..2k]$, where k is a power of 2 and not less than 4. We suppose that all $k \times k$ subarrays of A have been already sorted by the iterative merge sort. We now consider the process or merging the four subarrays into $A[1..2k, 1..2k]$ Since each subarray has been sorted independently from the others, we may consider the following contents of $A[k+1 ..2k, k+1..2k]$;

> For some p $(0 \leq p < 4k)$ all items in $A[k+1..2k, k+1..2k]$ except last p items are smaller than any item in the other three subarrays and the last p items are larger than any item in the other three subarrays.

Since the effect of the contents of $A[k+1..2k, k+1..2k]$ to $A[1, 1]$ does not appear before the $2k$th step of the merging process, the item in $A[1, 1]$ just after the $2k-1$st step of the merging process is the same for any initial configuration of $A[k+1..2k, k+1..2k]$. As shown in Fig. 5, for an appropriate value of p, this item in $A[1, 1]$ should be transferred to the right end position of a row which is not above the $k/2-1$st row. Therefore, this item in $A[1, 1]$ just after the $2k-1$st step of the merging process should move at least further $2.5k-2$ steps. We therefore have the following recurrence:

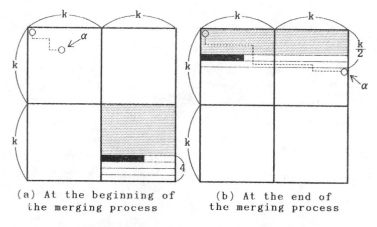

(a) At the beginning of   (b) At the end of
the merging process   the merging process

Fig. 5 The effect of $A[k+1..2k, k+1..2k]$ to $A[1, 1]$

$T(2k) \geq T(k) + 4.5k - 3 \quad (k \geq 4)$,

$T(4) \geq 10 \quad$ (from Lemma 17).

Solving this recurrence, we have

$T(n) \geq 4.5n - 3\log n - 2 \quad (n \geq 4)$. □

Lemma 18. There exists an initial pattern on the 4×4 mesh-connected processor array such that at least 7 steps are required to 1-roughly sort it by any pseudo-merge.

Proof. We consider an initial pattern on $A[1..4, 1..4]$ such that the key value of any item in $A[3..4, 1..2]$ is smaller than that of any items in $A[1..2, 1..4]$ and $A[3..4, 3..4]$. For Lemma 16, it takes at least 2 steps to 1-roughly sort each 2×2 subarray of $A[1..4, 1..4]$. Suppose that after 1-roughly sorting all the 2×2 subarrays of A we could 1-roughly sort the items in array A in less than 5 steps. Then in the next merge process the final position of the item in $A[3, 2]$ should be $A[1, 4]$. We should note that the third position of item in $A[3, 2]$ in the merge process cannot be $A[1, 3]$. That is, the item in $A[3, 2]$ cannot pass through any position of the first row of A. The item in $A[4, 2]$ or $A[3, 1]$ should be transferred to $A[1, 3]$ in the next merge process. In the former case, the item in $A[4, 2]$ should be transferred through the following route: $A[4, 2] \to A[4, 3] \to A[3, 3] \to A[2, 3] \to A[1, 3]$. However, this route is not possible without exchanging it by the item transferred to $A[1, 4]$ at some step in the merge process. Thus the former case is not possible to finish the merge process in 4 steps. In the latter case, the item in $A[3, 1]$ and the item in $A[3, 2]$ should be transferred to their final positions in the merge process through the following routes: $A[3, 1] \to A[2, 1] \to A[2, 2] \to A[2, 3] \to A[1, 3]$ and $A[3, 2] \to A[3, 3] \to A[3, 4] \to A[2, 4] \to A[1, 4]$. However, it is not possible to transfer both the items in $A[4, 1]$ and $A[4, 2]$ to $A[1, 1]$ and $A[1, 2]$ in not more than 4 steps without disturbing the transfer of items from $A[3 \ 1]$ and $A[3, 2]$. Thus any case leads us to a contradiction. Therefore, it is not possible that the input pattern is 1-roughly sorted in less than 7 steps by a pseudo-merge sort. □

Theorem 11. It takes at least $3.5n - \log n - 3$ steps to sort n^2 items ($n \geq 4$) on the $n \times n$ mesh-connected processor array by any iterative pseudo-merge sort.

Proof. Let $T(m)$ be the computing time for 1-roughly sorting m^2 items by an iterative pseudo-merge sort on the $m \times m$ mesh-connected processor array. Let us consider a subarray $A[1..2k, 1..2k]$, where k is a power of

2 such that $4 \leq k \leq n/4$. We suppose that all $k \times k$ subarrays of $A[1 .. 2k, 1 ..$
$2k]$ have been already 1-roughly sorted by the iterative pseudo-merge
sort. We may assume that any item in $A[k+1 .. 2k, k+1 .. 2k]$ is smaller than
any item in the other three subarrays. The effect of the contents of $A[k+1$
$.. 2k, k+1 .. 2k]$ to $A[1, 1]$ does not appear before the $2k$th step of the
pseudo-merging process. The item in $A[1, 1]$ just after the $2k$-1st step of
the pseudo-merging process should move at least further $k/2$ steps. We
therefore have the following recurrence:

$T(2k) \geq T(k) + 2.5k - 1 \quad (k \geq 4)$,

$T(4) \geq 7 \quad$ (from Lemma 18).

Solving this recurrence we have

$T(n/2) \geq 1.25n - \log n$.

From the same arguments as those used in the proof of Theorem 10, it
takes at least $2.25n - 3$ steps to obtain the completely sorted array $A[1 ..$
$n, 1 .. n]$ from the four 1-roughly sorted subarrays. We therefore have the
following inequality:

$T(n) \geq 3.5n - \log n - 3$.   □

5. Concluding remarks

We have shown that our parallel sorting algorithms are fast and simple
in their control structures. They are therefore suitable to be implemented
on a VLSI chip. The main tool used in this paper is function POTENTIAL
and related properties. This function will be useful for designing efficient
parallel sorting algorithms on the mesh-connected model and its variants.
Many variations of our algorithms can be considered. For example, we may
use the parallel bubbling in different directions, and/or allow a few types
of basic operations other than the parallel bubbling. Some of the variations may be somewhat faster than FPMSORT, but their control hardware
will be more complicated.

Finding good lower bounds on computing items for iterative merge
sorts or iterative pseudo-merge sorts is an interesting problem. The gaps
between the lower bounds derived in this paper and the computing times
of our algorithms are not tight enough. However, some smart ideas or
techniques will be required to derive tight lower bounds. Finding the
optimal computing time or a tight lower bound on computing times of
parallel sorts even on a small fixed sized processor array (e.g., 8×8
mesh-connected processor array) is not easy. We conjecture that $5.5n$ is a
lower bound on the computing times of iterative merge sorts and that $4.5n$
a lower bound on the computing times of iterative pseudo-merge sorts.

References

1. Ajtai, M., Komlos, J., and Szemeredi, E., "An O(N log N) sorting network", *Proc. 15th Annual ACM Symp. on Theory of Computing*, pp. 1-9, May 1983.

2. Akl, G.: *Parallel sorting algorithms*, Academic Press, Orlando, Florida, 1985.

3. Batcher, K. E., "Sorting networks and their applications", *Proc. AFIPS Spring Joint Computer Conf.*, 32, pp. 307-314, 1968.

4. Bilardi, G., and Preparata, F., "A minimum area VLSI architecture for O(log N) time sorting", *Proc. 16th Annual ACM Symp. on Theory of Computing*, pp. 64-70, May 1984.

5. Bitton, D., Dewitt, D. J., Hsiao, D. K., and Mrnon, J., "A taxonomy of parallel sorting", *ACM Computing Survey*, 16, pp. 287-318, 1984.

6. Knuth, D. E., *The Art of Computer Programming*, Vol. 3, *Sorting and Searching*, Addison-Wesley, Reading, Mass., 1973.

7. Kumar, M., and Hirschberg, D. S., "An efficient implementation of Batcher's odd-even merge algorithm and its application in parallel sorting schemes", *IEEE Trans. Comput.*, C-32, pp. 254-264, March 1983.

8. Lang, H. -W., Schimmler, M., Schmech, H. and Schroder, H.: "A fast sorting algorithm for VLSI", *ICALP 83, Lecture Notes in Comput. Science 154*, pp. 408-419, 1983.

9. Lang, H. -W., Schimmler, M., Schmech, H. and Schroder, H.: "Systoric sorting on a mesh-connected network", *IEEE Trans. Comput.*, C-34, pp. 625-658, 1985.

10. Leighton, T., "Tight bounds on the complexity of parallel sorting", *IEEE Trans. Comput.*, C-34, pp. 344-354, 1985.

11. Nassimi, D., and Sahni, S., "Bitonic sort on a mesh-connected parallel computer", *IEEE Trans. Comput.*, C-27, pp. 2-7, January 1979.

12. Sado, K. and Igarashi, Y.: "A divide-and-conquer method of the parallel sort", *IECE of Japan, Tech. Commit of Automata and Languages*, AL84-68, pp. 41-50, 1985.

13. Sado, K. and Igarashi, Y.: "A fast parallel pseudo-merge sort algorithm", *IECE of Japan, Tech. Commit of Automata and Languages*, AL85-16, pp. 21-30, 1985.

14. Saga, K., Sado, K. and Igarashi, Y.: "An iterative parallel pseudo-merge sort and its computing time", *IECE of Japan, Tech. Commit. of Computation*, COMP86-26, pp. 73-82, 1986.

15. Schnorr, C. P. and Shamir, A.: "An optimal sorting algorithm for mesh-connected computers", *Proc. 18th ACM Symposium on Theory of Computing*, pp. 255-263, 1986.

16. Thompson, C. D., and Kung, H. T., "Sorting on a mesh-connected parallel computer", *Commun. ACM*, 20, pp. 263-271, April 1977.

17. Thompson, C. D., "The VLSI complexity of sorting", *IEEE Trans. Comput.*, C-32, pp. 1171-1184 December 1983.

Game Solving Procedure H* Is Unsurpassed

T. Ibaraki

Department of Applied Mathematics and Physics

Faculty of Engineering

Kyoto University

Kyoto, Japan 606

Abstract   A search procedure X_1 for solving minimax game trees surpasses
a search procedure X_2 if $AREA(X_1) \subseteq AREA(X_2)$ holds for any game tree G,
where $AREA(X)$ denotes the set of nodes in G expanded by X. X_1 strictly
surpasses X_2 if X_1 surpasses X_2 and $AREA(X_1) \subset AREA(X_2)$ holds for at least
one game tree, where $\subset$ denotes proper inclusion. A search procedure X is
unsurpassed if no search procedure strictly surpasses X.

In this paper, we prove that a search procedure called H* is unsurpassed.

1. Introduction

Various search procedures, such as alpha-beta[4,6], SSS*[7] and H*
[1,3], are known for solving minimax game trees. All of these procedures
repeat the following step until the game value is correctly computed:

Select an open node (i.e., generated but not tested yet),

and, if it does not satisfy the cut condition, expand it to

generate its sons.

DISCRETE ALGORITHMS AND
COMPLEXITY

For a search procedure X and a given game tree G, AREA(X) denotes the set of nodes in G expanded before termination of X. As AREA(X) represents the amount of work required by X to solve the given game tree, it may be natural to call that a search procedure X_1 surpasses another search procedure X_2 if AREA(X_1) $\subseteq$ AREA(X_2) holds for any game tree. We say that X_1 strictly surpasses X_2 if X_1 surpasses X_2 and AREA(X_1) $\subset$ AREA(X_2) holds for some game tree, where $\subset$ denotes proper inclusion. A search procedure X is unsurpassed if no search procedure strictly surpasses X.

A remarkable achievement in this regard was first made by Stockman [7] by showing that SSS* surpasses alpha-beta. Later a complete characterization of the class of search procedures that surpass alpha-beta was given by [2]. However, no procedure has so far been proved to be unsurpassed. In this paper, we give a proof that a search procedure called H* is in fact unsurpassed.

2. Game Trees and Search Procedures

A minimax game tree G is a finite rooted tree consisting of two types of nodes, MAX and MIN. Without loss of generality, we assume that root P_0 is a MAX node. MAX and MIN nodes appear alternately along any path from P_0. A node is a terminal node if it has no son in G. For each terminal node P, a finite real number f(P), called the static evaluation value, is given. It represents the score given to the corresponding position of the game. The f-values can be extended to other nodes in G in the bottom-up manner:

$$f(P) := \begin{cases} \min_{Q \in S(P)} f(Q) & \text{if P is a MIN node} \\ \max_{Q \in S(P)} f(Q) & \text{if P is a MAX node,} \end{cases} \quad (1)$$

where S(P) denotes the set of sons of P in G. In particular, $f(P_0)$ given to root P_0 is called the game value. The aim of a search procedure is to compute $f(P_0)$.

When a search procedure is applied to G, subtrees of G are generated and expanded until $f(P_0)$ is computed. Such a subtree T is called a search tree. More precisely, it is a subtree T of G such that

1) T contains P_0, and

2) if T contains a son Q of a node P, then it contains all the sons of P.

A node P in T is called a tip node if T does not contain any son of P.

For each node P in a search tree T, lower and upper bounds L(P) and U(P) on f(P) are given, where they satisfy

$$L(P) \leq f(P) \leq U(P), \quad \text{for any P}$$
$$L(P) = f(P) = U(P), \quad \text{if P is a terminal node.}$$

It is possible to have $L(P) = -\infty$ and/or $U(P) = \infty$, though f(P) is always assumed to be finite. The updated values of L and U, denoted L_b and U_b, are defined in the bottom-up manner:

$$L_b(P) := \begin{cases} L(P), & \text{if P is a tip node,} \\ \max_{Q \in S(P)} L_b(Q), & \text{if P is a MAX node and} \\ & \text{is not a tip node,} \\ \min_{Q \in S(P)} L_b(Q), & \text{if P is a MIN node and} \\ & \text{is not a tip node.} \end{cases}$$

U_b is defined similarly, by interchanging L and U here. Define also the top-down values of L and U, denoted L_t and U_t, as follows:

$$L_t(P) := \max_{V \in AMAX(P)} L_b(V)$$
$$U_t(P) := \min_{W \in AMIN(P)} U_b(W),$$

where AMAX(P) (AMIN(P)) is the set of MAX (MIN) nodes in T, which are proper ancestors of P.

It is shown in [2] that a node P in T need not be expanded further (i.e., it does not provide any useful information of $f(P_0)$) if the following cut condition is met:

$$\max[L_t(P), L_b(P)] \geq \min[U_t(P), U_b(P)]. \tag{2}$$

It can be shown that

$$L_b(P) \leq f(P) \leq U_b(P) \tag{3}$$

holds for any P in T, and a node P in T satisfies the cut condition if and only if all of its descendants in T satisfy the cut condition. A search tree T solves the game if $L_b(P_0) = U_b(P_0)$ (=$f(P_0)$) holds for root P_0.

Starting with a search tree T consisting only of P_0, a search procedure grows T until it solves the game. This type of search procedures (called GSEARCH-B in [2]) are generally described as follows, where OPEN denotes the set of tip nodes in T, which have not been tested yet.

procedure GSEARCH

G1(initialization): Let OPEN:=$\{P_0\}$, $L_b(P_0):=L(P_0)$ and $U_b(P_0):=U(P_0)$.

G2(search): Halt if $L_b(P_0)=U_b(P_0)$. Otherwise select a node P from OPEN.

G3(test): Delete P from OPEN. Check if cut condition (2) holds. If so, return to G2.

G4(expansion): Generate all the sons Q of P, and compute their L(Q) and U(Q). Add these to OPEN, and update L_b, U_b, L_t and U_t of all nodes in the current search tree. Return to G2. []

Various search procedures, such as alpha-beta and SSS[*], can be realized by specifying how to select a node in step G2. Search procedure

H^* to be discussed in this paper has the following selection rule[3]. Call $L_b(P)$ for MAX nodes P and $U_b(P)$ for MIN nodes P the <u>optimistic bounds</u>. Let $\pi(P)$ denote the path from P_0 to P in T. For a tip node P in T, path $\pi(P)$ is called an <u>optimistic path</u> if, for each node $Q(\neq P)$ in the path, it contains a son of Q with the largest U_b if Q is a MAX node, and with the smallest L_b if Q is a MIN node (i.e., with the best optimistic bound). H^* selects a tip node P such that $\pi(P)$ is an optimistic path. This H^* can also be regarded as a search procedure $B^*[1]$ with PROVEBEST search rule.

As shown in [3], H^* has the following properties.

(1) No node P selected by H^* satisfies the cut condition.

(2) If $L_b(P_0)=U_b(P_0)$ holds for the current search tree, any node Q in its optimistic path satisfies $L_b(Q)=U_b(Q)=f(P_0)$.

As there may be more than one optimistic path in a search tree T, we need comment upon the tie breaking rule. For a node Q in T, let T(Q) denote the maximal subtree of T rooted at Q. In choosing a son R of Q, among those having the best optimistic bound, we assume that the tie breaking rule depends only on the information concerning T(Q), but not on the rest of T. Also, once a son R is selected, it will be persistently selected in later iterations unless the optimistic bound of R changes. Typical tie breaking rules are to select the leftmost one, the rightmost one, the one with the smallest $|U(R)-L(R)|$ and so on, among those sons R of Q with the best optimistic bound.

3. Outline of the Proof

In the subsequent sections, we shall prove that H^* is unsurpassed within search procedures of GSEARCH. For this, we show that, given any search procedure X of GSEARCH, there is a game tree G such that X expands at least one node not expanded by H^*.

For a given game tree G, let $\sigma(X)$ denotes the sequence of nodes expanded in step G4 of X. If $X \neq H^*$, then $\sigma(X) \neq \sigma(H^*)$ holds for some game tree G. In this case, consider the nodes at which $\sigma(X)$ and $\sigma(H^*)$ differ for the first time. Let P_X and P_H* denote such nodes in $\sigma(X)$ and $\sigma(H^*)$ respectively. Namely, up to this point, X and H^* have generated the same search tree T, but now they select different nodes P_X and P_H*, and expand them. Let R be the closest common ancestor of P_X and P_H*, and let Q_X and Q_H* denote the sons of R in paths $\pi(P_X)$ and $\pi(P_H*)$ respectively (see Fig. 1). Without loss of generality, we assume that R is a MAX node, since the other case can be similarly treated.

By the selection rule of H^*,

$$U_b(Q_H*) \geq U_b(Q_X)$$

holds in T. To prove that H^* is unsurpassed, the subsequent sections

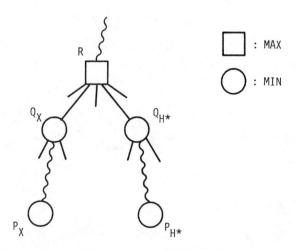

Fig. 1. Illustration of Q_X and Q_{H*} with their parent R.

construct game trees G, by extending the current search tree T, such that P_X (or some other node expanded by X) is not expanded by H^*. The proof is done for the following three cases:

A. $U_b(Q_X) < \infty$,

B. $U_b(Q_X) = U_b(Q_H^*) = \infty$ and $R \neq P_0$,

C. $U_b(Q_X) = U_b(Q_H^*) = \infty$ and $R = P_0$.

4. Proof for Case A

Assuming Case A, i.e., $U_b(Q_X) < \infty$, we first choose a finite number $a < \infty$ such that

$$
\begin{aligned}
&a = U_b(Q_H^*), && \text{if } U_b(Q_H^*) < \infty \\
&a > U_b(Q_X) \text{ and } a \geq L_b(Q_H^*), && \text{if } U_b(Q_H^*) = \infty,
\end{aligned}
\tag{4}
$$

and then assume that Q_H^* satisfies

$$
f(Q_H^*) = a.
\tag{5}
$$

This is justified because $L_b(Q_H^*) \leq a \leq U_b(Q_H^*)$ holds by (4).

In the rest of computation of H^*, Q_H^* always has a higher priority of being selected over Q_X (by the selection rule and the tie breaking rule of H^* discussed at the end of Section 2). There are two possible outcomes; either Q_H^* is solved (i.e., $L_b(Q_H^*) = U_b(Q_H^*) = a$ holds) or H^* becomes to select an optimistic path not visiting R.

In the former case,

$$
L_t(Q_X) \geq L_b(R) \geq L_b(Q_H^*) = a \geq U_b(Q_X)
$$

holds, and Q_X satisfies the cut condition. Therefore H^* does not expand its descendant P_X.

In the latter case, there is an ancestor W of R, with two sons V and V', such that V' is an ancestor of R (possibly V'=R) and, at this stage,

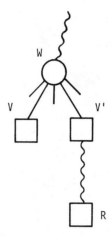

Fig. 2. Illustration of W and its sons.

H^* chooses an optimistic path containing W and V. This is illustrated in Fig. 2. Without loss of generality, we assume that W is a MIN node. By the selection rule of H^*, we have

$$L_b(V) \leq L_b(V')$$
$$L_b(V') > -\infty.$$

(6)

(The latter holds, because if $L_b(V')=L_b(V)=-\infty$, H^* keeps selecting V' by the tie breaking rule as discussed in Section 2.) Then choose a finite number b such that

$$b=L_b(V), \qquad\qquad \text{if } L_b(V) > -\infty$$
$$b<L_b(V') \text{ and } b\leq U_b(V), \text{ if } L_b(V)=-\infty$$

(7)

and assume

$$f(V)=b.$$

(8)

If H^* eventually finds

$$L_b(V)=U_b(V)=b,$$

then V' satisfies the cut condition because

$$U_t(V')\leq U_b(W)\leq U_b(V)=b\leq L_b(V').$$

This again means that H^* does not expand P_X (a descendant of V').

It is possible that H^* does not solve V but becomes to find an ancestor at which the optimistic path deviates from $\pi(W)$. Then we can repeat a similar argument. However, this situation cannot occur indefinitely because the depth of P_H* is finite. Consequently we have proved the next lemma.

Lemma 1. If Case A of Section 3 occures, H^* does not expand P_X for some game tree. []

5. Proof for Case B

Case B assumes that $U_b(Q_X)=U_b(Q_H*)=\infty$ and $R\neq P_0$, as illustrated in Fig. 3. Assumption $R\neq P_0$ means that R has its parent W in G, which is a MIN node. Let

$$L_{min}=min\{L_b(V)|V\in S(W), V\neq R\}$$

and choose a finite number c such that

$$c>L_{min}. \tag{9}$$

When H^* selects a node Y in $T(Q_H*)$, property $U_b(Y)=\infty$ can be shown in the following manner. By assumption $U_b(Q_H*)=\infty$. Let P be a node in the selected optimistic path, and assume $U_b(P)=\infty$. If P is a MIN node, all of its sons Q satisfy $U_b(Q)=\infty$, and hence so does the son in the optimistic path. On the other hand, if P is a MAX node, at least one of its sons Q

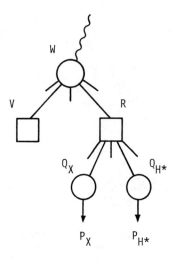

Fig. 3.   Illustration of the parent of R.

satisfies $U_b(Q)= \infty$. As H^* selects the son with the largest U_b, the son Q
in the optimistic path satisfies $U_b(Q)= \infty$.

If the selected Y is expanded, we assume that all $Z \in S(Y)$ satisfy

$$U(Z)= \infty$$
$$L(Z)=\max[c, L_b(Y)].$$

(10)

Therefore, expanding Y yields

$$L_b(Y) \geq c.$$

If Y is a MIN node, and has parent Q (a MAX node) in $T(Q_H^*)$, Q satisfies

$$L_b(Q) \geq c.$$

On the other hand, if Y is a MAX node and has parent Q (a MIN node) in

$T(Q_H^*)$, it is possible to have

$$L_b(Q) < c.$$

In this case, the optimistic path contains $Y' \in S(Q)$ with $L_b(Y')=L_b(Q)$, and H^* expands a descendant of Y'. Therefore, if we assume (10) also for such nodes, we shall eventually have

$$L_b(Y') \geq c.$$

Repeating this argument, we then obtain

$$L_b(Q) \geq c.$$

Note that, during this process, $U_b(Q_H^*)= \infty$ does not change, and H^* never selects Q_X in its optimistic path. Consequently, H^* eventually reaches the stage, either $L_b(Q_H^*) \geq c$ holds, or the optimistic path deviates from $\pi(Q_H^*)$ at a proper ancestor of R. In the former case, by $L_b(R) \geq c$, H^* selects a node V with $L_b(V)=L_{min}$ in its optimistic path. Therefore, in either case, H^* will select an optimistic path not visiting R, before selecting P_X. Now apply an argument similar to Case A to V and R, and we can prove the next lemma.

  <u>Lemma 2.</u> If Case B of Section 3 occurs, H^* does not expand P_X for some game tree. []

6. <u>Some Properties of H^*</u>

  Before dealing with Case C, we discuss some properties of H^*.

  Let root P_0 of a game tree G have m sons $Q_1, Q_2, ..., Q_m$, which are MIN nodes. Let $G(Q_i)$ denote the maximal subtree of G rooted at Q_i. For a search procedure X, $\sigma_i(X)$ denotes the subsequence of $\sigma(X)$ restricted to the nodes in $G(Q_i)$, whereas $\overline{\sigma}_i(X)$ denotes the sequence of the nodes expanded by X when it is applied to $G(Q_i)$.

Lemma 3. For a given game tree G, $\sigma_i(H^*)$ is a prefix of $\bar{\sigma}_i(H^*)$, i=1,2,...,m. (σ' is a prefix of σ if $\sigma = \sigma' \sigma''$ for some σ''.)

Proof. Since H^* applied to G or $G(Q_i)$ selects the nodes in $G(Q_i)$ solely on the basis of L_b and U_b in $G(Q_i)$, the orders of the nodes in $G(Q_i)$ selected by H^* applied to G and $G(Q_i)$ are the same . As no node selected by H^* satisfies the cut condition, this means that $\sigma_i(H^*)$ is a prefix of $\bar{\sigma}_i(H^*)$. (Note that $\sigma_i(H^*)$ can be a proper prefix of $\bar{\sigma}_i(H^*)$ since the computation of H^* applied to G may halt as a result of the computation in a different subtree $G(Q_j)$.) []

Now apply H^* to each $G(Q_i)$, and let K_i denote the set of nodes P in $G(Q_i)$ such that

$$U(P)= \infty, \text{ and } U_b(Q)= \infty \text{ for any ancestor } Q \text{ of } P, \quad (11)$$

when H^* selects P. Furthermore define

$$K= \bigcup_{i=1}^{m} K_i. \quad (12)$$

Lemma 4. In $\sigma(H^*)$, the nodes in K come before the nodes not in K.

Proof. Assume that a search tree T has at least one tip node in K. In this case $U_b(P_0)= \infty$ holds. Then, as discussed in Section 5 after (9), H^* selects a tip node P satisfying (11), i.e., in K. []

By lemma 3 and 4 we see that each $\sigma_i(H^*)$ ($\bar{\sigma}_i(H^*)$) starts with the initial portion consisting of the nodes in K_i, denoted $\rho_i(H^*)$ ($\bar{\rho}_i(H^*)$), followed by the portion consisting of the nodes not in K_i. Denote also the initial portion of $\sigma(H^*)$ consisting of the nodes in K by $\rho(H^*)$. $\rho(H^*)$ is obtained from $\rho_i(H^*)$, i=1,2,...,m, by merging them while preserving the order of nodes in each $\rho_i(H^*)$.

Now let X be a search procedure which has the following properties:

(1) it selects the nodes in K before any node not in K,

(2) $\rho_i(X)$ is a prefix of $\bar{\rho}_i(H^*)$, $i=1,2,\ldots,m$, and

(3) all the nodes not in K are selected by the rule of H^*.

In other words, such an X differs from H^* only in that the nodes in K can be selected from $G(Q_i)$, $i=1,2,\ldots,m$, in any order (the order within each $G(Q_i)$ must be the same as H^*). Denote the class of such search procedures by $C(H^*)$.

$\underline{\text{Lemma 5.}}$ Let $X \in C(H^*)$. Then all nodes in K are expanded by X.

$\underline{\text{Proof.}}$ Let $P \in K_i$. If P is selected by X,

$$U_t(P) = \min_{W \in \text{AMIN}(P)} U_b(W) = \infty$$

holds since $\rho_i(X)$ is a prefix of $\bar{\rho}_i(H^*)$. Therefore

$$\min[U_t(P), U_b(P)] = \min[U_t(P), U(P)] = \infty$$

and P does not satisfy the cut condition (2). Since any ancestor Q of P belongs to K, this shows that P is eventually selected and expanded by X. $\square$

This lemma implies that any $X \in C(H^*)$ satisfies $\rho_i(X) = \bar{\rho}_i(H^*)$ for all i. Since $H^* \in C(H^*)$ by definition, $\rho_i(H^*) = \bar{\rho}_i(H^*)$ and $\rho(H^*)$ is obtained by merging $\bar{\rho}_i(H^*)$, $i=1,2,\ldots,m$. As the nodes not in K are selected by the rule of H^*, this shows

$$\text{AREA}(X) = \text{AREA}(H^*), \quad \text{for } X \in C(H^*),$$

i.e., no X in $C(H^*)$ strictly surpasses H^*.

7. Proof for Case C

Case C assumes that $U_b(Q_X) = U_b(Q_H^*) = \infty$ and $R = P_0$. In this case, it is possible that both P_X and P_H^* belong to K, i.e., H^* has to expand P_X.

Therefore, it is necessary to take into account other nodes in order to prove that H^* is not strictly surpassed by any search procedure X.

As we have seen in the previous section, if $X \in C(H^*)$, a node P is expanded by X if and only if it is expanded by H^*. Therefore, we assume here $X \notin C(H^*)$ and show that there is at least one node which is expanded by X but not expanded by H^*.

As shown in Lemma 3, H^* has a property that $\sigma_i(H^*)$ is a prefix of $\bar{\sigma}_i(H^*)$. If there were a search procedure X strictly surpassing H^*, it must have a similar property.

Lemma 6. Let X be a search procedure. If $\sigma_i(X)$ is not a prefix of $\sigma_i(H^*)$ for some game tree, then X does not strictly surpass H^*.

Proof. Let P_X and P_H^* be the nodes in $\sigma_i(X)$ and $\sigma_i(H^*)$, respectively, at which these two sequences differ for the first time. Since the closest common ancestor of P_X and P_H^* now belongs to $G(Q_i)$, the argument of Case A or B in Section 3 or 4 can be applied to show that H^* does not expand P_X for some game tree. ☐

Combined with lemmas 4 and 5 for H^*, this tells that any X surpassing H^* has a $\sigma_i(X)$ consisting of $\rho_i(X)(= \rho_i(H^*))$ and then a sequence of the nodes not in K_i. In particular, $\rho_i(X)$ is a prefix of $\rho_i(H^*)$ $(= \bar{\rho}_i(H^*))$, i=1,2,...,m.

Lemma 7. Let X be a search procedure such that $\sigma_i(X)$ is a prefix of $\sigma_i(H^*)$, i=1,2,...,m, for any game tree. If X expands a node P_X not in K before a node in K, then X does not strictly surpass H^*.

Proof. Let P_X be the first such node and let T be the search tree when P_X is selected by X. Without loss of generality, assume that P_X belongs to $T(Q_1)$. Since $\sigma_1(X)$ is a prefix of $\sigma_1(H^*)$, P_X must be the node immediately after the $\rho_1(X)(= \rho_1(H^*))$ portion of $\sigma_1(X)$. This means that $U_b(Q_1) < \infty$ holds in the current search tree T. By assumption, there is a

$T(Q_i)$ containing a node P_H* in K, which is not expanded yet. Let P_H* belong to $T(Q_2)$ without loss of generality. This means $U_b(Q_2)= \infty$ in T. Now with $Q_X=Q_1$ and $Q_H*=Q_2$, apply the argument of Case A (Section 4) to show that there is a game tree, obtained by extending T, for which H^* does not expand P_X. []

The next lemma is the final step to show that X must be a member of $C(H^*)$ if it were to strictly surpass H^*.

Lemma 8. Let X be a search procedure such that, for any game tree, $\sigma_i(X)$ is a prefix of $\sigma_i(H^*)$, i=1,2,...,m, and X expands the nodes in K before any node not in K. Let

$$\sigma(X)= \rho(X) \mu(X).$$

If $\mu(X) \neq \mu(H^*)$, X does not strictly surpass H^*.

Proof. Let P_X and P_H* be the nodes in $\mu(X)$ and $\mu(H^*)$, respectively, at which these two sequences differ for the first time. Since $\sigma_i(X)$ is a prefix of $\sigma_i(H^*)$, P_X and P_H* belong to different $G(Q_i)$. Without loss of generality, let P_X and P_H* belong to $G(Q_1)$ and $G(Q_2)$ respectively. By P_X, $P_H* \notin K$ and by the definition of P_H*, $U_b(Q_1) \leq U_b(Q_2) < \infty$ holds for the search tree T at the time of selecting P_X and P_H*. Now with $Q_X=Q_1$ and $Q_H*=Q_2$, apply the argument of Case A (Section 4) to show that there is a game tree, obtained by extending T, for which H^* does not expand P_X. []

As we have shown in Section 6 that any $X \in C(H^*)$ does not strictly surpass H^*, the next theorem is finally proved.

Theorem 1. Search procedure H^* is unsurpassed. []

8. Discussion

Since the condition that X strictly surpasses Y is very strong, there

appears to be many unsurpassed search procedures. In fact, in collabora-
tion with Y. Katoh of Kyoto University, we could recently prove that SSS^*
is also unsurpassed.

Unfortunately, however, an unsurpassed procedure does not immediately
imply that it is efficient in practical applications. For example, judging
from the computational experience in [2], H^* appears to be inferior to
SSS^* and some versions of alpha-beta. In view of this, it is perhaps
necessary to introduce other measures that effectively compare the performance among unsurpassed search procedures.

This research was partially supported by the Ministry of Education,
Science and Culture of Japan under Scientific Research Grant-in-Aid.

References

[1] H. Berliner, The B^* tree search algorithm: A best-first proof procedure, Art. Int., 12, 23-40, 1979.

[2] T. Ibaraki, Generalization of alpha-beta and SSS^* search procedures,
Art. Int., 29, 73-117, 1986.

[3] T. Ibaraki, S. Suzuki, K. Inoue and T. Hasegawa, Heuristic search
algorithm H^* for solving minimax game trees, Kyoto Univ., Working
Paper, 1982.

[4] D. Knuth and R. Moore, An analysis of alpha-beta pruning, Art. Int.,
6, 293-326, 1975.

[5] J. Pearl, Heuristics: Intelligent Search Strategies for Computer
Problem Solving, Addison-Wesley, Reading Mass., 1984.

[6] J.R. Slagle and J.K. Dixon, Experiments with some programs that
search game trees, J. ACM, 16, 189-207, 1969.

[7] G. Stockman, A minimax algorithm better than alpha-beta? Art. Int.,
12, 179-196, 1979.

Algorithmic Problems

in Modeling and Electronic Prototyping

John Hopcroft

Cornell University

Abstract

During the past fifteen years there have been significant
advances in algorithm design, particularly in areas such as graph
theory, number theory and combinatorics. Most of the progress
has been on well defined problems with succinct definitions.
There has been less progress on problems whose scope and defini-
tional size are too complex to be fully comprehended by a single
individual. Problems in this class often have the property that
their specification evolves over time.

This paper is concerned with developing the science base
needed to support one such problem: electronic prototyping. Electronic prototyping involves modeling of physical objects to support
activities such as computer aided design, engineering analysis,

DISCRETE ALGORITHMS AND
COMPLEXITY

201

design verification and automated manufacturing. The size and complexity of a modeling system to support such activities requires new directions in algorithmic research.

There are two aspects of the problem that differentiate the work from earlier work in algorithm design. The first is that physical objects with shape and mass are far more complex to represent than mathematical objects such as graphs. The second is that the complexity of the systems involved is such that a full understanding of the details is beyond the comprehension of an individual given today's abstractions. A research effort is needed to aid in design decisions concerning representations and modularizations of these systems.

Introduction

During the past fifteen years significant progress has been made in the analysis and design of algorithms [1]. Most of the progress has been on algorithms for easily defined problems such as sorting, graph planarity, linear programming, etc. These problems have the characteristic that they have a short description that is easily stated. Designing an algorithm consists of converting the description of the desired solution to an algorithmic description for obtaining it. The design and implementation of such algorithms is often referred to as programming in the small.

There are a number of factors that led to the progress in this area. One of these factors was the paradigm of asymptotic complexity adopted in the early seventies [1]. The notion of asymptotic complexity gave a precise measure of goodness to an algorithm. It allowed researchers to compare competing algorithms and to explore the intrinsic complexity of a problem. Often the asymptotically optimal algorithm for a problem is not the best algorithm since it may lead to code that is too complex to write or maintain. Furthermore, the worst case might occur infrequently enough that another algorithm, with poorer worst case performance, is better in practice. In fact, the measure of asymptotic complexity often is not the correct measure. Nevertheless, the paradigm has been successful in directing research efforts and accounts for much of the progress in algorithm design.

Another paradigm was that of developing programs along with proofs of correctness from specifications. Invariant relations and preconditions played a major role [3,6]. The paradigm assumed that one is working on a problem whose nature is such that the specification is easier to write and get correct than the program itself. However, many problems for which we wish to design algorithms do not have simple descriptions, for example, text editors, geometric modelers, etc. In fact, the specification of what the algorithm is to do is not known except in general terms. Worse then that, the actual use of the algorithm will evolve with time. In other words, the development of the specification is intimately connected with the implementation and use of the software.

The existence of these paradigms shaped academic computer science research during the past fifteen years. Today computer science is broadening out into various applications areas. One of those areas, called electronic or computer prototyping [8], is concerned with representing physical objects in a computer so that we can manipulate and reason about them. The implementation effort for such a system is of sufficient magnitude that to be economically justifiable, the code must be usable for a wide spectrum of applications. This area of programming in the large is in need of a development analogous to that which took place during the seventies in programming in the small. What is needed is a science base that will aid the designer in making basic decisions that will have major consequences at a later time. This area is in need of research paradigms for its development. This paper talks about two aspects of the field, one having to do with partitioning software into modules and the other with the science base needed to represent physical objects.

The first area concerns techniques for partitioning large problems into manageable components along with the techniques to encapsulate the components so that their actual implementation is invisible to the rest of the system. If one can structure the interface between components so that the only transmission of information across the interface is through a specified set of questions and answers, then one can modify the implementation or even substitute a different implementation with only minor programming changes to conform the new module to the interface. This is basically the idea of object oriented programming.

The second area that needs development is a theory that allows one to understand how to represent physical objects. In the case of electronic prototyping one needs to represent solids. One is faced with a choice between various models such as an oct-tree[10], constructive solid geometry[11] or boundary representation[4]. It is important to have a theory to aid in understanding where the complexities will occur and how a model should be structured. Abstract models that capture the pertinent features without all the nitty gritty details can be extremely useful at the conceptual level.

In the early sixties, language specification and compiler construction was greatly aided by the abstraction of a context-free grammar. While the context-free grammar captured only part of the syntax of a language, it was sufficient to illuminate many of the inherent difficulties in parsing. The resulting theory of languages and parsing was a major contributor to the state of computer science where today the parsing phase of compiler construction is less than five percent of the total effort. A similar development of a science base for representing physical objects in a computer would greatly aid the design of solid modelers and electronic prototyping systems.

Electronic Prototyping

In this paper, we discuss one problem area: that of electronic prototyping. Electronic prototyping is the process of constructing models in a computer of physical objects so that we can verify designs. The commercial value promises to be great. For example, in designing a computer workstation, one currently builds a physical prototype to verify that no two parts occupy the same physical space and that every serviceable component has a free path for removal. With a computer model of the workstation, validation programs can be written to verify these design criteria. A change in design only requires rerunning the validation programs. This allows a designer to make changes much later in the design cycle. Another advantage of an electronic prototype over a physical prototype is that the electronic prototype will support engineering analyses such as heat flow or vibration analysis.

In the design of more complex systems such as a satellite with an antenna that deploys in space it may be the case that the antenna will not support its own weight under gravity and thus is hard to prototype with a physical model. An electronic prototype overcomes this difficulty as well as allowing integration of design with parts inventory, etc. Such prototypes will play an important role in off-line robot programming, in VLSI design, in injection molding and in studying gripping and rotation of objects.

Structuring a System

It is clear that complex systems must be broken into components whose internal designs can be isolated from one another.

An electronic prototyping system requires a number of components including modelers, simulators, languages, editors, etc. The modeling system must include abstract models to represent mass and inertia properties, geometric modelers for interference detection and dynamic modelers for equations of motion. Each of these systems is sufficiently complex to require man years of programming. Thus they must be designed so that they can be used in other systems.

One way to isolate a subsystem is by developing an interface so that all information to or from the subsystem is in the form of commands to the subsystem or responses to the commands. What is needed is a research effort to determine sets of commands adequate to support the flow of information to say a geometric modeler [2]. There are certain obvious questions that a geometric modeler must be able to answer:

(1) Do two objects intersect?

(2) Does a point of x lie on object A?

(3) Find the coordinates of a feature a.

(4) Determine the type of contact between objects A and B.

(5) What are the intersections of a ray with an object?

What is needed is a sufficiently complete set of manageable size so that algorithms that must interact with the modeler may do so efficiently.

Consider a display algorithm to compute a shaded image of an object. Suppose the algorithm is structured as follows. It first computes the projection on the view screen of each silhouette curve of the object. Next it partitions the view screen into regions where each region lies completely within a silhouette curve. In each region, a space coherent portion of the object is visible. To find the visible surface of the object for a given region, a ray is fired through some fixed point in the region and the surface closest to the view point is selected. This surface is the visible surface for the region. Shading the image requires for each point in the region the surface normal at the point on the surface that the ray intersects.

By distilling a set of commands sufficient to support the above algorithm and implementing the algorithm in terms of them, we have the desired feature that we can substitute any geometric modeler. However, we need an understanding of the types of commands that are needed to support a wide range of algorithms, not just a display algorithm: algorithms for motion

planning, for dynamic simulations, for finite element methods,
etc. A major advance in electronic prototyping could be achieved
if a kernel of commands that was problem independent but sufficient to support a wide range of applications could be achieved.

Representing a Physical Object

A second direction in which research is needed is at the component level. Within a geometric modeler, many design decisions
must be made. For example, should one use an oct-tree model or
a boundary representation? How does one represent an edge? In
a boundary representation should one approximate with polygonal patches or should one use a more general surface class such
as algebraic surfaces?

How does one represent physical objects in a computer: Wire
frame [5], oct-tree [10], constructive solid geometry (CSG) [11], or
boundary representation [4]? The answer, of course, depends on
the intended application. If we need to do interference checking
as in the workstation example, the wire frame model is not
appropriate. For image reconstruction the oct-tree model is desirable. For designing objects the CSG has advantages. For
engineering problems such as heat flow where finite element

techniques are used, the boundary representation has distinct advantages.

Within a representation there are many choices. For example, with the boundary representation one could use a manifold where the neighborhood of each point is homeomorphic to a disk or one could allow objects where components meet in lower dimensional intersections, such as two cubes meeting at a vertex or three triangular wedges meeting at a common line.

The difficulty is that the designer must make choices and these choices will have effects later on. Unlike the algorithm design of the past fifteen years, where the designer could fully comprehend the effects of choices and understand the entire algorithm and how components interrelate, the problems we are talking about are sufficiently complex that no single individual working on the problem understands the entire system. In fact the system is evolving as it is being designed and implemented. What is needed is a science base to help guide the designer in these situations.

Consider the problem of representing an edge. There are two obvious possibilities. The first is to represent the edge as the intersection of two surfaces in 3-space. The second is to use a parametric representation for the edge. Which method is better depends on the operations that must be supported and the complexity of the family of edges. Typical operations are

(1) Project edge onto a plane

(2) Traverse edge or its projection

(3) Intersect two edges

(4) Sort points in order that they occur on an edge

Traversing an edge represented by the intersection of two surfaces involves a Newton type iteration to track an edge whereas a parametric representation requires only function evaluation, usually a much simpler task. If the curve comes close to crossing itself, the Newton method may jump to the wrong branch. Tracking the curve with a parametric representation involves incrementing the parameter value and evaluating the coordinates of the corresponding point on the curve and avoids the difficulty of possibly losing the curve.

Sorting points along an edge represented by the intersection of two surfaces can be accomplished by walking along the edge and determining the order in which the points are encountered. For low degree algebraic edges, simpler techniques exist. Consider Fig. 1.

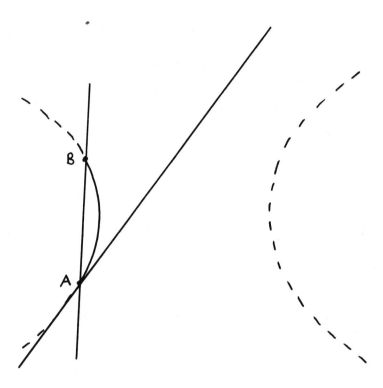

Fig. 1. Sorting points along a quadratic curve.

Given a quadratic edge from A to B and vectors tangent to the edge at A and B, proceed as follows. Construct a secant from A to B. Both tangent vectors must point to the same side of the secant since a quadratic can cross a line at most twice. Thus any points on the curve defining the edge that lie on the opposite side of the secant must be on a portion of the curve outside the edge segment. Points on the same side of the secant as the tangent may or may not be on the curve. By drawing a line tangent to the curve at A we can separate those points on the same side of the secant into those on the edge segment and those on a different branch of the curve. Note that the above test provides a method for determining whether a point C lies on the segment of a curve between two points A and B. This test is sufficient for sorting. Let A be the start of the curve and define $C < B$ whenever C is closer to A than B. Thus any comparison sorting algorithm can use this test to sort points along the curve.

On the other hand, given a parameterization $x = f_x(t)$, $y = f_y(t)$ and $z = f_z(t)$ of the edge with a parameter t in the range [0,1], the value of t for some point (x_0, y_0, z_0) can be determined by solving $x_0 = f_x(t)$ for t and selecting that solution satisfying the other two equations. Sorting can then be done by parameter value.

One of the difficulties with parametric representations is the complexity of the formulas for f_x, f_y, f_z and f_w. (Usually we deal in homogeneous space so we have a fourth function f_w.) If the f's are polynomial in t then the parameterization is called a rational parameterization.

Rational parameterizations are nice in that they are very easy to evaluate. Unfortunately not all curves have rational parameterizations. For curves not possessing such parameterizations, one must use computationally more complex functions. A curve as simple as the fourth degree curve arising from the intersection of two quadratic surfaces A and B has no rational parameterization provided that the curve is nondegenerate, i.e., the ideal $I(A,B)$ is prime. To see this, we first note that a nonsingular planar cubic has no rational parameterization and then show that the projection of a fourth degree space curve from a point on the curve onto a plane is a nonsingular cubic. If the fourth degree curve had a rational parameterization, then the nonsingular cubic would, a contradiction. Hence the fourth degree curve has no rational parameterization.

The proof that a nonsingular cubic has no rational parameterization involves the Riemann-Roch theorem from algebraic geometry [12]. Let C be a curve on the plane and let $\{p_1, p_2, \cdots, p_n\}$ be a set of points on C. With each point p_i associate a positive integer n_i and consider the set of all rational functions on C whose only zeros are at the points $\{p_1, p_2, \cdots, p_n\}$ and the order of the zero at p_i is at most n_i. The set of all such functions is called a linear series or divisor. The degree of the linear series is the sum of the integers associated with the p_i. The Riemann-Roch theorem states that the linear series is a vector space and relates the dimension of the space to the degree of the series, the genus of C and $i(D)$, the index of speciality.

Theorem (Riemann-Roch): Let C be a curve in the plane and L a linear series. Then

$$dim(L) = deg(L) - genus(C) + i(D) + 1$$

Proof: See Walker [12].

In the case where C is a nonsingular cubic, the genus is one and the index of speciality is zero. Thus the dimension of L equals the degree of L.

Now consider a linear series consisting of all rational functions having at most a simple zero at some point p. The degree of the series is one and hence the linear series is a vector space of

dimension one. Since the constant functions are all in the linear

series and since they form a vector space of dimension one, they

comprise the entire series. Now if the curve C had a rational

parameterization, then there would be a nonconstant function

$p - t$ having only a simple zero at p and thus the series would be

of dimension at least two. Thus we conclude that C has no

rational parameterization.

Theorem: A nonsingular cubic has no rational parameterization.

Proof: By the above argument.

Consider the intersection of two quadric surfaces G and H

where the ideal $I(G,H)$ is prime. The curve of intersection of G

and H is a fourth degree space curve not lying in a plane. The

projection of this curve onto a plane from a point of the curve is a

nonsingular cubic. First, to see that the projection is a cubic,

suppose that a line l intersected the projected curve in four or

more points. Then the plane containing the projection point and

the line l intersects the space curve in five points. This contrad-

icts Bezout's theorem [12]. Thus we conclude that the projection

from a point on the curve yields a degree three curve.

Theorem (Bezout's): In 3-space a curve of degree n intersects a surface of degree m in nm points unless a component of the curve lies in the surface.

Proof: See Walker [12].

To see that the cubic is nonsingular suppose that two points of the space curve project to the same point. Then some line from the projection point intersects the space curve in two additional points. Since the space curve is the intersection of two quadric surfaces, the line intersects each of these surfaces in at least three points. But again by Bezout's theorem this is impossible unless the line is contained in both quadrics G and H. However, this contradicts the fact that the ideal $I(G,H)$ is prime.

The fact that a nonplanar curve of intersection of two quadric surfaces does not have a rational parameterization does not mean that we cannot find a parameterization for the curve using a different class of parameterizations. In fact, any curve that is the intersection of two quadric surfaces can be parameterized in terms of square roots [9].

Consider two quadrics G and H. Consider the family of all surfaces F that can be expressed as $F = aG + bH$. This is a one parameter family of surfaces called a pencil. Any pair of surfaces in the pencil has the same curve of intersection. Thus we need not use G and H to define the curve but rather could select any two surfaces in the pencil. It is known that the pencil of any two quadric surfaces contains a ruled surface [9]. The ruled quadric surfaces such as the cylinder, cone or hyperbolic paraboloid can all be parameterized by means of a base curve and a line. By defining the curve as the intersection of a ruled quadric with another quadric, we can obtain a parameterization of the curve as follows. Parameterize the ruled quadric in terms of two parameters s and t. Let t describe a position on the base curve and s a position on the line. Now substitute the formulas for x, y and z in terms of s and t into the second quadric surface. Since s appears linearly in x, y and z and since x, y and z appear squared in the second surface, the result is a quadratic in s with coefficients that are rational functions of t. Solve for s in terms of t using the quadratic formula. Substituting the solution for s into the formulas for x, y and z yields a parameterization involving only square roots.

Example: Consider the intersection of two cylinders A and B where A is of unit radius centered on the z-axis and B is of radius two centered on the x-axis. The equations are

$x^2 + y^2 - 1 = 0$ and $y^2 + z^2 - 4 = 0$, respectively. The cylinder A has a base curve that is the intersection of the cylinder with the plane $z = 0$. This base curve can be parameterized by the equations

$$x = \frac{1 - t^2}{1 + t^2} \qquad y = \frac{2t}{1 + t^2} \qquad z = s$$

Substituting these equations into $y^2 + z^2 - 4 = 0$ yields the quadratic $s^2(1 - t^2) - (3 + 10t^2 + 3t^4) = 0$. Solving for s yields a parameterization for the curve of intersection involving only square roots.

$$x = \frac{1 - t^2}{1 + t^2} \qquad y = \frac{2t}{1 + t^2} \qquad z = \sqrt{\frac{3 + t^2 + 3t^4}{1 + t^2}}$$

Representing an edge is only one of literally hundreds of decisions that must be made. Each decision involves understanding mathematical, numerical and algorithmic aspects involved. A coherent body of knowledge that would allow the designer a conceptual picture and estimate the advantages and disadvantages of various choices would be a major step forward.

References

1. A. Aho, J. Hopcroft, J. Ullman (1974), *The Design and Analysis of Computer Algorithms*, Addison-Wesley, Reading MA.

2. A.P.Ambler, "Robotics and solid modelling: a discussion of the requirements robotic applications put on solid modelling systems." Technical Report.

3. E.W. Dijkstra, "Notes on structured programming". In Dahl, O.-J., C.A.R. Hoare and E.W. Dijkstra, *Structured Programming*, Academic Press, New York 1972. (Also appeared a few years earlier in the form of a technical report.)

4. C.M. Eastman and K. Preiss, "A review of solid shape modelling based on integrity verification." *Formative Technologies 16:2* (March 1984), Pittsburgh, PA. 66-80.

5. J.D. Foley and A. Van Dam, *Fundamentals of Interactive Computer Graphics*, Addison Wesley, Reading, MA. (1983).

6. C.A.R. Hoare, "An axiomatic approach to computer programming." *Comm. ACM 12* (October 1969), 576-580, 583.

7. C. Hoffmann and J. Hopcroft, "Automatic surface generation in computer aided design." *The Visual Computer* (1985) 1:92-100.

8. J. Hopcroft and D. Krafft, "The challenge of robotics for computer science." *Advances in Robotics 1, Algorithmic and Geometric Aspects of Robotics*, J. Schwartz and C. Yap, Eds., Lawrence Erlbaum Associates (1986), 7-42.

9. J.Levin, "A parametric algorithm for drawing pictures of solid objects composed of quadric surfaces." *Communications of the ACM 19:10* 555-563, (October, 1976).

10. D.J. Meagher, "Geometrical modelling using octree encoding." *Computer Graphics and Image Processing 19:2* 129-147, (1982)

11. A.A.G. Requicha and H.B. Voelcker, "Solid modelling: a historical summary and contemporary assessment." *IEEE Computer Graphics and Applications 2:2* 9-24 (1982).

12. R. Walker, *Algebraic Curves.* (1978) Springer-Verlag, New York.

Complementary Approaches to CNF Boolean Equations

Kazuo Iwama
Kyoto Sangyo University
Kyoto 603, Japan

Abstract. A new algorithm, called IS, developed specifically
for CNF SAT is presented and its complementary nature against
the conventional backtrack approach (BT) is investigated. It
is shown that IS runs faster on average as the number t of
clauses decreases or as the number s of literals in each
clause increses while BT runs faster as t increases or s
decreases. Adding to this general tendency, a strong evidence
is given which demonstrates that IS is actually faster than BT
for a faily large and practical set of CNF predicates.

1. Introduction.
     A number of approaches to attack hard (typically NP-hard)
combinatorial problems are known, most of which are claimed to
be "realistic" in the sense that they work well in most
average cases.   However, if, as widely believed, there are no
good algorithms which work efficiently for all instances,
those approaches should have some weak points.   That appears
to be true.   For example, when trying to solve CNF Boolean
equations (or their satisfiability, SAT) by backtracking
[3,4,6-10], it is known that the number of literals in each
clause plays an important role.   The more literals, the less
efficiently the approch works, which is clearly due to the
approach's fundamental structure.   Probabilistic approaches

DISCRETE ALGORITHMS AND
COMPLEXITY

[2,5] to the Hamilton Circuit Problem depend also on the degree of given graphs. The more the better in this case.

After knowing some specific weak point of one approach, it is quite natural to look for another approach which will compensate that weak point. To do so, completely new idea or angle of looking into the problem might be necessary since those weak points usually depend on the approach's backbone. It is a little surprising that there have been very few articles, as far as the author knows, which focus this complementary nature of algorithms for hard combinatorial problems. (Trivial ones like sequential searches of opposite directions usually do not help in the case of hard problems). Solving CNF SAT, for instance, most efforts have been made to improve backtracking or to analize the efficiency of backtracking, that did not change the approach's fundamental weak points. The main purpose of this paper is to introduce a new algorithm to solve CNF SAT that has nontrivial complementary nature against backtracking. The algorithm could be the first one specifically developed for CNF SAT since backtracking is rather a general method.

Among others, Purdom and Brown have investigated several aspects of solving CNF SAT by backtracking [3,6-9]. It was shown that (i) backtracking takes average time $\exp O(v^{(s-a)/(s-1)})$ for instances with v variables, s literals per clause and $t = v^a$ clauses, (ii) random CNF SAT can be solved in polynomial average time asymptotically whenever (a) $t(v) \leq n \log v$ or (b) $p(v) \leq n(\log v/v)^{3/2}$ or (c) $p(v) = $ constant, where the functions $t(v)$ and $p(v)$ are the number of clauses and the probability that a literal appears in a clause, respectively. The first result (i) says that backtracking works well when parameter a is large and s is small. In other words, we cannot expect much when a is small (≈ 1) and/or s is large. It should be noted that if a particular instance has more than $\log t$ literals in each clause then it must be satisfiable. Therefore "large s" means less than but close to $\log t$. All three conditions (a)-(c) of the second result also represent only extreme cases viewing from the above standard ($a \approx 1$ and $s \approx \log t$).

The new method called IS approach has completely opposite nature on its average run time; it is getting faster as a decreases or s increases. The following small example will clarify the idea. Let

$$f_0 = (x_1 + x_2)(x_3 + x_4)(\bar{x}_2 + \bar{x}_4)(\bar{x}_1 + \bar{x}_2)(\bar{x}_1 + x_3 + \bar{x}_4)(\bar{x}_1 + x_2 + \bar{x}_3)$$

and remember the clasic Karnaugh map used to minimize logic functions. Note that the first clause $(x_1 + x_2)$ of f_0 covers four maxterms (or cells of the map) $(x_1 + x_2 + x_3 + x_4)$, $(x_1 + x_2 + \bar{x}_3 + x_4)$, $(x_1 + x_2 + x_3 + \bar{x}_4)$ and $(x_1 + x_2 + \bar{x}_3 + \bar{x}_4)$. The second clause also covers four cells and so on. Note that cell $(x_1 + x_2 + x_3 + x_4)$ is covered by both the first and the second clauses. It is easy to see that f_0 is satisfiable if and only if the number of cells covered by at least one clause is less than 2^v (now v=4). In this particular case, the 1st and 2nd clauses overlaps on 1 cell, 2nd and 4th on 1, 3rd and 4th on 2, 3rd and 5th on 1, 4th and 5th on 1 and 3rd, 4th and 5th on 1 cell. Therefore by the inclusion-exclusion principle we can calcurate that

$$4+4+4+4+2+2-(1+1+2+1+1)+1=15$$

cells are covered, that means f_0 is satisfiable since $15 < 2^4$. In fact one can verify that no clauses cover cell $(x_1 + \bar{x}_2 + \bar{x}_3 + x_4)$, that means $(x_1, x_2, x_3, x_4) = (0,1,1,0)$ makes the whole f_0 1 (true). The efficiency of this approach clearly depends on t (the number of clauses) that can be considered as the size parameter. Also observe that it will work well if the number of overlaps is small and that we can expect on average that the number of overlaps decreases as the number of literals in each clause increases (under the same number of variables).

In the rest of the paper, basic definitions are given in Section 2. In Section 3 we formally investigate the IS algorithm introduced informally above and its complementary nature against backtracking. One might say that backtracking would still be better than IS in almost all region because the main theorem focuses only on how running time _varies_, like it decreases as parameter s increases. Therefore we should observe more quantitive aspects. A strong evidence is given that shows the IS approach is actually better than backtracking for a fairly large and practical set of instances. Finally in Section 4, we consider a basic strategy to solve CNF SAT of, for instance, 100 variables. Recommendation of the author is to use simultaneously three different approaches, random search, the IS approach and backtracking.

2. Preliminaries.

A (<u>CNF</u>) <u>predicate</u> is a product of <u>clauses</u> each of which is a sum of <u>literals</u> (variables x or their negation $\bar{x}$). For predicates f, <u>C(f)</u> denotes the set of all clauses of f. c_1 and c_2 in C(f) are said to <u>overlap</u> if there is no variable x such that one of the clauses c_1 and c_2 contains x and the other contains $\bar{x}$. Three or more clauses in C(f) <u>overlap</u> if every two of them overlap.

As a model of a problem set, we consider a <u>random source of instancecs</u> (<u>RSI</u>). <u>CNF(v,t,p)</u> is such an RSI. It generates CNF predicates over v variables, $x_1, x_2, \ldots, x_v$, each of which is formed by independently selecting t random clauses that are formed by independently selecting each literal (among 2v literals) with probability p. We can impose a filter on the RSI, for instance, the one that let pass through only the CNF predicates such that equal number of literals appear in all clauses. <u>UCNF(v,t,s)</u>, which can be viewed as another RSI, is CNF(v,t,s/2v) with the filter that let pass only the predicates with the same number s of literals in all the clauses. The next RSI has stronger regularity, which will play an important role in evaluating the performance of the IS approach. <u>RCNF(v,t,s)</u> is UCNF(v,t,s) with the filter that let pass only the CNF predicates such that for all clauses c, there are the same number of clauses that overlap with c. For example,

$$(x_1+x_2)(\bar{x}_1+x_3)(x_2+\bar{x}_3)(\bar{x}_1+x_3)$$

can be generated with probability > 0 by RCNF(3,4,2) since for every clause c there is exactly one clause (other than c itself) that overlaps with c.

Let A be an algorithm for CNF SAT and let g(v,t,s) be the expected running time of A when the instances generated by

UCNF(v,t,s) are given to A. Then it is said that the running time of A depends positively (negatively) on s for UCNF(v,t,s), or more simply A is s^+ (s^-) for UCNF(v,t,s), if g(v,t,s) is a monotone increasing (decreasing) function on argument s. Similarly for other arguments and RSIs.

Backtracking would be the most natural and direct method for CNF SAT. To improve backtracking, it is known to use a dynamic search order, i.e., deciding each time which variable should be selected out of unset variables using some heuristics [7,9]. However, as a counter part of the IS approach, we take the ordinary (fixed order) backtracking because our objective is to investigate the frame of the complementary nature between the two approaches. Moreover, it does not seem to lose much fairness since the IS approach at this introductory stage is also a very fundamental one. Backtracking (BT) is described as follows [8]: (1) The predicate is satisfiable if it contains no clauses; it is unsatisfiable if it cotains empty (all literals are false) clause. (2) Select the next variable. If both it and its negation occur as literals, generate two subproblems by setting the selected variable to 1 (true) and to 0 (false) and simplifying the two resulting predicates. Otherwise, generate one subproblem by setting the variable to the value that makes the literal 1. (3) Solve recursively the subproblems that have been generated. The original predicate is satisfiable if and only if any subproblem is satisfiable.

The following observation will be useful to understand the overall structure of the IS approach. Recall the predicate f_0 mentioned in Section 1. We can associate the graph G(f_0) of Fig.1 with this predicate, where the nodes n_1 to n_6 correspond to the clauses c_1 to c_6 of f_0 ($c_1 = (x_1 + x_2)$, $c_2 = (x_3 + x_4)$ and so on), and edges between two nodes show that the corresponding two clauses do NOT overlap. Hence two or more clauses that overlap are represented on the graph by two or more nodes which construct an independent set. (IS stands for independent sets.) In the rest of the paper it will often be said that a set of clauses are independent if they overlap or the set consists of a single clause.

3. IS approach and its complementary nature

We need a few more notations. Let f be a CNF predicate over v variables. For an independent set $S \subseteq C(f)$ of clauses, we define

$$LIT(S) = \bigcup_{c \text{ in } S} \{z \mid z \text{ is a literal in clause } c\},$$

$$SIZE(S) = a^{v-|LIT(S)|}.$$

Furthermore, for an integer i, $IND_f(i)$ (or simply IND(i) if f is clear) is defined as

$$IND(i) = \{S \mid S \text{ is an independent set of i clauses } \}.$$

In the example f_0 of Section 1, for instance,

$$IND(2) = \{\{c_1,c_2\},\{c_2,c_4\},\{c_3,c_4\},\{c_3,c_5\},\{c_4,c_5\}\},$$

$$LIT(\{c_3,c_4\}) = \{\overline{x}_1,\overline{x}_2,\overline{x}_4\},$$

$$SIZE(\{c_3,c_4\}) = 2^{4-3} = 2.$$

The following fact is straightforward.

(F1) SIZE(S) is the number of cells on the Karnaugh
     map that are covered by all clauses in S commonly.

Now we are ready to give the algorithm.

```
PROCEDURE IS
BEGIN
    sum:=0; i:=1;
    REPEAT
        compute IND(i) from IND(i-1);
        sum:= sum +    ∑         (-1)^{i-1}SIZE(S);
                    S in IND(i)

        IF i is odd AND sum<2^v (v is the number of
            variables) THEN answer "satisfiable" and stop;
        i:=i+1
    UNTIL IND(i)=φ;
```

IF sum=2^V THEN answer "unsatisfiable" ELSE
        answer "satisfiable"
    END.

Thus the algorthm counts the number N(f) of cells covered by at least one clause of f using the inclusion-exclusion principle. It should be noted that if the given predicate is satisfiable then it may be possible to quit the calculation before all the independent sets are generated. Let sum_i be the value of sum at the end of the ith iteration. Then it follows that:

(F2) $sum_i \geq N(f)$ if i is odd (proof is omitted).
Hence if $sum_i < 2^V$ for some odd i then N(f) must be less than 2^V, that means f is satisfiable.

The following result is our main theorem.

Theorem.   IS is (i) v^+, (ii) t^+ and (iii) s^- for RCNF(v,t,s).

It has been mentioned (implicitly in most cases) in several reports [e.g.,3] that BT is v^+, t^- and s^+. Thus this theorem shows the complementary nature of IS against BT.

Proof of Theorem.   Running time of algorithm IS for a given predicate f can be determined by the number of independent sets of the associated graph G(f) described in the preceeding section. Let n be the number of nodes and d be the degree of each node. (Recall that all nodes of G(f) has the same degree since the current RSI is RCNF(v,t,s).) Also let $p_I(k)$ be the probability that k nodes randomly taken from G(f) are independent. Then we can imply the following equations (proof is omitted).

(E1) $p_I(k) = \displaystyle\prod_{i=0,k-1} (n-g(i)-i)/(n-i)$, where

(E2) $g(i+1) = g(i)+d(n-g(i)-i-1)/(n-2i-1)$ $(g(0)=0)$.

(It should be mentioned that $p_I(k)$ has been checked experimentally using random regular graphs and Monte Carlo method. Agreement between the values by (E1) and the experimental values was very good.)   Therefore the expected number $N_I(k)$ and $N_I(f)$ of independent sets consisting of exactly k nodes and the total independent sets consisting of up to n nodes, respectively, are written as

$$(E3) \quad N_I(k) = {}_nC_k \cdot p_I(k)$$

$$= \prod_{i=0,k-1} (n-i-g(i))/(i+1),$$

$$N_I(f) = \sum_{k=1,n} N_I(k).$$

Observe that $g(i)$ is monotone increasing and therefore $n-i-g(i)$ is monotone decreasing. Thus $N_I(k)$ becomes maximum when $n-k+1-g(k-1)$ becomes the closest to k and after that it decreases rapidly ($n-i-g(i)$ approaches to 0 rapidly).

Now let us investigate the relation between the parameters v, t and s of the predicates f and the parameters n and d of the graphs $G(f)$. Clearly

$$n = t.$$

Suppose that there are two random clauses c_1 (a literals) and c_2 (b literals). Then the probability that c_1 and c_2 do not overlap, in other words the probability that an edge exists between c_1 and c_2 on graph $G(f)$, is

$$(E4) \quad 1- \sum_{i=0,a-1} ({}_{v-b}C_{a-i} \cdot 2^{-i} \cdot {}_bC_i)/{}_vC_a$$

or

$$(E5) \quad p_A(s) = 1- \sum_{i=0,s-1} ({}_{v-s}C_{s-i} \cdot 2^{-i} \cdot {}_sC_i)/{}_vC_s$$

if we set $a=b=s$. Suppose that the value $(t-1)p_A(s)$ exists between some integer j and $j+1$. Then almost all predicates generated by $RCNF(v,t,s)$ should have their associated regular graphs of degree j or $j+1$. However, since d does not have to be integers in (E2), the relation

$$d = (t-1)p_A(s)$$

would be more appropriate.

Now observe the following facts:

(F3) $p_A(s)$ is monotone increasing on s and so is d
   if t and v are fixed.

(F4) Since g(i) of (E2) is monotone increasing on d,
   $N_I(k)$ is monotone decreasing on d for all k.

It then follows that the number of independent sets of G(f) is monotone decreasing on s, or that IS is s^-.

(F5) $p_A(s)$ is monotone decreasing on v and so is d
   if t and s are fixed.

Hence, together with (F4), it follows that IS is v^+. Now suppose that v and s are fixed. Then $p_A(s)$ is fixed and it can be written as (recall that t=n)

$$d = c(n-1)$$

for some constant c. Look at the key factor (n-i-g(i)) of (E3). Although both n and g(i) are monotone increasing on n under the condition that d=c(n-1), it is not hard to see the whole (n-i-g(i)) is increasing on n if c<1. Therefore IS is t^+. ∎

It is intuitively obvious that the same result holds also for UCNF(v,t,s) and CNF(v,t,p). A crucial point for formal proof is how to evaluate the number of independent sets of nonregular random graphs, which seems to be much harder than the present analysis. If the RSI to algorithm IS is not RCNF(v,t,s) but UCNF(v,t,s) or CNF(v,t,s/2v), then the expected number of independent sets should differ from the calculation above. (One can see that there is a tendency that the number of independent sets increases because of the irregularity.) However, experiments show that the difference is not so large if parameter values (v, t and s) of the three RSIs are the same. Therefore the above analysis might also be useful for those nonregular RSIs as an approximation. Also note that irregularity in general helps to find good heuristics.

To make more quantitive competition between IS and BT, we evaluate the expected performance of BT. The following

approach is simpler than [3,6-9] but would better fit our
present purpose. Running time of BT should be evaluated by
the number of the nodes generated to form the backtrack tree.
Take a predicate f of v variables, t clauses and s literals in
each clause. Then we calculate the probability $p_E(w)$ that
some clause becomes empty (all literals are set to 0) when we
take w variables out of v and set each of them to 0 or 1
randomly. It can be written as

$$(E6) \quad p_E(w) = 1 - (1 - {}_{v-s}C_{w-s} 2^{-s} / {}_vC_w)^t$$

$$= 1 - (1 - \prod_{i=0,s-1} (w-i)/2(v-i))^t.$$

Assuming a symmetric distribution, we can get an expected
value w_0 of w by letting $p_E(w) = 1/2$. w_0 means that backtrack
occurs on average when the depth of the search tree gets to
w_0. Therefore a rough approximation is to assume that the
backtrack tree would be the tree all paths of which are of the
same length w_0. (As for the number of nodes, this assumption
is undercounting since the number of nodes increases as the
depth of the tree.)

Recall that each node of the backtrack tree has one or
two outgoing edges. Let $p_D(w)$ be the probability that a node
at the depth w is of outdegree two (outdegree one with
probability $(1-p_D(w))$, $N_B(f)$ be the expected number of the
nodes of the tree under the assumption above. Then $N_B(f)$ can
be written as

$$(E7) \quad N_B(f) = \sum_{w=1,w_0} 2^{K(w)}, \text{ where}$$

$$K(w) = \sum_{i=1,w} p_D(i)$$

namely K(w) is the expected number of the nodes with outdegree
two summed along a path from the root to the depth w. $p_D(w)$
is not easy. If we assume that each literal appears st/2v
times in f, then it can be written as

$$p_D(i) = 1 - (1 - (1-i/2v)^{s-1})^{st/2v}$$

Fig. 2 - Fig. 4 show specific values of N_I and N_B calculated by (E3) and (E7). We can observe the complementary nature between the two approaches and IS's competitiveness against BT.

4. Final remarks

What would be the best strategy if we have to decide the satisfiability of CNF predicates f of, say, 100 variables? A recommended one is to run simultaneously three algorithms, BT, IS and random search.

The following observation will support our strategy. (i) We should consider two new parameters q = the number of independent sets and r = the number of solutions (cells not covered) other than v, t and s. Of course the values of q and r cannot be known just by looking at the predicate f but those values are essential for our strategy. (ii) If r is high (e.g., 0.1 percent out of all cells), then the random search is very useful since its overhead is much smaller than BT. (iii) If r is low or zero then the random search does not work. Under such circumstance, if s is small then BT would be better in most cases. However, even if s is small, IS could be better if q is small. (Recall that the running time of IS directly depends on q, not s.) It should also be noted that the overhead of IS is much smaller than BT since the iteration structure of IS is simple. (iv) If s is large then IS would work better. Note that if s becomes larger under fixed v, t and r (r is very small) then, in tendency, q becomes smaller. That is another advocate of this observation.

We have discussed almost nothing about improvements of the IS approach. In principle, we can get better performance if we can decrease the number of independent sets, or overlaps, of given predicates. Several approaches to do this seem to exist, which is left to future reports.

Finally in this paper, we give a simple modification of IS, called backward IS, that calculates the overlaps from the smallest ones. Let INDS(i) = {S|S is an independent set such that LIT(S) contains i literals}.

```
PROCEDURE BIS
BEGIN
    sum:=0;  i:=v;
    REPEAT
        compute INDS(i);
        sum:=sum+      ∑          (-1)^(|S|-1).2^(v-i);
                    S in INDS(i)

        IF sum MOD 2^(v-i+1) ≠0 THEN answer "satisfiable"
            and stop;
        i:=i-1
    UNTIL i=0;
    answer "unsatisfiable"
END.
```

To compute INDS(i) is not easy. If we can generate all maximal independent sets [1,11] in advance then INDS(i) can be obtained successively from large i to small. It is expected that BIS works well if the number of solutions is very small.

Acknowledgements.   I would like to thank Professors Shuzo Yajima and Ronald Rivest for their valueable insights.

References
[1] E.   Akkoyunlu, "The   enumeration of   maximul   cliques of large graphs," SIAM J. Comput. 2 (1973).
[2] D.   Angluin and L.   Valiant, "Fast   probabilistic algorithms for Hamiltonian circuits and matchings," JCSS 18 (1979).
[3] C.   Brown and P. Purdom, Jr., "An average time analysis of backtracking," SIAM J. Comput. 10 (1981).
[4] J.   Fillmore and S.   Williamson, "On backtracking: A combinatorial description of the algorithm," SIAM J. Comput. 3 (1974).
[5] R.   Karp,   "The   probabilistic   analysis   of   some combinatorial   search   algorithms,"   in   Algorithms   and Complexity, Academic Press (1976).
[6] P.   Purdom, "Tree size by partial backtracking," SIAM J. Comput. 7 (1978).

[7] P. Purdom and C. Brown, "An analysis of backtracking with search rearrangement," SIAM J. Comput. 12 (1983).

[8] P. Purdom and C. Brown, "The pure literal rule and polynomial average time," SIAM J. Comput. 14 (1985).

[9] P. Purdom, C. Brown and E. Robertson, "Backtracking with multi-level dynamic search rearrangement," Acta Inform. 15 (1981).

[10] D. Schmidt and L. Druffel, "A fast backtracking algorithm to test directed graphs for isomorphism using distance matrices," JACM 23 (1976).

[11] S. Tsukiyama, M. Ide, H. Ariyoshi and I. Shirakawa, "A new algorithm for generating all the maximal independent sets," SIAM J. Comput. 6 (1977).

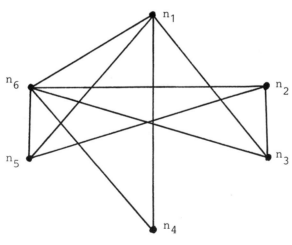

Fig.1 $G(f_0)$

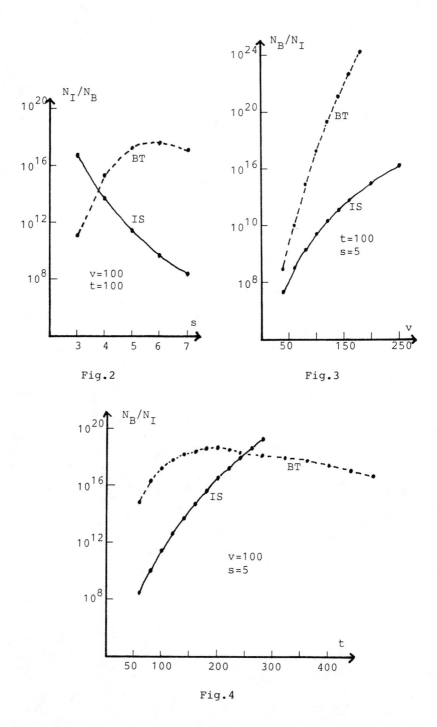

Fig.2

Fig.3

Fig.4

Open Problems
in Number Theoretic Complexity

(Preliminary version)
July 7, 1986

Leonard M. Adleman *
Department of Computer Science
University of Southern California
Los Angeles, CA 90089-0782

Kevin S. McCurley **
Department of Mathematics
University of Southern California
Los Angeles, CA 90089-1113

* Research sponsored by NSF Grant #53-4510-2651
** Research sponsored by the USC Faculty Research and Innovation Fund

Introduction.

In the past decade there has been a resurgence of interest in computational problems of a number theoretic nature. This period has been characterized by a growing awareness of the practical aspects of number theoretic computations and at the same time by an increased understanding of the relevance of deep theory to the problems which arise.

It is a particularly exciting time since progress in the area makes it reasonable to expect that some long standing problems (e.g. primality testing) may soon be settled, and at the same time interesting new problems have emerged. In this paper we present a collection of 36 open problems, some old and some new. We expect that none of these problems are easy; we are sure that many of them are hard.

DISCRETE ALGORITHMS AND
COMPLEXITY

237

Definitions, notation, and conventions.

In this paper:

$\mathbb{Z}$ denotes the integers,

$\mathbb{N}$ denotes the positive integers,

Primes denotes the set of primes in $\mathbb{N}$,

Squarefrees denotes the set of squarefree numbers in $\mathbb{N}$,

$\mathbb{Q}$ denotes the rationals.

For $a, b \in \mathbb{Z}$,

we write $a \mid b$ if there exists $k \in \mathbb{Z}$ with $b = ka$,

we write $a \nmid b$ if there does not exist $k \in \mathbb{Z}$ with $b = ka$,

$\gcd(a,b)$ denotes the greatest common divisor of a and b,

(a/b) denotes the Jacobi symbol if b is odd and $\gcd(a,b) = 1$,

$\langle a,b \rangle$ denotes the ordered pair.

For $n \in \mathbb{N}$,

$\mathbb{Z}/n\mathbb{Z}$ denotes the ring of integers modulo n,

$(\mathbb{Z}/n\mathbb{Z})^*$ denotes the corresponding multiplicative group,

$\varphi(n)$ denotes the number of elements in $(\mathbb{Z}/n\mathbb{Z})^*$,

$L(n)$ represents any function of the form $\exp((1+o(1))(\log n \, \log\log n)^{1/2})$.

If R is a ring, then we write $R[x]$ for the ring of polynomials with coefficients in R. The set of finite strings composed of the letters a and b is denoted $\{a,b\}^*$. For $n, a, b \in \mathbb{N}$ with $\gcd(n, 4a^3 + 27b^2) = 1$, let

$$S_{n,a,b} = \{ \langle x,y \rangle \mid x, y \in \mathbb{Z}/n\mathbb{Z} \ \& \ y^2 = x^3 + ax + b \} \cup \{ \infty \}.$$

When $p \in Primes$, $S_{p,a,b}$ is well known to be endowed with a group structure. We denote this group by $E_{p,a,b}$, and use $\#E_{p,a,b}$ for the number of elements of this group. More generally, if S is a set, we write $\#S$ for the cardinality of S.

In stating open problems we have chosen an ad hoc notation. For example, we label the first computational problem as C1, the corresponding open problem as O1 (or O1a and O1b if there are two), and the remarks concerning C1 and O1 we label as Rem1. Any additional references are given in Ref1. Computational problems C2 and C6 are stated in terms of a parameter S which is an arbitrary subset of $\mathbb{N}$. Computational problem C30 is stated in terms of a parameter $c \in \mathbb{N}$.

While it seems inappropriate to spend a great deal of time giving rigorous definitions of the complexity-theoretic notions used in this paper, it seems worthwhile to provide some guidance. More information on these notions may be found in [Gi], [AHU], [AM], and [GJ]. We assume the concept of a polynomial time computable function is understood. A computational problem C is thought of as a set of pairs $\langle x, S_x \rangle$, where x is an input for which an output is desired and S_x is the set of possible "correct" outputs on input x. For example

C1 $= \{\langle n,S_n\rangle \mid n \in Primes \Rightarrow S_n = \{1\} \ \& \ n \notin Primes \Rightarrow S_n = \{0\}\}$

C17 $= \{\langle\langle p,d\rangle,S_{\langle p,d\rangle}\rangle \mid d \in \mathbb{N} \ \& \ p \in Primes \ \& \ S_{\langle p,d\rangle} = \{f \in (\mathbb{Z}/p\mathbb{Z})[x] \mid \deg(f) = d$
     $\& \ f \ \text{irreducible}\}\}.$

C19 $= \{\ \langle p,S_p\rangle \mid p \in Primes \ \& \ S_p = \{g \mid g \in \mathbb{N}, \ 1 \le g \le p{-}1 \ \& \ g \ \text{generates}$
     $(\mathbb{Z}/p\mathbb{Z})^*\}\}$

C28 $= \{\langle\langle a,b,p,P,Q\rangle,S_{\langle a,b,p,P,Q\rangle}\rangle \mid a, \ b \in \mathbb{N}, \ p \in Primes, \ P, \ Q \in E_{p,a,b},$
     $(\exists n \in \mathbb{N})[nP = Q] \ \ \& \ S_{\langle a,b,p,P,Q\rangle} = \{n \mid n \in \mathbb{N} \ \& \ nP = Q\}\}$

If $C = \{\langle x,S_x\rangle\}$ is a computational problem then we let $\pi(C) = \{x \mid \langle x,S_x\rangle \in C\}$. We use $|x|$ to denote the length of an object x, where we hope that the meaning of "length" will be clear from the context.

Definition. C is in $\mathbb{P}$ iff there exists a polynomial time computable function f such that $\ (\forall x \in \pi(C)) \ [f(x) \in S_x]$.

Thus for example, in O18a below we ask if C18 is in $\mathbb{P}$. Any deterministic algorithm which runs in polynomial time with input–output behaviour consistent with that described in C18 would provide an affirmative answer to O18a. In particular how that algorithm behaves on an input $p \notin Primes$ is irrelevant.

Definition. C is in $\mathbb{R}$ iff there exists a c in $\mathbb{N}$ and a polynomial time computable function f such that

  i. $(\forall x \in \pi(C))(\forall \ |r| \le |x|^c) \ [f(x,r) \in S_x \ \text{or} \ f(x,r) = \text{"?"}]$

  ii. $(\forall x \in \pi(C)) \left[\dfrac{\#\{r \mid |r| \le |x|^c \ \& \ f(x,r) \in S_x\}}{\#\{r \mid |r| \le |x|^c\}} \ge \dfrac{1}{2} \right].$

Definition. C is in $\mathbb{NP}$ iff

  i. $(\forall x \in \pi(C))(\forall \ |r| \le |x|^c) \ [f(x,r) \in S_x \ \text{or} \ f(x,r) = \text{"?"}]$

  ii. $(\forall x \in \pi(C))(\exists y \in S_x)(\exists \ |r| \le |x|^c)[f(x,r) = y].$

Definition. C is recognized in $\mathbb{R}$ iff there exists a c in $\mathbb{N}$ and a polynomial time computable function f such that

  i. $(\forall x \in \pi(C))[S_x = \{1\} \Rightarrow (\forall \ |r| \le |x|^c) \ [f(x,r) = 1 \ \text{or} \ f(x,r) = \text{"?"}]]$

  ii. $(\forall x \in \pi(C)) \left[S_x = \{1\} \Rightarrow \dfrac{\#\{r \mid |r| \le |x|^c \ \& \ f(x,r) = 1\}}{\#\{r \mid |r| \le |x|^c\}} \ge \dfrac{1}{2} \right].$

  iii. $(\forall x \in \pi(C))[S_x \ne \{1\} \Rightarrow (\forall \ |r| \le |x|^c) \ [f(x,r) = \text{"?"}]].$

Definition. C is recognized in $\mathbb{NP}$ iff there exists a c in $\mathbb{N}$ and a polynomial time computable function f such that

i. $(\forall x \in \pi(C)) [S_x = \{1\} \Rightarrow (\forall |r| \leq |x|^c) [f(x,r) = 1 \text{ or } f(x,r) = "?"]]$

ii. $(\forall x \in \pi(C)) [S_x = \{1\} \Rightarrow (\exists |r| \leq |x|^c) [f(x,r) = 1]]$.

iii. $(\forall x \in \pi(C)) [S_x \neq \{1\} \Rightarrow (\forall |r| \leq |x|^c) [f(x,r) = "?"]]$.

For notions involving the reduction of one problem to another we will be even less formal.

Definition. f is a determinisitic solution to C iff $(\forall x \in \pi(C)) [f(x) \in S_x]$.

Let $D(C) = \{f \mid f \text{ is a deterministic solution to } C\}$.

For all deterministic algorithms A and functions f and g, we say that A translates f into g iff when given a subroutine for f, A computes g in polynomial time (where the time used in the subroutine for f is not counted).

Definition. $C1 \leq_{\mathbb{P}} C2$ iff there exists a deterministic algorithm A such that for all $f \in D(C2)$, there exists a $g \in D(C1)$ such that A translates f into g in polynomial time.

Definition. C is $\mathbb{NP}$-hard with respect to $\mathbb{P}$ iff for all C'
$$C' \text{ is in } \mathbb{NP} \Rightarrow C' \leq_{\mathbb{P}} C.$$

We will follow the convention of using $\mathbb{NP}$-hard to denote $\mathbb{NP}$-hard with respect to $\mathbb{P}$.

Definition. f is a random solution to C iff there exists a c in $\mathbb{N}$ such that

i. $(\forall x \in \pi(C))(\forall |r| \leq |x|^c) [f(x,r) \in S_x \text{ or } f(x,r) = "?"]$

ii. $(\forall x \in \pi(C)) \left[\dfrac{\#\{r \mid |r| \leq |x|^c \ \& \ f(x,r) \in S_x\}}{\#\{r \mid |r| \leq |x|^c\}} > \dfrac{1}{2} \right]$.

Let $R(C) = \{f \mid f \text{ is a random solution to } C\}$.

Definition. $C1 \leq_{\mathbb{R}} C2$ iff there exists a deterministic algorithm A such that for all $f \in D(C2)$, there exists a $g \in R(C1)$ such that A translates f into g in polynomial time.

Definition. C is NP-hard with respect to $\mathbb{R}$ iff for all C′

C′ is in NP $\Rightarrow$ C′ $\leq_{\mathbb{R}}$ C.

It is likely that some of the problems presented here will remain open for the forseeable future. However, it is possible in some cases to make progress by solving subproblems, or by establishing reductions between problems, or by settling problems under the assumption of one or more well known hypotheses (e.g. the various extended Riemann hypotheses, NP ≠ P, NP ≠ coNP).

For the sake of clarity we have often chosen to state a specific version of a problem rather than a general one. For example, questions about the integers modulo a prime often have natural generalizations to arbitrary finite fields, to arbitrary cyclic groups, or to problems with a composite modulus. Questions about the integers have natural generalizations to rings of integers in an algebraic number field, and questions about elliptic curves may generalize to arbitrary abelian varieties.

This list of problems reflects our own interests and should not be viewed as complete. The problems represented here arose from many different places and times. To those whose research has generated these problems or has contributed to our present understanding of them but to whom inadequate acknowledgement is given here, we apologize.

During the course of writing this paper we have benefited from conversations with several people, and we would like especially to thank Neal Koblitz, Jeff Lagarias, and Gary Miller for their contributions.

1. Primality testing.

C1   Input: $n \in \mathbb{N}$.
       Output: 1 if $n \in$ *Primes*,
                 0 otherwise.

O1a   Is C1 in $\mathbb{P}$?
O1b   Is C1 recognized in $\mathbb{R}$?

Rem1 A classical problem. The following quote appears in art. 329 of Gauss'
      Disquisitiones Arithmeticæ: (translation from [Kn, pp. 398])
            "The problem of distinguishing prime numbers from composites, and
            of resolving composite numbers into their prime factors, is one of the
            most important and useful in all of arithmetic. ... The dignity of science
            seems to demand that every aid to the solution of such an elegant and

celebrated problem be zealously cultivated."

It is known that the set of composites is recognized in $\mathbb{R}$ [SS]. If the extended Riemann hypothesis for Dirichlet L-functions is true, then C1 is in $\mathbb{P}$ [Mil]. There exists a constant $c \in \mathbb{N}$ and a deterministic algorithm for C1 with running time $O((\log n)^{c \log\log\log n})$ [APR]. If Cramér's conjecture on the gaps between consecutive primes is true, then C1 is recognized in $\mathbb{R}$ [GK]. C1 is recognized in $\mathbb{NP}$ [Pr]. Fürer [F] has shown that the problem of distinguishing between products of two primes that are $\not\equiv 1 \pmod{24}$ and primes that are $\not\equiv 1 \pmod{24}$ is in $\mathbb{R}$.

Ref1   [Guy], [Kn], [Len1], [CL], [Pom1], [Ra3], [Ra4], [Ri1], [Ri2], [Wil1].

2. Testing an infinite set of primes.

Let $S \subset \mathbb{N}$.

C2(S)   Input: $n \in \mathbb{N}$.
          Output: 1 if $x \in S$
                    0 if $x \notin S$.

O2   Does there exist an infinite set $S \subseteq Primes$ such that C2(S) is in $\mathbb{P}$?

Rem2   In light of Rem1 it is remarkable that O2 remains unsettled. The related problem of the existence of an infinite set $S \subseteq Primes$ such that C2(S) is recognized in $\mathbb{R}$ is addressed in [GK].

Ref2   See Ref1.

3. Prime greater than a given bound.

C3   Input: $n \in \mathbb{N}$.
          Output: $p \in Primes$ with $p > n$.

O3   Is C3 in $\mathbb{P}$?

Rem3   If Cramér's conjecture (see [C]) on the gaps between consecutive primes is true, then C3 $\leq_{\mathbb{P}}$ C1. Since the density of primes between n and $2n$ is approximately $1/\log n$, it follows that C3 $\leq_{\mathbb{R}}$ C1. This problem has cryptographic significance [DH], [RSA].

Ref3   [Ba3], [P]. See also Ref1.

4. Prime in an arithmetic progression.

C4   Input: a, n ∈ ℕ.
      Output: p ∈ *Primes* with p ≡ a (mod n) if gcd(a,n) = 1.

O4   Is C4 in ℙ ?

Rem4 It was conjectured by Heath-Brown [H-B] that if gcd(a,n) = 1, then the least
      prime p ≡ a (mod n) is $O(n \log^2 n)$, and this would imply that C4 $\leq_\mathbb{P}$ C1. If
      there are no Siegel zeroes, then the density of small primes in the arithmetic
      progression a modulo n is sufficient to conclude that C4 $\leq_\mathbb{R}$ C1   [Bom].
      Without hypothesis, it is known [EH] that Heath-Brown's conjecture is true for
      almost all pairs a, n with gcd(a,n) = 1. Hence if C1 is in ℙ, then one can
      solve C4 in deterministic polynomial time for almost all inputs. See also Rem20.

Ref4   [AM]

5. Integer factoring.

C5   Input: n ∈ ℕ.
      Output: $p_1, p_2, \ldots, p_k \in$ *Primes* and $e_1, e_2, \ldots, e_k \in$ ℕ such that

$$n = \prod_{i=1}^{k} p_i^{e_i}, \text{ if } n > 1.$$

O5a   Is C5 in ℙ ?
O5b   Is C5 in ℝ ?

Rem5 Another classical problem, mentioned by Gauss in his *Disquisitiones Arithmeticæ*
      (see Rem1). There are a large number of random algorithms for C5 whose
      running time is believed to be $L(n)^c$ for varying constants c ≥ 1 [Pom2],
      [Len2], [SL]. The only random algorithm of this class whose running time has
      actually been proved to be $L(n)^c$ is due to Dixon [Dix]. Dixon's algorithm is

unfortunately not practical. A determination of the complexity of C5 would have significance in cryptography [RSA].

Ref5   [Dix], [Guy], [Kn], [Len2], [MB], [Pom2], [Ri1], [Ri2], [Sha2], [Sch1], [SL], [Wil2].

6. Factoring a set of positive density.

Let $S \subseteq \mathbb{N}$.

C6(S)   Input: $n \in \mathbb{N}$.

Output: $p_1, p_2, \ldots, p_k \in Primes$ and $e_1, e_2, \ldots e_k \in \mathbb{N}$ such that

$$n = \prod_{i=1}^{k} p_i^{e_i}, \quad \text{if } n > 1 \text{ and } n \in S.$$

O6   Does there exist a set S such that

$$\varliminf_{x \to \infty} \frac{1}{x} \#\{ n \mid n \leq x \ \& \ n \in S \} > 0$$

and C6(S) is in $\mathbb{P}$?

Rem6   Assuming the necessary hypotheses for the running time analysis for Lenstra's elliptic curve factoring method (see [Len2]), it is probably possible to prove that a set S satisfying

$$\varliminf_{x \to \infty} \frac{\#\{ n \mid n \leq x \ \& \ n \in S \}}{\dfrac{x \ (\log\log x)^2}{\log x \ \log\log\log x}} > 0.$$

can be factored in random polynomial time. This set will still have density zero, however. A related question is whether factoring a set of positive density is random polynomial time equivalent to C5. The set *Squarefrees* has density $6/\pi^2$, however it is not even clear that C5 $\leq_{\mathbb{R}}$ C6(*Squarefrees*).

7. Squarefree part.

C7   Input: $n \in \mathbb{N}$.

Output: $r, s \in \mathbb{N}$ with $n = r^2 s$ and $s \in Squarefrees$.

O7a   Is C7 in $\mathbb{P}$?

O7b   Is $C5 \leq_{\mathbb{R}} C7$?

Rem7   See Rem13. Clearly $C7 \leq_{\mathbb{P}} C5$. The analogous question for $f \in \mathbb{Q}[x]$ or $(\mathbb{Z}/p\mathbb{Z})[x]$ is solvable in polynomial time by performing calculations of the form $\gcd(f,f')$, where f' is the (formal) derivative of f. (see [Kn, pp. 421]).

8. Squarefreeness.

C8   Input: $n \in \mathbb{N}$.
Output: 1 if $n \in$ *Squarefrees*,
        0 otherwise.

O8   Is C8 in $\mathbb{P}$?

Rem8   A generalization of this is given n and $k \in \mathbb{N}$, to determine if n is divisible by the kth power of a prime. Another generalization is to output $\mu = \mu(n)$, where
$$\mu(n) = \begin{cases} 1, & \text{if } n = 1 \\ 0, & \text{if there exists a } p \in \text{\textit{Primes}} \text{ with } p^2 \,|\, n, \\ (-1)^k, & \text{if } n \text{ is a product of } k \text{ distinct primes.} \end{cases}$$
Shallit and Shamir have shown that this generalization is reducible to the problem of computing the function d mentioned in Rem9.

9. Number of distinct prime factors.

C9   Input: $n \in \mathbb{N}$.
Output: $\omega(n) = \#\{p \mid p \in \text{\textit{Primes}} \ \& \ p \,|\, n\}$.

O9   Is C9 in $\mathbb{P}$?

Rem9   Clearly $C1 \leq_{\mathbb{P}} C9$, since we can easily check to see if n is a perfect power. An interesting variant of C9 is to output $\Omega(n) = e_1 + \ldots + e_k$, where
$$n = \prod_{i=1}^{k} p_i^{e_i}$$
is the prime factorization of n. Another variant is to output $d(n) = \#\{k \mid k \in \mathbb{N} \ \& \ k \,|\, n\}$, and still another variant is to output the multiset $\{e_1, \ldots, e_k\}$. Shallit and Shamir [ShSh] have proved that the last two variants

are polynomial time equivalent to each other. As a consequence we have that C9 is polynomial time reducible to the problem of computing the function d mentioned above.

10. Roots modulo a composite.

C10   Input: e, a, n $\in$ $\mathbb{N}$.
        Output: $x \in \mathbb{N}$ such that $x^e \equiv a \pmod{n}$, if $\gcd(e, \varphi(n)) = 1$ and $\gcd(a,n) = 1$.

O10   Is C5 $\leq_{\mathbb{R}}$ C10 ?

Rem10   When the restriction that $\gcd(e, \varphi(n)) = 1$ is dropped, it is known that C5 $\leq_{\mathbb{R}}$ C10 [Ra2]. A resolution of this problem would have important consequences in public-key cryptography [RSA]. It is known that C10 $\leq_{\mathbb{P}}$ C23.

11. Quadratic residuosity modulo a composite.

C11   Input: a, n $\in$ $\mathbb{N}$.
        Output: 1 if there exists an $x \in \mathbb{N}$ such that $x^2 \equiv a \pmod{n}$ and $\gcd(a,n) = 1$,
              0 otherwise.

O11a   Is C11 in $\mathbb{P}$?
O11b   Is C5 $\leq_{\mathbb{R}}$ C11 ?

Rem11   It is easy to show that C11 $\leq_{\mathbb{P}}$ C5. There is an obvious generalization where the exponent 2 is replaced by another exponent k that is either fixed for the problem or supplied as an input. The presumed difficulty of C11 has been used as a basis for cryptographic systems [GM1], [GM2], [Y], [BBS]. C11 is related to C9 since the proportion of residues modulo n that are quadratic residues is $2^{-\omega(n)}$, where $\omega(n)$ is the number of distinct prime divisors of n. Therefore given an algorithm for C11, one can obtain a confidence interval for $\omega(n)$ by checking random values.

12. Quadratic non-residue modulo a prime.

C12   Input: p $\in$ $\mathbb{N}$.

Output: $b \in \mathbb{N}$ such that there does not exist $c \in \mathbb{N}$ with $c^2 \equiv b \pmod{p}$, if $p \in Primes$.

O12   Is C12 in $\mathbb{P}$?

Rem12 C12 is easily seen to be in $\mathbb{R}$, since polynomial time algorithms for the corresponding problem of distinguishing quadratic residues from nonresidues can be based on the Jacobi symbol and the law of quadratic reciprocity, or else on Euler's criterion:

$$p \in Primes \text{ and } p \nmid a \Rightarrow a^{\frac{p-1}{2}} \equiv \left(\frac{a}{p}\right) \pmod{p}.$$

Curiously, Gauss was aware of Euler's criterion, but was apparently unimpressed by its efficiency [G, art. 106]:

"Although it is of almost no practical use, it is worthy of mention because of its simplicity and generality ... But as soon as the numbers we are examining are even moderately large this criterion is practically useless because of the amount of calculation involved".

Under the extended Riemann hypothesis, C12 is in $\mathbb{P}$ [Mil]. It is also known that the least quadratic nonresidue is almost always small [Erd], so C12 can be solved in deterministic polynomial time for almost all inputs.

Ref12   [Ank], [Ba1].

13. Quadratic signature.

C13   Input: $\sigma \in \{-1,1\}^*$.
       Output: The least $p \in Primes$ such that for all i with $1 \le i \le |\sigma|$, $(p_i/p) = \varepsilon_i$, where $|\sigma|$, the length of σ, is the number of symbols in σ, p_i is the ith prime, and ε_i is the ith symbol of σ.

O13   Is C13 in $\mathbb{P}$?

Rem13 If n has the form $m^2 q$ with q an odd prime and m odd, then for any a with $\gcd(a,n) = 1$ we have $(a/n) = (a/q)$. It follows that if C13 is in $\mathbb{P}$, then n could be partially factored since, assuming the extended Riemann hypothesis, q can be determined by a signature of length $O(\log^2 n)$ [Mil], [Ank]. The notion of quadratic signature can be generalized; see [AMc].

14. Square roots modulo a prime.

C14   Input: a, p $\in$ $\mathbb{N}$.
Output: $x \in \mathbb{N}$ with $x^2 \equiv a \pmod p$ if $p \in$ *Primes* and such an x exists.

O14   Is C14 in $\mathbb{P}$?

Rem14 Among the researchers who have presented algorithms for C14 are [G, art. 319-322], [Ton], [Leh], [Sha1], [Ber1], [Ra1], [AMM]. It is now known that C14 is in $\mathbb{R}$. It is also known that C14 $\leq_{\mathbb{P}}$ C12 and that on the extended Riemann hypothesis, C14 is in $\mathbb{P}$. There is a natural generalization of C14 where the exponent 2 is replaced by a fixed k. Another generalization has k as part of the input. For this version there is a random time $O((k \cdot \log p)^c)$ algorithm based on known algorithms for C15. One can also use a discrete logarithm algorithm (see Rem21) to solve this variant, resulting in a random time $O(L(p))$ algorithm, which for large k will be faster.

Ref14 Many additional references are given in [LN, pp. 182]. See also Ref16.

15. Polynomial roots modulo a prime.

C15   Input: p $\in$ $\mathbb{N}$, f $\in$ $(\mathbb{Z}/p\mathbb{Z})[x]$.
Output: $a \in \mathbb{Z}$ with $f(a) \equiv 0 \pmod p$ if $p \in$ *Primes* and such an a exists.

O15   Is C15 in $\mathbb{P}$?

Rem15 See Rem14. C15 is in $\mathbb{R}$ [Ber3], [CZ], [Ra1]. If the extended Riemann hypothesis is assumed and f has abelian Galois group over the rationals, then the problem is in $\mathbb{P}$ [Hua].

Ref15 See Ref16.

16. Factoring polynomials modulo a prime.

C16   Input: p $\in$ $\mathbb{N}$, f $\in$ $(\mathbb{Z}/p\mathbb{Z})[x]$.
Output: irreducible $g_1, \ldots, g_k \in (\mathbb{Z}/p\mathbb{Z})[x]$, and $e_1, \ldots, e_k \in \mathbb{N}$ such that

$$f = \prod_{i=1}^{k} g_i^{e_i}, \text{ if } p \in Primes.$$

O16   Is C16 in $\mathbb{P}$?

Rem16 See Rem 15. C16 is in $\mathbb{R}$ [Ber3], [CZ], [Ra1]. The corresponding problem over $\mathbb{Q}$ is in $\mathbb{P}$ [LLL].

Ref16   [Ber1], [Ber2], [Kn, pp. 420-441], [LN, pp. 147-185].

17. Irreducible polynomials.

C17   Input: d, p $\in \mathbb{N}$.
       Output: irreducible f $\in (\mathbb{Z}/p\mathbb{Z})[x]$ with degree(f) = d, if p $\in$ *Primes*.

O17   Is C17 in $\mathbb{P}$?

Rem17 C17 is in $\mathbb{R}$ [Ber2], [Ra1]. C17 is in $\mathbb{P}$ if the extended Riemann hypothesis is true [AL]. There is a c $\in \mathbb{N}$ and a deterministic polynomial time algorithm which on input d, p with p $\in$ *Primes* outputs an irreducible f $\in (\mathbb{Z}/p\mathbb{Z})[x]$ of degree greater than cd/logp and less than or equal to d [AL]. Since irreducible quadratics yield quadratic nonresidues, it is clear that C12 $\leq_\mathbb{P}$ C17, and also from the results on C14 that C14 $\leq_\mathbb{P}$ C17.

18. Recognition of a primitive root modulo a prime.

C18   Input: b, p $\in \mathbb{N}$.
       Output: 1 if b is a generator of $(\mathbb{Z}/p\mathbb{Z})^*$ and p $\in$ *Primes*,
       0 if b is not a generator of $(\mathbb{Z}/p\mathbb{Z})^*$ and p $\in$ *Primes*.

O18a   Is C18 in $\mathbb{P}$?
O18b   Is C18 recognized in $\mathbb{R}$?

Rem18 It is known that C18 $\leq_\mathbb{P}$ C5, since b is a primitive root modulo p if and only if p $\nmid$ b and $\forall q[[\, q \in$ *Primes* & $q \mid$ p-1] $\Rightarrow b^{(p-1)/q} \not\equiv 1 \pmod{p}]$. A generalization of C18 where a third input c $\in \mathbb{N}$ is given and the output is 1 if and only if b has order c is also of interest.

19. Finding a primitive root modulo a prime.

C19   Input: $p \in \mathbb{N}$.
       Output: $g \in \mathbb{N}$ such that $1 \le g \le p-1$ and g generates $(\mathbb{Z}/p\mathbb{Z})^*$, if $p \in Primes$.

O19   Is C19 in $\mathbb{P}$?

Rem19 The density of generators is sufficient that it is easily shown that C19 $\le_{\mathbb{R}}$ C18.
       If the extended Riemann hypothesis is true, then the least generator is small
       [Wang], and C19 $\le_{\mathbb{P}}$ C18. An interesting variant of C19 involves finding
       elements of $(\mathbb{Z}/p\mathbb{Z})^*$ of desired order. C19 has an obvious extension to an
       arbitrary finite field, or for that matter to any cyclic group.

20. Calculation of orders modulo a prime.

C20   Input: $a, p \in \mathbb{N}$.
       Output: $k = \min\{x \mid x \in \mathbb{N}, a^x \equiv 1(\mathrm{mod}\ p)\}$, if $p \in Primes$ and $\gcd(a,p) = 1$.

O20   Is C20 in $\mathbb{P}$?

Rem20 The variant in which p is not required to be prime is random polynomial time
       equivalent to C5 [Mil]. A related question: is the problem of factoring numbers
       of the form $p - 1$, with p prime, polynomial time reducible to C20 ? If C4 is
       in $\mathbb{P}$, then the problem of factoring numbers of the form $p - 1$ with p prime is
       polynomial time equivalent to C5.

21. Discrete logarithm modulo a prime.

C21   Input: $g, b, p \in \mathbb{N}$.
       Output: $x \in \mathbb{N}$ with $g^x \equiv b\ (\mathrm{mod}\ p)$, if $p \in Primes$ and such an x exists.

O21   Is C21 in $\mathbb{P}$?

Rem21 If the prime factors of $p - 1$ are less than $\log^c p$, then the problem is in $\mathbb{P}$ [PH].

The fastest known algorithms for solving C21 have running times of L(p) [COS]. The resolution of O21 would have important consequences in cryptography [ElG], [BM]. There is an obvious generalization of C21 to an arbitrary finite field. Bach [Ba2] has asked if the problem of factoring numbers of the form $p - 1$, with p prime, is polynomial time reducible to C21.

Ref21 [O].

22. Discrete logarithm modulo a composite.

C22   Input: g, b, n $\in \mathbb{N}$.
         Output: $x \in \mathbb{N}$ with $g^x \equiv b \pmod{n}$, if such an x exists.

O22a   Is C22 in $\mathbb{P}$?
O22b   Is C5 $\leq_{\mathbb{P}}$ C22 ?

Rem22 Clearly C21 $\leq_{\mathbb{P}}$ C22. It is also known that C5 $\leq_{\mathbb{R}}$ C22 [Ba2]. The resolution of O22 would have consequences in public-key cryptography [Mc]. There is an obvious generalization to an arbitrary group (see also C28).

23. Calculation of $\varphi(n)$.

C23   Input: n $\in \mathbb{N}$.
         Output: $\varphi(n)$.

O23   Is C5 $\leq_{\mathbb{P}}$ C23 ?

Rem23 It is known that C5 $\leq_{\mathbb{R}}$ C23 [Mil], and it is obvious that C23 $\leq_{\mathbb{P}}$ C5. C5 is known to be random polynomial time equivalent to the problem of computing $\sigma(n)$, the sum of the positive integral divisors of n [BMS].

24. Point on an elliptic curve.

C24   Input: a, b, p $\in \mathbb{N}$.
         Output: x, y $\in \mathbb{N}$ with $y^2 \equiv x^3 + ax + b \pmod{p}$, if $p \in Primes$ and
         $p \nmid 4a^3 + 27b^2$.

O24   Is C24 in $\mathbb{P}$?

Rem24 One can show that C24 is in $\mathbb{R}$, since there is an easy argument to show that
        C24 $\leq_\mathbb{R}$ C14: choose random values of x, evaluate the right hand side, and use a
        random algorithm for C14 to try to solve for y. A theorem of Hasse implies that
        the probability of choosing a successful x is approximately 1/2.

25. Binary quadratic congruences.

C25   Input: k, m, n $\in \mathbb{N}$.
        Output: x, y $\in \mathbb{N}$ with $x^2 - ky^2 \equiv m$ (mod n), if n is odd and gcd(km,n) = 1.

O25   Is C25 in $\mathbb{P}$?

Rem25 C25 is in $\mathbb{R}$ [AEM]. If the extended Riemann hypothesis and Heath-Brown's
        conjecture on the least prime in an arithmetic progression are true, then C25 is in
        $\mathbb{P}$ [Sh]. C25 arose from cryptography [OSS], [PS]. In fact, C25 is only one
        example of a wide range of questions concerning solutions of $f \equiv 0$ (mod n),
        where f is a multivariate polynomial with coefficients in $\mathbb{Z}/n\mathbb{Z}$. Such questions
        can vary greatly in their complexity as the form of the question changes. We may
        ask questions about determining if a solution exists, finding a solution, finding the
        least solution, or finding the number of solutions. We may vary the form of the
        polynomial or the properties of n (e.g. prime, composite, squarefree). As an
        example of the variation in complexity, even for the polynomial $f(x) = x^2 - a$
        we have the following situation:
        1. The problem of deciding from inputs   a, p $\in \mathbb{N}$ whether
            $x^2 - a \equiv 0$ (mod p) has a solution when p is prime is in $\mathbb{P}$ (see
            Rem12.)
        2. The problem of finding from inputs a, p $\in \mathbb{N}$ a solution of
            $x^2 - a \equiv 0$ (mod p) when p is prime is in $\mathbb{R}$ (see Rem14).
        3. The problem of finding from inputs   a, n $\in \mathbb{N}$ a solution of
            $x^2 - a \equiv 0$ (mod n) is random equivalent to the problem of
            factoring n (see Rem10).
        4. The problem of finding from inputs   a, n $\in \mathbb{N}$ the least positive
            integer solution of $x^2 - a \equiv 0$ (mod n) is $\mathbb{NP}$-hard [MA].
        We therefore view the problem of classifying all problems concerning solutions of
        $f \equiv 0$ (mod n) according to their complexity as an important metaproblem.

26. Key distribution.

C26   Input: g, p, a, b ∈ ℕ.

Output: c ∈ ℕ, where c ≡ g^{xy} (mod p), if p ∈ *Primes*, g is a primitive root modulo p, a ≡ g^x (mod p), and b ≡ g^y (mod p).

O26   Is C21 ≤$_ℝ$ C26 ?

Rem26 The motivation for this problem comes from cryptography [DH]. It is obvious that C26 ≤$_ℙ$ C21. There is a generalization where p is replaced by a composite n, and we ask only for an output c when a and b are powers of g. For this generalization is the problem equivalent to C5 or C22 (see [Ba2], [Mc])?

Ref26   [O], [ElG].

27. Construction of an elliptic curve group of a given order.

C27   Input: p, n ∈ ℕ.

Output: a, b ∈ ℕ with #E$_{p,a,b}$ = n, if p ∈ *Primes* and such an a, b exist.

O27   Is C27 in ℙ ?

Rem27 There is a polynomial time algorithm that, given p, a, and b with p∤4a^3 + 27b^2, computes #E$_{p,a,b}$ [Sch2].

28. Discrete logarithms in elliptic curve groups.

C28   Input: a, b, p ∈ ℕ, P, Q ∈ S$_{p,a,b}$.

Output: n ∈ ℕ with P = nQ, if p ∈ *Primes* and such an n exists.

O28   Is C28 in ℙ ?

Rem28 The presumed difficulty of this problem has been used as the basis for a public key cryptosystem and digital signature scheme [Ko], [Mil1]. Whereas for the discrete logarithm problem in the multiplicative group modulo a prime there is a subexponential algorithm (see Rem21), no such algorithm is known to exist for C28. A related problem is given a, b, and p to construct a minimal set of generators for $E_{p,a,b}$.

29. Shortest vector in a lattice.

C29   Input: $b_1, \ldots, b_n \in \mathbb{Z}^n$.
       Output: $v \in \Lambda$ with $\|v\|_2 = \min\{\|x\|_2 \mid x \in \Lambda, x \neq 0\}$, where
       $\Lambda = \mathbb{Z}b_1 \oplus \ldots \oplus \mathbb{Z}b_n$, if $b_1, \ldots, b_n$ span $\mathbb{R}^n$.

O29   Is C29 $\mathbb{NP}$-hard ?

Rem29 The corresponding problems with norms $\|\cdot\|_\infty$ and $\|\cdot\|_1$ are known to be
       $\mathbb{NP}$-hard [L1], [vEB]. See also Rem30.

30. Short vector in a lattice.

Let $c \in \mathbb{N}$
C30(c) Input: $b_1, \ldots, b_n \in \mathbb{Z}^n$.
       Output: $v \in \Lambda$ with $v \neq 0$ and $\|v\|_2 \leq n^c \min\{\|x\|_2 \mid x \in \Lambda, x \neq 0\}$, where
       $\Lambda = \mathbb{Z}b_1 \oplus \ldots \oplus \mathbb{Z}b_n$, if $b_1, \ldots, b_n$ span $\mathbb{R}^n$.

O30   Does there exist a $c \in \mathbb{N}$ for which C30(c) is in $\mathbb{P}$?

Rem30 In [LLL] it was shown that there is a polynomial time algorithm that produces a
       nonzero vector v in Λ with $\|v\|_2 \leq 2^{(n-1)/2} \min\{\|x\|_2 \mid x \in \Lambda, x \neq 0\}$, and in
       [S] it was shown that for any $\varepsilon > 0$ there is a polynomial time algorithm A_ε that
       produces a nonzero vector v with $\|v\|_2 \leq (1+\varepsilon)^n \min\{\|x\|_2 \mid x \in \Lambda, x \neq 0\}$. A
       number of related problems in simultaneous diophantine approximation are
       discussed in [L1] and [Fr].

Ref30 [LLS].

31. Galois group of a polynomial.

C31   Input: $f \in \mathbb{Q}[x]$
       Output: $n = [K:\mathbb{Q}]$, where K is the splitting field of f.

O31   Is C31 in $\mathbb{P}$?

Rem31 n is the order of the Galois group associated with f. Polynomial time algorithms
       exist for determining if n is a power of 2 or if the Galois group is solvable
       [LM]. Many other properties of the Galois group can also be determined in
       polynomial time [Ka].

32. Class numbers.

C32   Input: $d \in \mathbb{N}$.
       Output: h(-d), the order of the group of equivalence classes of binary quadratic
       forms with discriminant -d under composition.

O32   Is C32 in $\mathbb{P}$?

Rem32 This is related to classical questions of Gauss [G, art. 303]. It appears that the
       results of Shanks [Sh1], [Sh2], Schnorr & Lenstra [SL], Seysen [Se], and
       Schoof [Sch1] establish that $C5 \leq_{\mathbb{R}} C32$, and that ERH implies $C5 \leq_{\mathbb{P}} C32$. It
       is remarked in [BMS] that it is not even known if C32 is in $\mathbb{NP}$. The best
       known algorithm for computing h(-d) is due to Shanks [Sha2]. The question
       could also be stated in terms of the class number of orders in the field $\mathbb{Q}(\sqrt{-d})$.

Ref32 [Go], [Sha1], [Sch1], [L4].

33. Solvability of binary quadratic diophantine equations.

C33   Input: $a, b, c, d, e, f \in \mathbb{Z}$.
       Output: 1 if there exists $x, y \in \mathbb{Z}$ with $ax^2 + bxy + cy^2 + dx + ey + f = 0$ and
              there does not exist a $g \in \mathbb{Z}$ with $b^2 - 4ac = g^2$.
       0 otherwise.

O33a   Is C33 $\mathbb{NP}$-hard ?
O33b   Is C33 $\mathbb{NP}$-hard with respect to $\mathbb{R}$?

Rem33 It is known that C33 is recognized in $\mathbb{NP}$ [L2]. Without the constraint that
       $b^2 - 4ac$ is not a square, the problem is known to be $\mathbb{NP}$-hard [MA]. Certain
       variants of C33 are known to be $\mathbb{NP}$-hard with respect to $\mathbb{R}$ [AM].

34. Solvability of anti-Pellian equation.

C34   Input: $d \in \mathbb{Z}$.
       Output: 1 if there exist $x, y \in \mathbb{Z}$ with $x^2 - dy^2 = -1$.
       0 otherwise.

O34   Is C34 in $\mathbb{P}$?

Rem34 There exist choices of d for which the smallest solution of $x^2 - dy^2 = -1$ cannot
      be written down in polynomial space [L2]. It is known that C34 is in $\mathbb{NP}$
      [L3]. If the factorization of d is provided as part of the input, then the problem is
      recognized in $\mathbb{R}$, and if in addition we assume the extended Riemann hypothesis,
      then the problem is in $\mathbb{P}$ [L3].

35. Greatest common divisors in parallel.

C35   Input: $a, b \in \mathbb{N}$.
       Output: gcd(a,b).

O35   Is C35 in $\mathbb{NC}$?

Rem35 The best known results for computing greatest common divisors in parallel are
      contained in [BK], [CG] and [KMR]. One may ask a similar question for the
      modular exponentiation problem: given $a, b, n \in \mathbb{N}$, compute $a^b \pmod{n}$. For
      a definition of $\mathbb{NC}$ see [Co1] or [Co2].

36. Integer multiplication in linear time.

C36   Input: $a, b \in \mathbb{N}$.
       Output: ab.

O36   Does there exist an algorithm to solve C36 that uses only $O(\log(ab))$ bit
       operations ?

Rem36 The best known algorithm is due to Schönhage and Strassen and uses
      $O(\log(ab) \cdot \log\log(ab) \cdot \log\log\log(ab))$ bit operations [ScSt].

Ref36 [Kn, pp. 278-301].

References.

[AL] L. M. Adleman and H. W. Lenstra, Jr., Finding irreducible polynomials over finite fields, *Proc. 18th Annual ACM Symposium on Theory of Computing* (Berkeley, 1986), 350–355, Association for Computing Machinery, New York, 1986.

[AEM] L. M. Adleman, D. Estes, and K. McCurley, Solving bivariate quadratic congruences in random polynomial time, to appear in *Math. Comp.*

[AM] L. M. Adleman and K. Manders, Reducibility , Randomness, and Intractibility, *Proc. 9th Annual ACM Symposium on Theory of Computing*, 151-163, Association for Computing Machinery, New York, 1977.

[AMM] L. M. Adleman, K. Manders, and G. Miller, On taking roots in finite fields, *Proc. 18th Annual IEEE Symposium on Foundations of Computer Science* (Providence, Rhode Island, 1977), IEEE Computer Society, 175-178.

[AMc] L. M. Adleman and R. McDonnell, An application of higher reciprocity to computational number theory, *Proc. 22nd Annual IEEE Symposium on Foundations of Computer Science,* IEEE Computer Society, 1982, 100-106.

[APR] L. M. Adleman, C. Pomerance, and R. Rumely, On distinguishing prime numbers from composite numbers, *Annals of Math.*, **117** (1983), 173-206.

[AHU] A. Aho, J. Hopcroft, and J Ullman, *The Design and Analysis of Computer Algorithms*, Addison-Wesley, Reading, 1974.

[Ank] N. Ankeny, The least quadratic nonresidue, *Annals of Math.* **55** (1952), 65–72.

[Ba1] E. Bach, *Analytic Methods in the Analysis and Design of Number Theoretic Algorithms,* MIT Press, Cambridge, 1985.

[Ba2] E. Bach, Discrete Logarithms and Factoring, Technical Report UCB/CSD 84/186, Computer Science Division (EECS), University of California, Berkeley, California, June, 1984.

[Ba3] E. Bach, How to generate prefactored random numbers, preprint, 1984.

[BMS] E. Bach, G. Miller, and J. Shallit, Sums of divisors, perfect numbers, and factoring, *Proc. 16th Annual ACM Symposium on Theory of Computing* (1984), Association for Computing Machinery, New York, 1984.

[Ber1] E. Berlekamp, Factoring polynomials over finite fields, *Bell System Tech. J.* **46** (1967), 1853-1859.

[Ber2] E. Berlekamp, *Algebraic Coding Theory*, McGraw-Hill, New York, 1968.

[Ber3] E. Berlekamp, Factoring polynomials over large finite fields, *Math. Comp.* **24** (1970), 713-735.

[BBS] L. Blum, M. Blum, and M. Shub, A simple unpredictable pseudo-random number generator, *SIAM J. Comp.* **15** (1986), 364-383.

[BM]   M. Blum and S. Micali, How to generate cryptographically strong sequences of pseudorandom bits, *SIAM J. Comp.* **13** (1984), 850-864.

[Bom]   E. Bombieri, Le grand crible dans la théorie analytique des nombres. Avec une sommaire en anglais. *Astérisque*, No. 18. *Société Mathemématique de France,* Paris, 1974.

[BK]   R. Brent and H. Kung, Systolic VLSI arrays for linear time gcd computation, *VLSI 83, IFIP,* F. Anceau and E. Aas (eds.), pp. 145-154, *Elsevevier,* 1983.

[CZ]   D Cantor and H. Zassenhaus, A new algorithm for factoring polynomials over finite fields, *Math. Comp.* **36** (1981), 587-592.

[CG]   B. Chor and O. Goldreich, An Improved Parallel Algorithm for Integer GCD, preprint, 1985.

[CL]   H. Cohen and H. W. Lenstra, Jr., Primality testing and Jacobi sums, *Math. Comp.* **42** (1984), 297-330.

[Co1]   S. Cook, A Taxonomy of Problems with Fast Parallel Algorithms, *Information and Control* **64** (1985), 2-22.

[Co2]   S. Cook, Towards a complexity theory of synchronous parallel computation, *Enseignment Math., 27* (1981), 99-124.

[COS]   D. Coppersmith, A. Odlyzko, and R. Schroeppel, Discrete logarithms in GF(p), to appear in *Algorithmica.*

[C]   H. Cramér, On the order of magnitude of the difference between consecutive prime numbers, *Acta Arith.* **2** (1936), 23–46.

[Dh]   W. Diffie and M. E. Hellman, New directions in cryptography, *IEEE Transactions on Information Theory* **22** (1976), 644-654.

[Dix]   J. D. Dixon, Asymptotically fast factorization of integers, *Math. Comp.* **36** (1981), 255-260.

[EH]   P. D. T. A. Elliot and H. Halberstam, The least prime in an arithmetic progression, *Studies in Pure Mathematics,* Academic Press, London, 1971, 59-61.

[ElG]   T. ElGamal, A Public Key Cryptosystem and a Signature Scheme Based on Discrete Logarithms, *IEEE Transactions on Information Theory* **31** (1985), 469-472.

[vEB]   P. van Emde Boas, Another NP-complete partition problem and the complexity of computing short vectors in lattices, Math. Dept. Report 81-04, Univ. Amsterdam, 1981.

[Erd]   P. Erdös, Remarks on number theory. I, *Mat. Lapok* **12** (1961), 10-17.

[Fr]   M. A. Frumkin, Complexity Questions in Number Theory, *J. Soviet Math.* **29** (1985), 1502-1517. (Translated from *Zapiski Nauchnykh Seminarov Leningradskogo Otdeleniya Matematicheskogo Instituta im. V. A. Steklova AN SSSR,* vol. 118 (1982), 188-210.)

[F]   M. Fürer, Deterministic and Las Vegas primality testing algorithms, Proc. ICALP 1985.

[GJ] M. Garey and D. Johnson, *Computers and Intractibility: A Guide to the Theory of NP-Completeness*, W. H. Freeman, San Francisco, 1979.

[G] K. F. Gauss, *Disquisitiones Arithmeticæ*, Leipzig, Fleischer, 1801. Translated into English by Arthur A Clarke, S.J., Yale University Press, New Haven, 1966.

[Gi] J. Gill, Computational complexity of probabilistic Turing machines, *SIAM J. Comp.* **4** (1977), 675-695.

[Go] D. Goldfeld, Gauss' class number problem for imaginary quadratic fields, *Bull. Amer. Math. Soc.* **13** (1985), 23-38.

[GK] S. Goldwasser and J. Kilian, Almost all primes can be quickly certified, *Proc. 18th Annual ACM Symposium on Theory of Computing* (Berkeley, 1986), 316–329, Association for Computing Machinery, New York, 1986.

[GM1] S. Goldwasser and S. Micali, Probabilistic Encryption & How to Play Mental Poker Keeping Secret All Partial Information, *Proc. 14th Annual ACM Symposium on Theory of Computing* (1982), 365-377, Association for Computing Machinery, New York, 1982.

[GM2] S. Goldwasser and S. Micali, Probabilistic Encryption, *Journal of Computer and System Science* **28** (1984), 270-299.

[Guy] R. Guy, How to factor a number, *Proceedings of the fifth Manitoba Conference on Numerical Mathematics* (Univ. of Manitoba, Winnipeg, Manitoba, 1975), pp. 49-89. *Congress. Numer., XXVII,* 1977.

[H-B] D. R. Heath-Brown, Almost-primes in arithmetic progressions and short intervals, *Math. Proc. Cambridge Philos. Soc.* **83** (1978), 357-375.

[Hua] M. Huang, Riemann hypothesis and finding roots over finite fields, *Proc. 17th Annual ACM Symposium on Theory of Computing* (1985), 121-?, Association for Computing Machinery, New York, 1985.

[KMR] R. Kannan, G. Miller, and L. Rudolph, Sublinear parallel algorithm for computing the greatest common divisor of two integers, *Proc. 25th IEEE Symposium on Foundations of Computer Science*, (1984), 7-11.

[Ka] W. Kantor, Polynomial-time algorithms for finding elements of prime order and Sylow subgroups, *J. Algorithms* **4** (1985), 478-514.

[Kn] D. E. Knuth, *The Art of Computer Programming, Vol. 2: Seminumerical Algorithms,* second edition, *Addison-Wesley, Reading, MA,* 1981.

[Ko] N. Koblitz, Elliptic curve cryptosystems, preprint, 1985.

[L1] J. Lagarias, The computational complexity of simultaneous diophantine approximation problems, *SIAM J. Comput.* **14** (1985), 196-209.

[L2] J. Lagarias, Succinct certificates for the solvability of binary quadratic Diophantine equations, *Proc. 20th IEEE Symposium on Foundations of Computer Science,* (1979), 47-54, IEEE Computer Society.

[L3] J. Lagarias, On the computational complexity of determining the solvability or unsolvability of the equation $X^2 - DY^2 = -1$, *Trans. Amer. Math. Soc.* **260** (1980), 485-508.

[L4]   J. Lagarias, Worst-Case Complexity Bounds for Algorithms in the Theory of Integral Quadratic Forms, *J. Algorithms* **1** (1980), 142-186.

[LLS]   J. Lagarias, H. W. Lenstra, Jr., and C.-P. Schnorr, Korkine-Zolotarev bases and successive minima of a lattice and its reciprocal lattice, preprint.

[LM]   S. Landau and G. Miller, Solvability by radicals is in polynomial time, *J. Comp. and Sys. Sci.* **30** (1985), 179-208.

[Leh]   D. H. Lehmer, Computer Technology applied to the theory of numbers, *Studies in Number Theory*, 117-151, Math. Assoc. Amer. (distributed by Prentice Hall, Englewood Cliffs, NJ), 1969.

[Len1]   H. W. Lenstra, Jr., Primality testing algorithms (after Adleman, Rumely, and Williams), Sém. Bourbaki **33** (1980/81), exp. 576, pp. 243-257 in *Lecture Notes in Math.* **901**, *Springer-Verlag, NY,* 1981.

[Len2]   H. W. Lenstra, Jr., Factoring integers with elliptic curves, preprint, May, 1986.

[LLL]   A. K. Lenstra, H. W. Lenstra, Jr., and L. Lovàsz, Factoring polynomials with rational coefficients, *Math. Ann.* **261** (1982), 515-534.

[LN]   R. Lidl and H. Niederreiter, *Finite Fields, Addison-Wesley, Reading, MA,* 1983.

[MA]   K. Manders and L. Adleman, NP-Complete Decision Problems for Binary Quadratics, *J. Comp. Sys. Sci.* **16** (1978), 168-184.

[MB]   M. Morrison and J. Brillhart, A Method of Factoring and the Factorization of F_7, *Mathematics of Computation* **29** (1975), 183-205.

[Mc]   K. McCurley, Digital signatures and public-key cryptosystems based on discrete logarithms and factoring, preprint, 1986.

[Mil]   G. Miller, Riemann's hypothesis and tests for primality, *J. Comp. Sys. Sci.* **13** (1976), 300-317.

[Mill]   V. Miller, Use of Elliptic Curves in Cryptography, to appear in *Proc. Crypto `85.*

[O]   A. Odlyzko, The discrete logarithm problem and its cryptographic significance, *Advances in Cryptology* (Proc. Eurocrypt 1984), *Lecture Notes in Computer Science* **209** , *Springer-Verlag, NY,* 224-314.

[P]   D. A. Plaisted, Fast verification, testing, and generation of large primes, *Theor. Comp. Sci.* **9** (1979), 1-16.

[PH]   S. Pohlig and M. Hellman, An improved algorithm for computing discrete logarithms over GF(p) and its cryptographic significance, *IEEE Trans. Information Th.* **24** (1978), 106-110.

[PS]   J. Pollard and C.-P. Schnorr, Solution of $x^2 + ky^2 \equiv m \pmod{n}$, with application to digital signatures, to appear in *IEEE Trans. Information Th.*

[Pom1]   C. Pomerance, Recent developments in primality testing, *Math. Intelligencer* **3** (1980/81), 97-105.

[Pom2]   C. Pomerance, Analysis and comparison of some integer factoring methods, pp. 89-139 in *Computational Methods in Number Theory*: Part 1, H. W. Lenstra and R. Tijdeman, eds., Math. Centre Tract 154, Math. Centre, Amsterdam, 1982.

[Pr] V. Pratt, Every prime has a succinct certificate, *SIAM J. Comput.* **4** (1975), 214–220.

[Ra1] M. O. Rabin, Probabilistic algorithms in finite fields, *SIAM J. Comput.* **9** (1980), 273-280.

[Ra2] M. O. Rabin, *Digitalized signatures and public-key functions as intractible as factorization,* MIT Laboratory for Computer Science report TR-212 (1979).

[Ra3] M. O. Rabin, Probabilistic algorithm for testing primality, *J. Number Th.* **12** (1980), 128-138.

[Ra4] M. O. Rabin, pp. 35-36 in *Algorithms and Complexity,* ed. by J. F. Traub, *Academic Press,* New York, 1976.

[Ri1] H. Riesel, *Prime Numbers and Computer Methods for Factorization, Birkhäuser, Boston,* 1985.

[Ri2] H. Riesel, Modern Factorization methods, *BIT* **25** (1985), 205-222..

[RSA] R. Rivest, A. Shamir, and L. Adleman, "A method for obtaining digital signatures and public key cryptosystems", *Communications of the ACM* **21** (1978), 120-126.

[S] C.-P. Schnorr, A hierarchy of polynomial time basis reduction algorithms, preprint.

[ScSt] A. Schönhage and V. Strassen, Schnelle Multiplikation grosser Zahlen, *Computing* **7** (1971), 281-292.

[Sch1] R. Schoof, Quadratic fields and factorisation, *Computational Methods in Number Theory,* Part 1, H. W. Lenstra and R. Tijdeman, eds., Math. Centre Tract 154, Math. Centre, Amsterdam, 1982.

[Sch2] R. Schoof, Elliptic curves over finite fields and the computation of square roots modulo p, *Math. Comp.* **44** (1985), 483-494.

[Sh] J. Shallit, An Exposition of Pollard's Algorithm for Quadratic Congruences, Technical Report 84-006, Department of Computer Science, University of Chicago, December, 1984.

[ShSh] J. Shallit and A. Shamir, Number-theoretic functions which are equivalent to number of divisors, *Information Processing Letters* **20** (1985), 151-153.

[Sha1] D. Shanks, Five number-theoretic algorithms, *Proc. Second Manitoba Conference on Numerical Mathematics* **(1972)**, 51-70.

[Sha2] D. Shanks, Class number, a theory of factorization, and genera, *Proc. Symp. Pure Math.* **20** (1971), 415-440.

[SL] C.-P. Schnorr and H. W. Lenstra, Jr., A Monte Carlo factoring algorithm with linear storage, *Math. Comp.* **43** (1984), 289-311.

[SS] R. Solovay and V. Strassen, A fast Monte-Carlo test for primality, *SIAM J. Comput.* **6** (1977), 84-85.

[Ton] A. Tonelli, Bemerkung über die Auflösung quadratischer Congruenzen, *Göttinger Nachr.* **1891**, 314-346.

[Wang] Y. Wang, On the least primitive root of a prime, *Sci. Sinica,* **10** (1961), 1-14.

[Wil1] H. C. Williams, Primality testing on a computer, *Ars Combinatorica* **5** (1978), 127-185.

[Wil2] H. C. Williams, Factoring on a computer, *Math. Intelligencer* **6** (1984), 29-36.

[Y] A. Yao, Theory and applications of trapdoor functions, *Proc. 23rd IEEE Symposium on Foundations of Computer Science,* (1982), *IEEE,* 80-91.

Decision Problem of the Security for Cryptographic Protocols

Toru FUJIWARA,   Kenichi TANIGUCHI   and   Tadao KASAMI

Department of Information and Computer Sciences

Faculty of Engineering Science

Osaka University

Toyonaka,   Osaka 560,   Japan

Abstract.   We discuss the problem of deciding whether a given cryptographic protocol is secure or not under a certain environment. We present sufficient conditions under which the security problem is decidable. The classes of protocols which satisfy the conditions are larger than that considered by Dolev, et al. The security problem for the classes is shown to be solved in polynomial time.

1. Introduction.

Many cryptographic protocols for key distribution or digital signature have been proposed. It is assumed that the encryption and decryption functions used for these protocols are secure. Even though we make this assumption, in most cases it is not easy to decide whether the proposed protocol is vulnerable to an "active" saboteur or not. An "active" saboteur may impersonate another user and may alter or replay the massage.

In this paper, we formulate the problem of deciding whether a given cryptographic protocol is secure or not. A protocol is said to be secure

DISCRETE ALGORITHMS AND
COMPLEXITY

if the saboteurs cannot get the information to be protected (the secret
message or the signatures of other users) by executing any combination
of operations provided by the system on information obtained through
wiretapping. A formal definition of the security problem is defined in
the next section. In section 3, we show that the security problem is
undecidable even though we make many restrictions on the operations used
in the protocols. In sections 4 and 5 we give a sufficient condition
under which the security problem is decidable. Several practical
protocols are in this class. The security problem for the class can be
solved in polynomial time. In section 6 we relax the sufficient
condition mentioned in section 5.

In [1, 2], Dolev, et al. also discussed the decision problem for
the security. But in their model, a cryptographic key is not an argument
of the encryption and decryption functions. That is, their encryption
(or decryption) function is a mapping from plaintext (or ciphertext) to
ciphertext (or plaintext). But for a key distribution protocol, since
keys which are distributed or generated in the protocol are used in
later steps of the protocol, the encryption function should be defined
as a mapping from both plaintext and key to ciphertext. This makes the
problem difficult. In this paper, we consider the case where the
encryption and decryption functions have two arguments.

2. Formal Definition of the Security Problem.

Let F be a set of function symbols which contains constant symbols.
For $f \in F$, let $a(f)$ be the number of arguments of f. Let $T_{VAR}(F)$ be the
infinite set of terms on F with variables and let $T(F)$ be the set of
terms without variables.

For a given cryptographic protocol, the problem of its security is
defined by (F, A, I, O, G) where F, A, I, O and G are defined as

follows:

(1) F is a finite set of function symbols. F contains the symbols of operations of the protocol, i.e. function symbols of encryption, decryption and so on.

(2) A is a finite set of axioms by which we represent the properties of the functions. We assume that saboteurs cannot use any knowledge on the properties of functions except for the axioms in A. The congruence relation defined by A is denoted by $\equiv$.

(3) I is a finite subset of $T(F)$. I contains terms which correspond to information that saboteurs know, e.g. their keys and/or information through wiretapping.

(4) O is a subset of F. O contains symbols of operations which are available for the saboteurs.

Let Q be a set of terms which correspond to such information that the saboteurs can get by executing any combination of operations provided by the system on the information corresponding to terms in I. Q is defined as follows:

i) $I \subset Q$,

ii) for $f \in O$ and t_1, t_2, $\cdots$, $t_{a(f)} \in Q$,

   $f(t_1, t_2, \cdots, t_{a(f)}) \in Q$,

and

iii) for $t_1 \in Q$ and $t_2 \in T(F)$ such that $t_1 \equiv t_2$, $t_2 \in Q$. $\Delta\Delta$

For $t \in T_{VAR}(F)$, let $\{X_1, X_2, \cdots, X_h\}$ be the set of all variables which appear in t. To represent these variables explicitly, we denote t as $t[X_1, X_2, \cdots, X_h]$. For $t[X_1, X_2, \cdots, X_h]$ and terms t_1, t_2, $\cdots$, $t_h \in T_{VAR}(F)$, let $t[t_1, t_2, \cdots, t_h]$ be the term which is obtained from t by substituting t_i with X_i for $1 \leq i \leq h$.

(5) $G = \{g_1, g_2\}$ is a set of two terms in $T_{VAR}(F)$. Suppose that g_1 and g_2 contain variables $\{X_{11}, X_{12}, \cdots, X_{1h_1}\}$ and $\{X_{21}, X_{22}, \cdots, X_{2h_2}\}$,

respectively, where $X_{1j} = X_{2j}$ are the same variables for $1 \leq j \leq h_0 \leq$ $\min\{h_1, h_2\}$. We define that the protocol described by (F, A, I, O, G) is secure if and only if there exist no t_1, t_2, $\cdots$, t_{h_0}, t_{1h_0+1}, t_{1h_0+2}, $\cdots$, t_{1h_1}, t_{2h_0+1}, t_{2h_0+2}, $\cdots$, t_{2h_2} in Q such that

$$g_1[t_1, t_2, \cdots, t_{h_0}, t_{1h_0+1}, t_{1h_0+2}, \cdots, t_{1h_1}]$$
$$\equiv g_2[t_1, t_2, \cdots, t_{h_0}, t_{2h_0+1}, t_{2h_0+2}, \cdots, t_{2h_2}].$$

$$\Delta\Delta$$

Example 1: Consider the following cryptographic protocol which uses a symmetric cryptosystem (common key cryptosystem). In this protocol secret messages are exchanged between users called terminal nodes. This system involves a host node as well as terminal nodes. Each terminal has a unique terminal secret key. All the terminal secret keys are also stored at the host node but any terminal node knows no terminal secret key except for his own secret key. For each user a, let K(a) be the terminal secret key of the user a. Let E(X, Y) (or D(X, Y)) be an encryption (or decryption) function which maps from cryptographic key X and a plaintext (or ciphertext) Y to the ciphertext (or plain text). When user a send a secret message m to user b, the following communications are done as shown in Figure 1.

(Step 1) User a generates a random number r (which is used as a session key), and he send the host node his name a, the destination name b, and E(K(a), r).

(Step 2) The host node gets r and returns E(K(b), r) to user a.

(Step 3) User a sends E(r, m) and E(K(b), r) to user b.

(Step 4) User b computes m using E(r,m), E(K(b), r) and K(b).

Assume that any information on any channel can be wiretapped. Consider the case where user a sends message m to b. The security problem whether or not user c, the saboteur, can know the secret message m is described as follows:

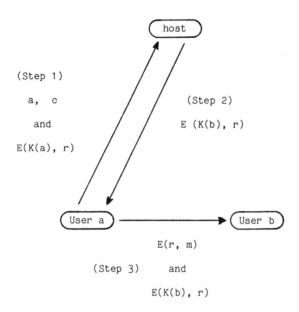

Fig.1 A cryptographic protocol.

F = { f, E, D, K, r, m, a, b, c } ,

A = { f(X, Y, Z) == E(K(Y), D(K(X), Z)) ,

     D(X, E(X, Y)) == Y ,

     E(X, D(X, Y)) == Y } ,

I = { a, b, c, K(c), E(K(a), r), E(K(b), r), E(r, m) } ,

O = { f, E, D } ,

G = { X, m } .

The first axiom in A corresponds to the operation to compute E(K(b),r) using a, b and E(K(a) ,r). The second and third axioms means that the encryption and decryption functions are secure. That is, on these functions saboteurs can only use the knowledge that the encryption (or decryption) function is the inverse function of the decryption (or encryption) function.

This protocol is not secure since

$$D(D(K(c), f(a, c, E(K(a), r))), E(r, m)) \equiv m.$$

That is, user c can compute the message m as follows:

(Step 2-1) User c wiretaps $E(K(a), r)$ and $E(r, m)$.

(Step 2-2) User c sends to the host node the source name a, the

destination name c, and $E(K(a), r)$, as if a wants

to send a message to user c using the session key r

(see Step 1 above).

(Step 2-3) The host node returns $E(K(c), r)$ to user a, and user c

wiretaps this.

(Step 2-4) User c can compute m using $E(r, m)$, $E(K(c), r)$ and his secret

key $K(c)$.

$$\Delta\Delta$$

Hereafter we consider the class of the security problems. An

instance of SP is (F, A, I, O, G), and the question is whether the

protocol described by (F, A, I, O, G) is secure or not.

3. Undecidability of the Security Problem SP.

In this section, we show that SP is undecidable by reducing Post's

Correspondence Problem (PCP) to a restricted class of SP.

An instance of PCP consists of two lists, $L_1 = w_{11}, w_{12}, \cdots, w_{1k}$

and $L_2 = w_{21}, w_{22}, \cdots w_{2k}$ of strings over some alphabet Σ, say $\{0, 1\}$.

The question is whether there is a sequence of integers $i_1, i_2, \cdots i_m$

with $m \geq 1$ such that

$$w_{1i_1} w_{1i_2} \cdots w_{1i_m} = w_{2i_1} w_{2i_2} \cdots w_{2i_m}.$$

PCP is known to be undecidable.

Let SP_1 denote the subclass of SP whose instance has the following

form:

$F = \{c, H_0, H_1, H_{r0}, Hh_{r1}, PROJ_0, PROJ_1,$

$\quad CONC, S, MARK, GEN_1, GEN_2, \cdots, GEN_n, REV_1, REV_2\}$.

$A = \{ H_{r0}(S(H_0(X))) == S(X)$,

$\quad H_{r1}(S(H_1(X))) == S(X)$,

$\quad PROJ_1(CONC(X, Y)) == X$,

$\quad PROJ_2(CONC(X, Y)) == Y$,

$\quad GEN_j(X) == CONC(f_{1j}(PROJ_1(X)), f_{2j}(PROJ_2(X)))$,

$\qquad\qquad for\ 1 \leq j \leq n\}$,

where f_{1j} and f_{2j} are composite functions of E_0 and E_1 ,

$\quad MARK(X) == CONC(S(PROJ_1(X)), S((PROJ_2(X)))$,

$\quad REV_0(X) == CONC(H_{r0}(PROJ_1(X)), H_{r0}((PROJ_2(X)))$,

$\quad REV_1(X) == CONC(H_{r1}(PROJ_1(X)), H_{r1}((PROJ_2(X)))\}$.

$I = \{ CONC(f_{1j}(c), f_{2j}(c))$, $for\ 1 \leq j \leq n\}$.

$O = \{GEN_1, GEN_2, \cdots, GEN_n, MARK, REV_0, REV_1\}$.

$G = \{ X , CONC(S(c), S(c))\}$.

For each n, f_{1j} and f_{2j} for $1 \leq j \leq n$, we have an instance of SP_1.

<u>Theorem 1</u> : SP_1 is undecidable, and hence, SP is undecidable.

Proof: For a given instance of PCP,

$$L_1 = w_{11}, w_{12}, \cdots, w_{1k}\ and\ L_2 = w_{21}, w_{22}, \cdots w_{2k}$$

over an alphabet $\{0, 1\}$, define

$n = k$,

$f_{1j}(X) = E_{a_{j1}}(E_{a_{j2}}(\cdots(E_{a_{j\ell_{1j}}}(X))\cdots))$,

$f_{2j}(X) = E_{b_{j1}}(E_{b_{j2}}(\cdots(E_{b_{j\ell_{2j}}}(X))\cdots))$

for $1 \leq j \leq n$, where a_{jh} and b_{jh} are the h-th symbols in w_{1j} and w_{2j}, respectively, and ℓ_{1j} and ℓ_{2j} are the lengths of w_{1j} and w_{2j}, respectively.

It is easy to see that the instance of PCP has a solution if and only if the solution of security problem defined above is not secure.

ΔΔ

4. The Security Problem and the Term Rewriting System.

In this section, we consider instances of SP, (F, A, I, O, G), which satisfy conditions under which we can regard axioms as rewriting rules from its left-hand side to the right-hand side.

Condition 1: F is partitioned into two sets F_1 and F_2, and A is also partitioned into two sets A_1 and A_2. F_1 and A_1 satisfies (a), (b) and (c), and F_2 and A_2 satisfies (d), (e) and (f).

(a) Each axiom in A_1 has the form

$$f(X_1, X_2, \cdots, X_{a(f)}) == t$$

where $f \in F_1$, $X_1, X_2, \cdots, X_{a(f)}$ are distinct variables and $t \in T_{VAR}(F_2)$.

(b) For each f in F_1 there is exactly one axiom in A_1 which contains f in its left-hand side.

(c) Any variable in the right-hand side of the axiom in A_1 appears only once in its right-hand side (right linear) and appears in its left-hand side.

(d) Left-hand and right-hand sides of each axiom in A_2 are terms in $T_{VAR}(F_2)$.

(e) Any variable in the right-hand side of the axiom in A_2 appears in its left-hand side.

(f) As a term rewriting system, A_2 has the Church-Rosser property and the finite termination property.

$$\Delta\Delta$$

F_1 is the set of function symbols which corresponds to operations available in the protocol and these operations are defined by the axioms in A_1. Function symbols in F_2 are the primitive functions which are used to define operations, and the axioms in A_2 represent their properties.

In Example 1,

$$F_1 = \{ f \} ,$$

$$A_1 = \{ f(X, Y, Z) == E(K(Z), D(K(Y), X)) \} \ ,$$

$$F_2 = \{ E, D, K, r, m, a, b, c \} \ ,$$

and

$$A_2 = \{ D(X, E(X, Y)) == Y \ , \quad E(X, D(X, Y)) == Y \quad \} \ .$$

Let (F, A, I, O, G) be an instance of SP which satisfies Condition 1. It follows from (a) and (f) in Condition 1 that A has the Church-Rosser property and the finite termination property.

For $t \in T_{VAR}(F)$, let $norm_A(t)$ be the normal form of t which is obtained by rewriting term t using A as the term rewriting rules. Let O' be the set such that

(1) for $f \in O \cap F_1$

$$norm_A(t_R) \in O' \ ,$$

where t_R is the right-hand side of the axiom in A_1 such that f appears in its left-hand side,

(2) for $f \in O \cap F_2$ and distinct variables X_1, X_2, $\cdots$, $X_{a(f)}$,

$$f(X_1, X_2, \cdots, X_n) \in O'.$$

Let $\bar{Q}$ be the set such that

(1) for $t \in I$, $norm_A(t) \in \bar{Q}$,

(2) for $t[X_1, X_2, \cdots, X_h] \in O'$ and $u_1, u_2, \cdots, u_h \in \bar{Q}$,

$$t[u_1, u_2, \cdots, u_h] \in \bar{Q}.$$

Then we have Lemma 1.

Lemma 1: For any $t \in Q$, there is a term $t' \in \bar{Q}$ such that

$$norm_A(t) = norm_{A_2}(t') \ ,$$

where $norm_{A_2}(t')$ is the normal form of t' which is obtained by rewriting term t' using A_2 as the term rewriting rules. $\Delta\Delta$

Define

$$T_0 = \{ norm_A(t) \mid t \in I \} \cup O' \ ,$$

$$T_1 = \{ norm_A(g_1), norm_A(g_2) \} \cup T_0 \ ,$$

$$T_{1*} = \{ t \mid t \text{ is a subterm of a term } t_1 \text{ in } T_1 \} \ ,$$

and

$$T_{1*}^2 = \{ (t_1, t_2) \mid t_1, t_2 \in T_{1*} \} \, .$$

Let EQ^2 be a subset of T_{1*}^2 such that for $(t_1[X_{11}, X_{12}, \cdots, X_{1h_1}],$ $t_2[X_{21}, X_{22}, \cdots, X_{2h_2}]) \in T_{1*}^2,$

$$(t_1[X_{11}, X_{12}, \cdots, X_{1h_1}], t_2[X_{21}, X_{22}, \cdots, X_{2h_2}]) \in EQ^2$$

if and only if there are $u_{11}, u_{12}, \cdots, u_{1h_1}, u_{21}, u_{22}, \cdots u_{2h_2}$ in $\bar{Q}$ such that

$$t_1[u_{11}, u_{12}, \cdots, u_{1h_2}] \equiv t_2[u_{21}, u_{22}, \cdots, u_{2h_2}] \, .$$

Hereafter we assume that Condition 2 holds for G.

Condition 2: g_1 and g_2 have no common variables. For any variable X in g_1 (or g_2), X appears only once in g_1 (or g_2).   ΔΔ

For the instance of SP in Example 1 or in [7, 8], G satisfies this condition. Lemma 2 follows from the definition of the security, EQ^2 and Condition 2.

Lemma 2: A protocol $(F_1 \cup F_2, A_1 \cup A_2, I, O, \{g_1, g_2\})$ of SP that satisfies Conditions 1 and 2 is "secure" if and only if

$$(\mathrm{norm}_{A_1}(g_1), \mathrm{norm}_{A_1}(g_2)) \notin EQ^2. \qquad \text{ΔΔ}$$

From Lemma 2, if we can compute EQ^2 for a given $(F_1 \cup F_2, A_1 \cup A_2, I, O, \{g_1, g_2\})$ which satisfies Conditions 1 and 2, then we can decide whether the protocol is secure or not.

5. A Simple Sufficient Condition under which the Security Problem Is Decidable.

In this section we give a simple sufficient condition under which the security problem is decidable.

Condition 3:

(3-a) $\{E, D\} \subset F_2$ and $a(E) = a(D) = 2.$

(3-b) For any f in F_2 except for E and D, $a(f) = 1.$ ΔΔ

Condition 4: A_2 consists of two axioms :

$$D(X, E(X, Y)) == Y \quad \text{and} \quad E(X, D(X, Y)) == Y. \qquad \Delta\Delta$$

We show SP is decidable under Conditions 1 to 4 by reducing it to a problem on one-dimensional strings.

First, we define generation rules and reduction rules. Let Σ be a finite set of terminal symbols and S be the unique nonterminal symbol. There are no other nonterminal symbols except for S. For $\alpha \in \Sigma^* \cup \Sigma^*\{S\}$, $S \to \alpha$ is called a generation rule. For a set of generation rules GR and $\alpha_0 \in \Sigma^*\{S\}$, a set of strings (sentential forms) which are generated from α_0, denoted $SF(GR,\alpha_0)$, is defined as follows:

(1) $\alpha_0 \in SF(GR,\alpha_0)$,

(2) if $\alpha S \in SF(GR,\alpha_0)$ and $S \to \beta \in GR$, then $\alpha\beta \in SF(GR,\alpha_0)$. $\qquad \Delta\Delta$

Let $L_\Sigma(GR,\alpha_0)$ be $SF(GR,\alpha_0) \cap \Sigma^*$.

In this paper, we consider reduction rules which have the form $\alpha \to \lambda$ where α is in Σ^+ and λ is the null string. For a set of reduction rules RR and $L \subset \Sigma^*$, let $L_R(RR,L)$ be the set of strings such that

(1) $L \subset L_R(RR,L)$,

(2) for $\alpha_1\alpha\alpha_2 \in L_R(RR,L)$ and $\alpha \to \lambda \in RR$, $\alpha_1\alpha_2 \in L_R(RR,L)$. $\qquad \Delta\Delta$

For $t \in T_{1*}(F)$, consider a tree representation of term t as shown in Figure 2. We regard a pair of an inner node on the path from the root to the rightmost leaf and its leftmost subtree(function symbol and its first argument) or a leaf (constant or variable) as a symbol. Let Σ be a set of those symbols except a symbol for a leaf whose label is a variable. Note that Σ is a finite set, and we regard symbols in Σ as terminal symbols. We define st(t) as a string of symbols in $\Sigma \cup \{S\}$ along the path from the root to the rightmost leaf (If the label of the right-most leaf is a variable, then the symbol for this variable is always the unique nonterminal symbol S). The terminal symbol for a pair of a function symbol f and its first argument t is denoted by f_t, and that for a constant c in F is denoted by the same symbol, c. For example,

$$st(E(K(Y), D(K(X), Z))) = E_{K(Y)}D_{K(X)}S .$$

For $t \in T_{1*}$, define

$$L(t) = L_{\Sigma}(GRULE(T_0), st(t))$$

where $GRULE(T_0) = \{S \to st(t) | t \in T_0 \}$.

The strings in L(t) correspond to terms in the set $\bar{Q}'$ which is defined as follows:

(1) For $t \in I$, $norm_{A_1}(t) \in \bar{Q}'$,

(2) For $t \in O'$ whose rightmost leaf is a constant, $t \in \bar{Q}'$,

and

(3) For $t \in O'$ whose rightmost leaf is a variable X, terms obtained from t by substituting X for any term in $\bar{Q}'$ are also in $\bar{Q}'$.   ΔΔ

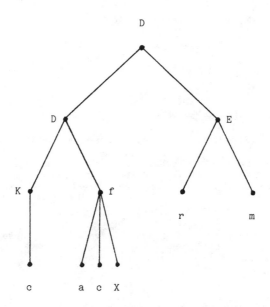

$$t = D(D(K(c),f(a,c,X)), E(r,m))$$

Fig. 2   The tree representation of a term t.

For the instance of SP in Example 1

$$\Sigma = \{E_X, D_X, E_{K(Z)}, D_{K(Y)}, E_{K(a)}, E_{K(b)}, E_r, K, a, b, c, m, r\}$$

$$GRULE(T_0) = \{ S \rightarrow E_X, \quad S \rightarrow D_X S, \quad S \rightarrow E_{K(Z)} D_{K(Y)} S,$$

$$S \rightarrow E_{K(a)} r, \ S \rightarrow E_{K(b)} r, \quad S \rightarrow Kc$$

$$S \rightarrow E_r m, \quad S \rightarrow a, \ S \rightarrow b, \ S \rightarrow c \ \} \ .$$

For $P \subset T_1^2*$, we define a set RRULE (P) of reduction rules and a set

EQSYMB(P) of pairs of symbols in Σ.

[Definition of RRULE(P)]

For $(t_1, t_2) \in P$, if $E_{t_1}, D_{t_2} \in \Sigma$, then

$D_{t_2} E_{t_1} \rightarrow \lambda \in$ RRULE(P) and $E_{t_1} D_{t_2} \rightarrow \lambda \in$ RRULE(P) .　　ΔΔ

[Definition of EQSYMB(P)]

(1)　For any $a \in \Sigma$, $(a,a) \in$ EQSYMB(P) .

(2)　For $(t_1, t_2) \in P$, if $E_{t_1}, E_{t_2} \in \Sigma$ then $(E_{t_1}, E_{t_2}) \in$ EQSYMB(P),

and if $D_{t_1}, D_{t_2} \in \Sigma$, then $(D_{t_1} D_{t_2}) \in$ EQSYMB(P) .　　ΔΔ

For P, a subset of T_1^2*, and t_1, $t_2 \in T_1*$, the value of predicate

$E(P, t_1, t_2)$ is True if and only if there are $\alpha_1 \in L_R(RRULE(P), L(t_1))$

and $\alpha_2 \in L_R(RRULE(P), L(t_2))$ such that

(1) the lengths of α_1 and α_2 are the same and

(2) $(a_{1j}, a_{2j}) \in$ EQSYMB(P), for $1 \leq j \leq h$,

where a_{1j} and a_{2j} are the j-th symbol in α_1 and α_2, respectively, and

h is the length of α_1 (or α_2).　　ΔΔ

Since $L_R(RRULE(P), L(t_i))$ for $1 \leq i \leq 2$ are regular sets, we can

evaluate $E(P, t_1, t_2)$ for any P, t_1 and t_2 by a similar method to

evaluate whether the intersection of two regular sets is empty or not.

Lemma 3: Let P be a subset of EQ^2 and t_1 and t_2 be terms in T_1*. If $E(P,$

$t_1, t_2) =$ True then $(t_1, t_2) \in EQ^2$.

　　　　　　　　　　　　　　　　　　　　　　ΔΔ

<u>Lemma 4</u>: Let P be a subset of EQ^2. If $E(P, t_1, t_2)$ = False for any t_1, t_2 such that both t_1 and t_2 are terms in T_{1*} and (t_1, t_2) is not in P, then $P = EQ^2$.

ΔΔ

By using Lemmas 3 and 4, we can compute EQ^2 as follows.

[Procedure to compute EQ^2]

(Step 1) $P_0 := \{ (t, t) \mid t \in T_{1*} \}$

(Step 2)

  i := 1

  repeat

    $P_{i+1} := P_i \cup \{(t_1, t_2) \mid (t_1, t_2) \in P_i$ and $E(P, t_1, t_2)$ = True $\}$

    i := i+1

  until $P_i = P_{i+1}$

(Step 3) $EQ^2 := P_i$

  end

ΔΔ

Let n_0 be the size of the security problem. Let n be the size of the description of all of F_2, A_2, $\{norm_{A_1}(t) \mid t \in I\}$, {axioms in A_1 whose left-hand sides include function symbols $f \in O \cap F_1$}, $\{f(X_1, X_2, \cdots, X_{a(f)}) \mid f \in O \cap F_2$ and $X_1, X_2, \cdots, X_{a(f)}$ are distinct variables} and $\{norm_1(g_1), norm_1(g_2)\}$. Note that we assume that each symbol (function symbol, etc.) can be represented in a constant length. Then we have Theorem 2.

<u>Theorem 2</u>: The time complexity of the algorithm to solve an instance of SP which satisfies Conditions 1, 2, 3 and 4 is $O(n^8)$.   ΔΔ

Note that $n \leq O(n_0^2)$, and the size of the problem used in [1] corresponds to n defined here.

6. Sufficient Condition Under Which the Security Problem Is Decidable.

The conditions 3 and 4 described above can be relaxed so that A_2 can contain, for example, the following forms of axioms:

(A1) IF(true , X , Y) = X ,

(A2) $f_1(X, f_2(X, f_3(X , Y))) == Y$,

(A3) $f_4(X, f_5(X, c_1))) == c_2$,

(A4) $f_6(X, f_7(X, Y))) == c_3$,

(A5) $f_8(X, f_9(X, Y))) == f_{10}(Y)$.

The axioms (A1) and (A2) are also cancellation rules as the axioms for E and D. The third axiom (A3) has the form obtained from the axiom for E and D by replacing Y in the left-hand and right-hand sides by constants c_1 and c_2, respectively. The left-hand sides of the last two axioms, (A4) and (A5), have the same forms as the axioms for E and D, but the right-hand sides are constants or f(Y) where $f \in F_2$.

When the set A contains axioms of above forms, we can decide its security as follows:

(1) When A contains axioms such as (A1), by considering the strings along the path from the root to each leaf as well as the rightmost leaf, we can solve the security problem.

(2) Let EQ^3 be a set such that for terms $t_1[X_{11}, X_{12}, \cdots X_{1h_1}]$, $t_2[X_{21}, X_{22}, \cdots X_{2h_2}]$, $t_3[X_{31}, X_{32}, \cdots X_{3h_3}])$ in T_{1*},

$$(t_1[X_{11}, X_{12}, \cdots X_{1h_1}], t_2[X_{21}, X_{22}, \cdots X_{2h_2}],$$
$$t_3[X_{31}, X_{32}, \cdots X_{3h_3}]) \in EQ^3 ,$$

if and only if there are $u_{j1}, u_{j2}, \cdots, u_{jh_j}$ in $\bar{Q}$, for $1 \le j \le 3$, such that

$$t_1[u_{11}, u_{12}, \cdots, u_{1h_1}]$$
$$\equiv t_2[u_{21}, u_{22}, \cdots, u_{2h_2}]$$
$$\equiv t_3[u_{31}, u_{32}, \cdots, u_{3h_3}] \ .$$

When A contains axioms such as (A2), the term $f_1(t_1, f_2(t_2, f_3(t_3, t_4)))$ can be rewritten into t_4 if and only if $(t_1, t_2, t_3) \in EQ^3$. We can compute EQ^3 as well as EQ^2.

(3) When A contains axioms such as (A3), (A4) and/or (A5). By considering rewriting rules such as

  (R3) $f_{4_X} f_{5_X} c_1 \to c_2$,

  (R4) $f_{6_X} f_{7_X}{}^* \to c_3$,

and (R5) $f_{8_X} f_{9_X} \to f_{10}$,

we can solve the security problem. The rewriting rule (R5) means that any string whose prefix is $f_{6_X} f_{7_X}$ can be rewriten into c_3.

                                                                    ΔΔ

Next we give a relaxed sufficient condition. For $t \in T_{VAR}(F)$, let tree(t) be the tree representation of the term t. For a leaf v of tree(t), we say that the path p from the root to the leaf v is a trunk of tree(t) if and only if

(1) tree(t) has only one node. That is, v is the root.

or

(2) for every subterm t_s of t such that the root of tree(t_s) is not on the path p but is a child of some node on p, t_s is a variable or a term containing no variable.

                                                                    ΔΔ

The typical trunk of a tree is shown in Figure 3.

Conditions 3 and 4 can be replaced by Condition 5.

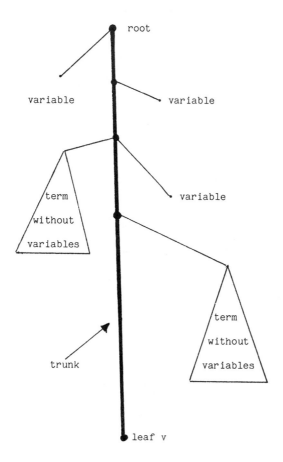

Fig. 3   Typical trunk of a tree.

Condition 5:   For each axiom $t_L == t_R$ in A_2, if t_R contains variables, then the axiom satisfies (1), otherwise satisfies (2).

(1) t_R is a variable X or has a form f(X) where f ϵ F_2 and X is a variable. The variable X appears in t_L only once but $t_L \neq X$. The path from the root of tree(t_L) to the node whose label is X is a trunk of tree(t_L).

(2) t_R is a constant in F_2 and tree(t_L) has a trunk.

$\Delta\Delta$

Next we show a method for solving the security problem which satisfies this relaxed condition.

Let N_+ and N_+^* be the set of positive integers and the set of sequences of positive integers, respectively. Let λ be the empty sequence in N_+^*. For $t \in T_{VAR}(F_2)$, we define the set of occurrences, $Occ(t)$, of subterms of t and the subterm of t at occurrence v, t/v, for $v \in Occ(t)$ as follows:

(1) If t is a constant in F_2 or a variable, then

$$Occ(t) = \{ \lambda \}, \text{ and } t/\lambda = t.$$

(2) If $t = f(t_1, t_2, \cdots, t_{a(f)})$, then

$$Occ(t) = \{ \lambda \} \cup \{ i{\cdot}v \mid 1 \leq i \leq a(f) \text{ and } v \in Occ(t_i) \},$$

$$t/\lambda = t,$$

and

$$t/i{\cdot}v = t_i/v, \text{ for } 1 \leq i \leq a(f).$$ $\Delta\Delta$

For term $t \in T_{VAR}(F_2)$ and an occurrence $v \in Occ(t)$, we say that v is a leaf occurrence of t, if and only if the subterm t/v is a constant in F_2 or a variable.

Let T_{2*} be a set of terms such that

$$T_{2*} = T_{1*} \cup \{\text{left-hand and right-hand sides of each axiom in } A_2\}.$$

Define a set of terminal symbols Σ and a string st(t, v)$\in \Sigma^* \cup \Sigma^*\{S\}$ for $t \in T_{2*}$, $v \in Occ(t)$ as follows:

(1) If t is a constant in F_2, then $t \in \Sigma$ and st(t, λ) = t.

(2) If t is a variable, then st(t, λ) = S.

(3) If $t = f(t_1, t_2, \cdots, t_{a(f)})$ where $f \in F_2$ and a(f) > 0, then

$$f_{t_1,t_2,\cdots,t_{i-1},*,t_{i+1},\cdots,t_{a(f)}} \in \Sigma, \text{ for } 1 \leq i \leq a(f), \text{ and}$$

$$st(t, v) = f_{t_1,t_2,\cdots,t_{i-1},*,t_{i+1},\cdots,t_{a(f)}} {\cdot}st(t, v_1),$$

where $v = i{\cdot}v_1$.

The set of generation rules $GRULE(T_0)$ and the set of strings $L(t)$

for $t \in T_{1*}$ are redefined as follows:

$$GRULE(T_0) = \{\ S \rightarrow st(t,v)\ |\ t \in T_0\ \text{and}$$

$$v \text{ is a leaf occurrence of } t\},$$

$$L(t) = \{\ \alpha\ |\ \alpha \in L_\Sigma(GRULE(T_0),\ st(t,v))\ ,$$

$$\text{for leaf occurrences } v \text{ of } t\}.$$

As we mentioned before, since we consider reduction rules which

have the form $\alpha \rightarrow a$ or $\alpha* \rightarrow a$ where $\alpha \in \Sigma^*$, $a \in \Sigma$ and $* \notin \Sigma \cup \{S\}$, we

redefine $L_R(RR,L)$ as follows:

(1) $L \subset L_R(RR,L)$.

(2) For $\alpha_1 \alpha \alpha_2 \in L_R(RR,L)$,

 (2.1) if $\alpha \rightarrow \beta \in RR$ where $\beta \in \Sigma \cup \{\lambda\}$, then $\alpha_1 \beta \alpha_2 \in L_R(RR,L)$,

and

 (2.2) if $\alpha* \rightarrow \beta \in RR$ where $\beta \in \Sigma \cup \{\lambda\}$, then $\alpha_1 {}^R \in L_R(RR,L)$.

Let m be the maximum number of occurrences of the same variable in

a left-hand side of an axiom in A_2. For an integer i where $2 \leq i \leq m$,

let T_{1*}^i be a set such that

$$T_{1*}^i = \{\ (t_1,\ t_2,\ \cdots,\ t_i)\ |\ t_j \in T_{1*},\ \text{for } 1 \leq j \leq i\ \}.$$

Let EQ^i be a subset of T_{1*}^i such that for terms $t_1[X_{11},\ X_{12},\ \cdots,\ X_{1h_1}]$,

$t_2[X_{21},\ X_{22},\ \cdots,\ X_{2h_2}],\ \cdots,\ t_i[X_{i1},\ X_{i2},\ \cdots,\ X_{ih_i}])$ in T_{1*},

$$(t_1[X_{11},\ X_{12},\ \cdots,\ X_{1h_1}],\ t_2[X_{21},\ X_{22},\ \cdots,\ X_{2h_2}],\ \cdots,$$

$$t_i[X_{i1},\ X_{i2},\ \cdots,\ X_{ih_i}]) \in EQ^i$$

if and only if there are $u_{j1},\ u_{j2},\ \cdots,\ u_{jh_j}$ in $\bar{Q}$, for $1 \leq j \leq i$, such

that

$$t_1[u_{11},\ u_{12},\ \cdots,\ u_{1h_1}]$$

$$\equiv t_2[u_{21},\ u_{22},\ \cdots,\ u_{2h_2}]$$

$$\cdots\cdots$$

$$\equiv t_i[u_{i1},\ u_{i2},\ \cdots,\ u_{ih_i}]\ .$$

To solve the security problem which satisfies the relaxed

condition, we compute

$$EQ^{m*} = \bigcup_{i=2}^{m} EQ^i$$

instead of EQ^2 in the previous section. Before that, we define mappings
$\psi_f \colon \Sigma \to F_2$, $\psi_* \colon \Sigma \to N$ and $\psi_t \colon \Sigma \times N \to T_{VAR}(F)$ where N is the set of
nonnegative integers.

(1) For $a \in \Sigma$ which corresponds to a constant in F,

$\qquad \psi_f(a) = a$ and $\psi_*(a) = 0$.

(2) For $b = f_{t_1, t_2, \cdots, t_{i-1}, *, t_{i+1}, \cdots, t_{a(f)}} \in \Sigma$,

$\qquad \psi_f(b) = f$, $\psi_*(b) = i$, and

$\qquad \psi_t(b,j) = t_j$,   for $1 \le j \le i-1$ or $i+1 \le j \le a(f)$.

We say that terminal symbols a and b are the same type if and only if
$\psi_f(a) = \psi_f(b)$ and $\psi_*(a) = \psi_*(b)$.

$\qquad$ Let

$$t_{1*}^{m*} = \bigcup_{i=1}^{m} T_{1*}^i .$$

For $P \subset T_{1*}^{m*}$, we redefine a set RRULE (P) of reduction rules and define a
set $EQSYMB^q(P)$ for $2 \le q \le m$ instead of EQSYMB(P).

[Definition of RRULE(P)]

(1) For an axiom $t_L == X$ or $t_L == f(X)$ in A_2 where X is a variable,
$\qquad$ consider the occurrence v_L where $t_L/v_L = X$. For $st(t_L, v_L) =$
$b_1 b_2 \cdots b_q S$,

$\qquad\qquad a_1 a_2 \cdots a_q \to \lambda \in RRULE(P),$

$\qquad\qquad\qquad\qquad$ if the right-hand side of the axiom is X,

$\qquad\qquad a_1 a_2 \cdots a_q \to f_* \in RRULE(P),$

$\qquad\qquad\qquad\qquad$ if the right-hand side of the axiom is f(X), where a_1, a_2, $\cdots$, a_q satisfy the following properties.

(i) For $1 \le i \le q$, a_i and b_i are the same type.

(ii) For $1 \le i \le q$ and $1 \le j \le a(\psi_f(b_i))$, $j \ne i$, if $\psi_t(b_i,j)$ does

not contains any variable, then $\psi_t(a_i,j) = \psi_t(b_i,j)$. Otherwise, for

each variable Y that appears r times in t_L where $r \ge 2$,

$$(\psi_t(a_{i_1}, j_1), \psi_t(a_{i_2}, j_2), \cdots, \psi_t(a_{i_r}, j_r)) \in P,$$

where

$$\psi_t(b_{i_1}, j_1) = \psi_t(b_{i_2}, j_2) = \cdots = \psi_t(b_{i_r}, j_r).$$

(2) For an axiom $t_L == c$ in A_2 where c is a constant in F_2, there is a

trunk p in $tree(t_L)$ which satisfies Condition 5-(2). Note that the

trunk p may not uniquely determined but any trunk that satisfies this

condition may be chosen. Let v_L be the occurrence of t_L that subterm

t_L/v_L is a constant or a variable which corresponds to the end point

of trunk p.

(2.1) If t_L/v_L is a constant, then for $st(t_L, v_L) = b_1 b_2 \cdots b_q$,

$a_1 a_2 \cdots a_q \to c \in RRULE(P)$,

where a_1, a_2, $\cdots$, a_q satisfy (i) and (ii) described above.

(2.2) If t_L/v_L is a variable, then for $st(t_L, v_L) = b_1 b_2 \cdots b_q S$,

$a_1 a_2 \cdots a_q * \to c \in RRULE(P)$,

where a_1, a_2, $\cdots$, a_q satisfy (i) and (ii) described above.

$\Delta\Delta$

[Definition of $EQSYMB^q(P)$]

(1) For $a \in \Sigma$, q-tuple $(a, a, \cdots, a) \in EQSYMB^q(P)$.

(2) For a_1, a_2 $\cdots$, a_q which are the same type, if

$$(\psi_t(a_1, j), \psi_t(a_2, j), \cdots, \psi_t(a_q, j)) \in P,$$

for $1 \le i \le q$, $1 \le j \le a(\psi_f(b_i))$, and $j \ne i$, then

$(a_1, a_2, \cdots, a_q) \in EQSYMB^q(P)$. $\Delta\Delta$

For P, a subset of EQ^{m*}, and t_1, t_2, $\cdots t_q \in T_{1*}$, the value of the

predicate $E(P, t_1, t_2, \cdots t_q)$ is True if and only if there are $\alpha_i \in$
$L_R(RRULE(P), L(t_i))$ for $1 \le i \le q$ such that

  (1) the lengths of α_i for $1 \le i \le q$ are the same and

  (2) $(a_{1j}, a_{2j}, \cdots, a_{qj}) \in EQSYMB(P)$, for $1 \le j \le h$ where a_{ij} is
the j-th symbol in α_i and h is the length of α_1.

Then we have Lemmas 5, 6 and Theorem 3 which correspond to Lemmas 3, 4

and Theorem 2, respectively.

Lemma 5: Let P be a subset of EQ^{m^*} and $t_1, t_2, \cdots t_q$ are terms in T_{1^*}.
If $E(P, t_1, t_2, \cdots, t_q)$ is True, then $(t_1, t_2, \cdots, t_q) \in EQ^q$.

$$\Delta\Delta$$

Lemma 6: Let P be a subset of EQ^{m^*}. If $E(P, t_1, t_2, \cdots, t_q) = $ False for
any $t_1, t_2, \cdots, t_q$ such that every $t_1, t_2, \cdots, t_q$ is term in T_{1^*} and
$(t_1, t_2, \cdots, t_q)$ is not in P, then $P = EQ^{m^*}$.

$$\Delta\Delta$$

Theorem 3: For an axiom $t_L == t_R$ in A_2, let $\ell(t_L)$ be the number of
function symbols on the path from the root of $tree(t_L)$ to the leaf t_L/v_L
where v_L is defined in the definition of RRULE(P). Let ℓ be the maximum
value of $\ell(t_L)$ for all axioms in A_2. The time complexity of the
algorithm to solve the security problem which satisfies Conditions 1, 2
and 5 is

$$O(mn^{4m} + \ell n^{m+\ell+4})$$ $\Delta\Delta$

Assume that m and ℓ are constants. Under the relaxed condition, the
time complexity of solving the security problem is still in polynomial.

7. Conclusion.

In this paper we have formalized the security problem of the
cryptographic protocols. We have give sufficient conditions under which
the security problem is decidable. The key management system proposed by

Ehrsam, et al. [5] satisfies the relaxed sufficient condition.

We have assumed that sorts (data types) of function are the same.

When we have various sorts of functions, we can define the security of cryptographic protocols in the same manner as mentioned in this paper. In this case, the condition such that all the axioms in A_1 have right linear property can be relaxed as follows.

Condition 6:　If all normal forms of terms of certain sorts are constants in F and all the constants of the sort are in I, then variables of these sorts may appear multiple time in the right-hand sides of the axioms in A_1.　　　　　　　　　　　　ΔΔ

By modifying the definition of O' as follows, we can solve the security problem in the same manner.

[modified definition of O']

For $t_L == t_R$ in A_1 which is not right linear, any term that can be obtained from t_R by substituting any constant of the sort for the variables which appears twice or more in t_R is in O'.　　　ΔΔ

The digital signature protocol proposed by Needham, et al. [6] satisfies this relaxed sufficient condition.

The details of the relaxed sufficient condition and the algorithm to solve the security problem are given in [3, 4] (proofs are given in [4]).

References

[1]　D. Dolev and A. C. Yao : "On the Security of Public Key Protocols," IEEE Trans. on IT, Vol. IT-29, No.2, pp.198-208 (1982).

[2]　D. Dolev, S. Even and R. M. Karp : "On The Security of Ping-Pong Protocols," Information and Control, Vol. 55, No. 1-3, pp.57-68 (1982).

[3]　T. Fujiwara, K. Taniguchi and T. Kasami : "Decision Problem of the

Security for Cryptographic Protocols," Trans. of IECE of Japan,
Vol. J69-D, No.6, pp. 984-992, (June 1986).

[4] T. Fujiwara, K. Taniguchi and T. Kasami : "On a Decision Problem of
the Security for Cryptographic Protocols," Research Report of Dept.
of Information and Computer Sciences, Osaka University (July 1985)
(in Japanese).

[5] W. F. Ehrsam, S. M. Matyas and W. L. Tuchman : "A Cryptographic key
management scheme for implementing the Data Encryption Standard,"
IBM system J., Vol.17, No.2, pp.106-125 (1978).

[6] R. M. Needham and M. D. Schroeder : "Using Encryption for authenti
cation in large networks of computers," Commun. ACM, Vol.21, No.12,
pp.993-999 (1978).

[7] T. Kasami, S. Yamamura and K. Mori : "A Key Management Scheme for
End-to-End Encryption and a Formal Verification of Its Security,"
Trans. of IECE of Japan, Vol. J65-D, No.6, pp. 695-702, (June
1982).

[8] T. Fujiwara, T. Kasami and S. Yamamura : "A Formal Verification for
the Security of a Digital Signature Protocol," Papers of IECE
of Japan, AL81-90, pp. 13-18 (Jan. 1982) (in Japanese).

A Digital Signature Scheme
Secure Against Adaptive Chosen Message Attack *
(Extended Abstract)
(Revision September 5, 1986)

Shafi Goldwasser**
Silvio Micali**
Ronald L. Rivest **

Abstract

We present a digital signature scheme based on the computational difficulty of integer factorization.

The scheme possesses the novel property of being robust against an adaptive chosen message attack: an adversary who receives signatures for messages of his choice (where each message may be chosen in a way that depends on the signatures of previously chosen messages) can not later forge the signature of even a single additional message. This may be somewhat surprising, since the properties of having forgery being equivalent to factoring and being invulnerable to an adaptive chosen message attack were considered in the folklore to be contradictory.

More generally, we show how to construct a signature scheme with such properties based on the existence of a "claw-free" pair of permutations – a potentially weaker assumption than the intractibility of integer factorization.

The new scheme is potentially practical: signing and verifying signatures are reasonably fast, and signatures are compact.

I. INTRODUCTION.

The idea of a "digital signature" first appeared in Diffie and Hellman's seminal paper, "New Directions in Cryptography"[DH76]. They propose that each user A publish a "public key" (used for validating signatures), while keeping secret a "secret key" (used for producing signatures). In their scheme user A's signature for a message M is a value which depends on M and on A's secret key, such that anyone can verify the validity of A's signature using A's public key. However, while knowing A's public key is sufficient to allow one to validate A's signatures, it does not allow one to easily forge A's signatures. They also proposed a way of implementing signatures based on "trap-door functions" (see section II.A).

The notion of a digital signature is useful and is a legal replacement for handwritten signatures [LM78, Ma79]. However, a number of technical problems arise if digital signatures are implemented using trap-door functions as suggested by Diffie and Hellman [DH76]; these problems have been addressed and solved in part elsewhere. For example, [GMY83] showed how to handle arbitrary or sparse messages sets and how to ensure that if an enemy sees previous signatures (for messages that he has not chosen) it does not help him to forge new signatures (this is a "non-adaptive chosen message attack" – see section III).

The signature scheme presented here, using fundamentally different ideas than those presented by Diffie and Hellman, advances the state of the art of signature

* This research was supported by NSF grant MCS-80-06938, an IBM/MIT Faculty Development Award, and DARPA contract N00014-85-K-0125.

** MIT Laboratory for Computer Science, Cambridge, Mass. 02139 schemes with provable security properties even further; it has the following important characteristics:

- What we prove to be difficult is *forgery*, and not merely obtaining the secret key used by the signing algorithm (or obtaining an efficient equivalent algorithm).
- Forgery is proven to be difficult for a "most general" enemy who can mount an *adaptive chosen message attack*. (An enemy who can use the real signer as "an oracle" can not in time polynomial in the size of the public key forge a signature for any message whose signature was not obtained from the real signer.) In contrast to all previous published work on this problem, we prove the scheme invulnerable against such an adaptive attack where each message whose signature is requested may depend on all signatures previously obtained from the real signer. We believe that an adaptive chosen message attack to be the most powerful attack possible for an enemy who is restricted to using the signature scheme in a natural manner.
- The properties we prove about the new signature scheme do not depend in any way on the set of messages which can be signed or on any assumptions about a probability distribution on the message set.
- Our scheme can be generalized so that it can be based on "hard" problems other than factoring whenever one can create claw-free trap-door pair generators.

Our scheme can be based on any family of pairs of claw-free permutations, yielding a signature scheme that is *invulnerable* to a chosen message attack even if the claw-free trap-door permutations are *vulnerable* to a chosen message attack when used to make a trap-door signature scheme (see section II).

Fundamental ideas in the construction are the use of randomization, signing by using two authentication steps (the first step authenticates a random value which is used in the second step to authenticate the message), and the use of a tree-like branching authentication structure to produce short signatures.

We note that our signature scheme is not of the simple Diffie-Hellman "trap-door" type. For example, a given message can have many signatures.

Our signature scheme is seemingly "paradoxical", in that we prove that forgery is equivalent to factoring even if the enemy uses an *adaptive* chosen message attack. We can restate the paradox as follows:

- Any general technique for forging signatures can be used as a "black box" in a construction that enables the enemy to factor one of the signer's public moduli (he has two in our scheme), but
- The technique of "forging" signatures by getting the real signer to play the role of the "black box" (i.e. getting the real signer to produce some desired genuine signatures) does not help the enemy to factor either of the signer's moduli.

Resolving this paradox was previously believed to be impossible and contradictory [Wi80, misled by Rivest].

The rest of this paper is organized as follows. In section II we present definitions of what it means to "break" a signature scheme and what it means to "attack" a signature scheme. In section III we review previously proposed signature schemes. In section IV we review more closely the nature of the "paradox", and discuss how it can be resolved. In section V we describe the complexity-theoretic foundations of our scheme, and in section VI we give the details of our signature scheme. In section VII we prove that it has the desired properties. In the last section we discuss some ways to improve the running time and memory requirements of this scheme.

II. FUNDAMENTAL NOTIONS

To properly characterize the results of this paper, it is helpful to answer the following questions:
- What is a digital signature scheme?
- What kinds of attacks can the enemy mount against a digital signature scheme?
- What is meant by "breaking" the signature scheme?

II.A. WHAT IS A DIGITAL SIGNATURE SCHEME?

A *digital signature scheme* contains the following components:

- A *message space* M which is the set of messages to which the signature algorithm may be applied. Without loss of generality, we assume in this paper that all messages are represented as binary strings – that is $M \subseteq \{0,1\}^+$.

- A *security parameter* k, which is chosen by the user when he creates his public and secret keys. The parameter k determines a number of quantities (length of signatures, overall security, etc.).

- A *signature bound* B which is an integer bounding the total number of signatures that can be produced with an instance of the signature scheme. This value is typically bounded above by a low-degree polynomial in k, but may be infinite.

- A *key generation algorithm* G which any user A can use on input 1^k (i.e. k in unary) to generate in polynomial time a pair (P_A^k, S_A^k) of matching *public* and *secret* keys. The secret key is sometimes called the *trap-door information*.

- A *signature algorithm* which produces a signature $\sigma(M, S_A)$ for a message M using the secret key S_A. Here σ may receive other inputs as well. For example, in the scheme we propose first, σ has an additional input which is the number of previously signed messages.

- A *verification algorithm* $V(S, M, P_A)$ which tests whether S is a valid signature for message M using the public key P_A.

Any of the above algorithms may be "randomized" algorithms that make use of auxiliary random bit stream inputs. We note that G *must* be a randomized algorithm, since part of its output is the secret key, which must be unpredictable to an adversary. The signing algorithm σ may be randomized – we note in particular that our signing algorithm is randomized and is capable of producing many different signatures for the same message. In general, the verification algorithm need not be randomized, and ours is not.

We note that there are other kinds of "signature" problems which are not dealt with here; the most notable being the "contract signing problem" where two parties wish to exchange their signatures to an agreed-upon contract *simultaneously* (for example, see [EGL82], [BGMR85], [Bl83]).

II.A.1 A Classical Example: Trap-Door Signatures

To create a signature scheme Diffie and Hellman proposed that A use a "trap-door function" f: informally, a function for which it is easy to evaluate $f(x)$ for any argument x but for which, given only $f(x)$, it is computationally infeasible to find any y with $f(y) = f(x)$ without the secret "trap-door" information. According to their suggestion, A publishes f and anyone can validate a signature by checking that $f(signature) = message$. Only A possesses the "trap-door" information allowing him to invert f: $f^{-1}(message) = signature$. (Trap-door functions will be formally defined in section V.) We call any signature scheme that fits into this model (i.e. uses trap-door functions and signs by apply f^{-1} to the message) a *trap-door signature scheme*.

We note that not all signature schemes are trap-door schemes, although most of the proposals in the literature are of this type.

II.B. KINDS OF ATTACKS

We distinguish two basic kinds of attacks:

- **Key-Only Attacks** in which the enemy knows only the real signer's public key, and
- **Message Attacks** where the enemy is able to examine some signatures corresponding to either known or chosen messages before his attempt to break the scheme.

We identify the following four kinds of message attacks, which are characterized by how the messages whose signatures the enemy sees are chosen. Here A denotes the user whose signature method is being attacked.

- **Known Message Attack:** The enemy is given access to signatures for a set of messages $M_1, \ldots, M_t$. The messages are known to the enemy but are not chosen by him.
- **Generic Chosen Message Attack:** Here the enemy is allowed to obtain from A valid signatures for a chosen list of messages $M_1, \ldots, M_t$ before he attempts to break A's signature scheme. These messages are *chosen* by the enemy, but they are *fixed* and *independent* of A's public key (for example the M_i's may be chosen at random). This attack is *nonadaptive*: the entire message list is constructed before any signatures are seen. This attack is "generic" since it does not depend on the A's public key; the same attack is used against everyone.
- **Directed Chosen Message Attack:** This is similar to the generic chosen message attack, except that the list of messages to be signed may be created after seeing A's public key but before any signatures are seen. (The attack is still nonadaptive.) This attack is "directed" against a particular user A.
- **Adaptive Chosen Message Attack:** This is more general yet: here the enemy is also allowed to use A as an "oracle"; not only may he request from A signatures of messages which depend on A's public key but he may also request signatures of messages which depend additionally on previously obtained signatures.

The above attacks are listed in order of increasing severity, with the adaptive chosen message attack being the most severe natural attack an enemy can mount. That the adaptive chosen message attack is a natural one can be seen by considering the case of a notary public who must sign more-or-less arbitrary documents on demand. In general, the user of a signature scheme would like to feel that he may sign arbitrary documents prepared by others without fear of compromising his security.

II.C. WHAT DOES IT MEAN TO "BREAK" A SIGNATURE SCHEME?

One might say that the enemy has "broken" user A's signature scheme if his attack allows him to do any of the following with a non-negligible probability:

- **A Total Break:** Compute A's secret trap-door information.
- **Universal Forgery:** Find an efficient signing algorithm functionally equivalent to A's signing algorithm (based on possibly different but equivalent trap-door information).
- **Selective Forgery:** Forge a signature for a particular message chosen *a priori* by the enemy.
- **Existential Forgery:** Forge a signature for at least one message. The enemy has no control over the message whose signature he obtains, so it may be random or nonsensical. Consequently this forgery may only be a minor nuisance to A.

Note that to forge a signature means to produce a *new* signature; it is not forgery to obtain from A a valid signature for a message and then claim that he has now "forged" that signature, any more than passing around an authentic handwritten signature is an instance of forgery. For example, in a chosen message attack it does not constitute selective forgery to obtain from the real signer a signature for the target message M.

Clearly, the kinds of "breaks" are listed above in order of decreasing severity – the least the enemy might hope for is to succeed with an existential forgery.

We say that a scheme is respectively *totally breakable, universally forgeable, selectively forgeable*, or *existentially forgeable* if it is breakable in one of the above senses. Note that it is more desirable to prove that a scheme is not even existentially forgeable than to prove that it is not totally breakable. The above list is not exhaustive; there may be other ways of "breaking" a signature scheme which fit in between those listed, or are somehow different in character.

We utilize here the most realistic notion of forgery, in which we say that a forgery algorithm succeeds if it succeeds probabilistically with a non-negligible probability. To make this notion precise, we say that the forgery algorithm succeeds if its chance of success is at least as large as one over a polynomial in the security parameter k. (We could not hope for much more, since there will always be some exponentially small chance that a forgery algorithm could guess the secret key exactly by randomly flipping coins.)

To say that the scheme is "broken", we not only insist that the forgery algorithm succeed with a non-negligible probability, but also that it must run in probabilistic polynomial time.

We note here that the characteristics of the signature scheme may depend on its message space in subtle ways. For example, a scheme may be existentially forgeable for a message space M but not existentially forgeable if restricted to a message space which is a sufficiently small subset of M.

The next section exemplifies these notions by reviewing previously proposed signature schemes.

III. PREVIOUS SIGNATURE SCHEMES AND THEIR SECURITY

In this section we list a number of previously proposed signature schemes and briefly review some facts about their security.

Trap-Door Signature Schemes [DH76]: Any trap-door signature scheme is existentially forgeable with a key-only attack since a valid (message, signature) pair can be created by beginning with a random "signature" and applying the public verification algorithm to obtain the corresponding "message". A common heuristic for handling this problem in practice is to require that the message space be sparse (i.e. requiring that very few strings actually represent messages – for example this can be enforced by having each message contain a reasonably long checksum.) In this case this specific attack is not likely to result in a successful existential forgery.

Rivest-Shamir-Adleman [RSA78]: The RSA scheme is selectively forgeable using a directed chosen message attack, since RSA is *multiplicative*: the signature of a product is the product of the signatures. (This can be handled in practice as above using a sparse message space.)

Merkle-Hellman [MH78]: Shamir showed the basic Merkle-Hellman "knapsack" scheme to be universally forgeable using just a key-only attack [Sh82]. (This scheme was perhaps more an encryption scheme than a signature scheme, but had been proposed for use as a signature scheme as well.)

Rabin [Ra79]: As noted earlier, Rabin's signature scheme is totally breakable if the enemy uses a directed chosen message attack. However, for non-sparse message spaces selective forgery is as hard as factoring if the enemy is restricted to a known message attack.

Williams [Wi80]: This scheme is similar to Rabin's. The proof that selective forgery is as hard as factoring is slightly stronger, since here only a single instance of selective forgery guarantees factoring (Rabin needed a probabilistic argument). Williams uses effectively (as we do) the properties of numbers which are the product of a prime $p \equiv 3$ (mod 8) and a prime $q \equiv 7$ (mod 8). Again, this scheme is totally breakable with a directed chosen message attack.

Lieberherr [Li81]: This scheme is similar to Rabin's and Williams', and is totally breakable with a directed chosen message attack.

Shamir [Sh78]: This knapsack-type signature scheme has recently been shown by Tulpan [Tu84] to be universally forgeable with a key-only attack for any practical values of the security parameter.

Goldwasser-Micali-Yao [GMY83]: This paper presents for the first time signature schemes which are not of the trap-door type, and which have the interesting property that their security characteristics hold for *any* message space. The first signature scheme presented in [GMY83] was proven not to be even existentially forgeable against a *generic* chosen message attack unless factoring is easy. However, it is not known to what extent *directed* chosen message attacks or adaptive chosen message attacks might aid an enemy in "breaking" the scheme.

The second scheme presented there (based on the RSA function) was also proven not to be even existentially forgeable against a generic chosen message attack. This scheme may also resist existentially forgery against an adaptive chosen message attack, although this has not been proven. (A proof would require showing certain properties about the density of prime numbers and making a stronger intractability assumption about inverting RSA.) We might note that, by comparison, the scheme presented here is much faster, produces much more compact signatures, and is based on much simpler assumptions (only the difficulty of factoring or more generally the existence of trap-door permutation pair generators).

Several of the ideas and techniques presented in [GMY83], such as bit-by-bit authentication, are used in the present paper.

Ong-Schnorr-Shamir [OSS84a]: Totally breaking this scheme using an adaptive chosen message attack has been shown to be as hard as factoring. However, Pollard [Po84] has recently been able to show that the "OSS" signature scheme is universally forgeable in practice using just a key-only attack; he developed an algorithm to forge a signature for any given message without obtaining the secret trap-door information. A more recent "cubic" version has recently been shown to be universally forgeable in practice using just a key-only attack (also by Pollard). An even more recent version [OSS84b] based on polynomial equations was similarly broken by Estes, Adleman, Kompella, McCurley and Miller [EAKMM85] for quadratic number fields.

El Gamal[EG84]: This scheme, based on the difficulty of computing discrete logarithms, is existentially forgeable with a generic message attack and selectively forgeable using a directed chosen message attack.

Okamoto-Shiraishi[OS85]: This scheme, based on the difficulty of solving quadratic inequalities modulo a composite modulus, was shown to be universally forgeable by Brickell and DeLaurentis [BD85].

IV. THE PARADOX OF PROVING SIGNATURE SCHEMES SECURE

The paradoxical nature of signature schemes which are provably secure against chosen message attacks made its first appearance in Rabin's paper, "Digitalized Signatures as Intractable as Factorization". The signature scheme proposed there works as follows. User A publishes a number n which is the product of two large primes. To sign a message M, A computes as M's signature one of M's square roots modulo n. (When M is not a square modulo n, A modifies a few bits of M to find a "nearby" square.) Here signing is essentially just extracting square roots modulo n. Using the fact that extracting square roots modulo n enables one to factor n, it follows that selective forgery in Rabin's scheme is equivalent to factoring if the enemy is restricted to at most a known message attack.

However, it is true (and was noticed by Rabin) that an enemy might totally break the scheme using a directed chosen message attack. By asking A to sign a value $x^2 \bmod n$ where x was picked at random, the enemy would obtain with probability $\frac{1}{2}$ another square root y of x^2 such that $\gcd(x + y, n)$ was a prime factor of n.

Rabin suggested that one could overcome this problem by, for example, having the signer concatenate a fairly long randomly chosen pad U to the message before signing it. In this way the enemy can not force A to extract a square root of any particular number.

However, the reader may now observe that the proof of the equivalence of selective forgery to factoring no longer works for the modified scheme. That is, being able to selectively forge no longer enables the enemy to directly extract square roots and thus to factor. Of course, breaking this equivalence was really the whole point of making the modification.

IV.A. THE PARADOX

We now "prove" that it is impossible to have a signature scheme for which it is both true that forgery is provably equivalent to factoring, and yet the scheme is invulnerable to adaptive chosen message attacks. The argument is essentially the same as the one given in [Wi80]. By *forgery* we mean in this section any of universal, selective, or existential forgery – we assume that we are given a proof that forgery of the specified type is equivalent to factoring.

Let us begin by considering this given proof. The main part of the proof presumably goes as follows: given a subroutine for forging signatures, a constructive method is specified for factoring. (The other part of the equivalance, showing that factoring enables forgery, is usually easy, since factoring usually enables the enemy to totally break the scheme.)

But it is trivial then to show that an adaptive chosen message attack enables an enemy to totally break the scheme. The enemy merely executes the constructive method for factoring given in the proof, using the real signer instead of the forgery subroutine! That is, whenever he needs to execute the forgery subroutine to obtain the signature of a message, he merely performs an "adaptive chosen message attack" step – getting the real user to sign the desired message. In the end the unwary user has enabled the enemy to factor his modulus! (If the proof reduces factoring to universal or selective forgery, the enemy has to get real user to sign a particular message. If the proof reduces factoring to existential forgery, the enemy need only get him to sign anything at all.)

IV.B. BREAKING THE PARADOX

How can one hope to get around the apparent contradictory natures of equivalence to factoring and invulnerability to an adaptive chosen message attack?

The key idea in resolving the paradox is to have the constructive proof that forgery is as hard as factoring be a *uniform* proof which makes *essential* use of the fact that the forger can forge for *arbitrary* public keys with a non-negligible probability of success. However, in "real life" a signer will only produce signatures for a *particular* public key. Thus the constructive proof can not be applied in "real life" (by asking the real signer to unwittingly play the role of the forger) to factor.

In our scheme this concept is implemented using the notion of "random rooting". Each user publishes not only his two composite moduli n_1 and n_2, but also a "random root" R_ϵ. (Here ϵ denotes the empty string.) This value R_ϵ is used when validating the user's signatures. The paradox is resolved in our case as follows:

- It is provably equivalent to factoring for an enemy to have a *uniform* algorithm for forging; uniform in the sense that if for all pairs of composite numbers n_1 and n_2 if the enemy can randomly forge signatures for a significant fraction of the possible random roots R_ϵ, then he can factor either n_1 or n_2.

- The above proof *requires* that the enemy be able to pick R_ϵ himself – the forgery subroutine is fed triples (n_1, n_2, R_ϵ) where the R_ϵ part is chosen by the enemy according the procedure specified in the constructive proof. *However*, the user has picked a fixed R_ϵ at random to put in his public key, so an adaptive chosen message attack will not enable the enemy to "forge" signatures corresponding to any other values of R_ϵ. Thus the constructive method given in the proof can not be applied!

V. GENERAL NOTATION AND CONVENTIONS

V.A Notation and Conventions for Strings

Let $\alpha = \alpha_0\alpha_1 \ldots \alpha_i$ be a binary string, then $\bar{\alpha}$ will denote the integer $\sum_{k=1}^{i} 2^{\alpha_k}$. The strings in $\{0,1\}^*$ are ordered as follows: if $\alpha = \alpha_0 \ldots \alpha_i$ and $\beta = \beta_0 \ldots \beta_j$ are binary strings, we write $\alpha < \beta$ if either $i < j$ or $i = j$ and $\bar{\alpha} < \bar{\beta}$. We write $\alpha \leq \beta$ if either $\alpha < \beta$ or $\alpha = \beta$. We let $PREFIX_\alpha$ denote the set of strings which are prefixes of α.

V.B Notation and Conventions for Probabilistic Algorithms.

We introduce some generally useful notation and conventions for discussing probabilistic algorithms. (We make the natural assumption that all parties, including the enemy, may make use of probabilistic methods.)

We emphasize the number of inputs received by an algorithm as follows. If algorithm A receives only one input we write "$A(\cdot)$", if it receives two inputs we write "$A(\cdot, \cdot)$" and so on.

We write "PS" for "probability space"; in this paper we only consider countable probability spaces. In fact, we only deal with probability spaces arising from probabilistic algorithms.

If $A(\cdot)$ is a probabilistic algorithm, then for any input i, the notation $A(i)$ refers to the PS which assigns to the string σ the probability that A, on input i, outputs σ. We point out the special case that A takes no inputs; in this case the notation A refers to the algorithm itself, whereas the notation $A()$ refers to the PS defined by running A

with no input. If S is a PS, we denote by $\mathbf{P}_S(e)$ the probability that S associates with element e. Also, we denote by $[S]$ the set of elements which S gives positive probability. In the case that $[S]$ is a singleton set $\{e\}$ we will use S to denote the value e; this is in agreement with traditional notation. (For instance, if $A(\cdot)$ is an algorithm that, on input i, outputs i^3, then we may write $A(2) = 8$ instead of $[A(2)] = \{8\}$.)

If $f(\cdot)$ and $g(\cdot, \cdots)$ are probabilistic algorithms then $f(g(\cdot, \cdots))$ is the probabilistic algorithm obtained by composing f and g (i.e. running f on g's output). For any inputs $x, y, \ldots$ the associated probability space is denoted $f(g(x, y, \ldots))$.

If S is a PS, then $x \leftarrow S$ denotes the algorithm which assigns to x an element randomly selected according to S; that is, x is assigned the value e with probability $\mathbf{P}_S(e)$.

The notation $\mathbf{P}(x \leftarrow S; y \leftarrow T; \ldots : p(x, y, \ldots))$ denotes the probability that the predicate $p(x, y, \ldots)$ will be true, after the (ordered) execution of the algorithms $x \leftarrow S$, $y \leftarrow T$, etc.

We let $\mathcal{RA}$ denote the set of probabilistic polynomial-time algorithms. We assume that a natural representation of these algorithms as binary strings is used.

By 1^k we denote the unary representation of integer k, i.e.

VI. THE COMPLEXITY THEORETIC BASIS OF THE NEW SCHEME

A particular instance of our scheme can be constructed if integer factorization is computationally difficult. However, we will present our scheme in a general manner without assuming any particular problem to be intractable. This clarifies the exposition, and helps to establish the true generality of the proposed scheme. We do this by introducing the notion of a "claw-free permutation pair", and constructively showing the existence of such objects under the assumption that integer factorization is difficult.

This section builds up the relevant concepts and definitions in stages. In subsection VI.A. we give a careful definition of the notions of a trap-door permutation and a trap-door permutation generator. These notions are not directly used in this paper, but serve as a simple example of the use of our notation. (Furthermore, no previous definition in the literature was quite so comprehensive.) The reader may, if he wishes, skip section VI.A without great loss.

In subsection VI.B. we define claw-free permutation pairs and claw-free permutation pair generators.

In subsection VI.C. we show how to construct claw-free permutation pair generators under the assumption that factoring is difficult.

Finally, in subsection VI.D. we show how to construct an infinite family of pairwise claw-free permutations, given a generating pair f_0, f_1, of claw-free permutations.

Altogether, then, this section provides the underlying definitions and assumptions required for constructing our signature scheme. The actual construction of our signature scheme will be given in section VII.

VI.A Trap-door Permutations

Informally, a family of trap-door permutations is a family of permutations f possessing the following properties:

- It is easy, given a integer k, to randomly select permutations f in the family which have k as their security parameter, together with some extra "trap-door" information allowing easy inversion of the permutations chosen.
- It is hard to invert f without knowing f's trap-door.

We can interpret the two properties above by saying that any user A can easily randomly select a pair of permutations, (f, f^{-1}), inverses of each other. This will enable A to easily evaluate and invert f; if now A publicizes f and keeps secret f^{-1}, then inverting f will be hard for all other users.

In the informal discussion above, we used the terms "easy" and "hard". The term "easy" can be interpreted as "in polynomial time"; "hard", however, is of more difficult interpretation. By saying that f is hard to invert we cannot possibly mean that f^{-1} cannot be easily evaluated at any of its arguments.* We mean, instead, that f^{-1} is hard to evaluate at a *random* argument. Thus, if one wants (as we do) to use trap-door functions to generate problems computationally hard for an "adversary", he must be able to randomly select a point in the domain of f and f^{-1}. This operation is easy for all currently known candidates of a trap-door permutation, and we explicitly assume it to be easy in our formal treatment.

Definition: Let G be an algorithm in $\mathcal{RA}$ that on input 1^k, outputs an ordered triple (d, f, f^{-1}) of algorithms. (Here $D = [d()]$ will denote the domain of the trap-door permutation f and its inverse f^{-1}.) We say that G is a *trap-door permutation generator* if there is a polynomial p such that

(1) Algorithm d always halts within $p(k)$ steps and defines a uniform probability distribution over the finite set $D = [d()]$. (I.e., running d with no inputs uniformly selects an element from D.)

(2) Algorithms f and f^{-1} halt within $p(k)$ steps on any input $x \in D$. Furthermore, the functions $x \mapsto f(x)$ and $x \mapsto f^{-1}(x)$ are inverse permutations of D.

(3) For all (inverting) algorithms $I(\cdot, \cdot, \cdot, \cdot) \in \mathcal{RA}$, for all c and sufficiently large k:

$$\mathbf{P}\big((d, f, f^{-1}) \leftarrow G(1^k); z \leftarrow d(); y \leftarrow I(1^k, d, f, z) : y = f^{-1}(z)\big) < k^{-c}.$$

We make the following informal remarks corresponding to some of the parts of the above definition.

(1) This condition makes it explicit that it is possibly to sample the domain of f in a uniform manner.

(3) This part of the definition states that if we run the experiment of generating (d, f, f^{-1}) using the generator G and security parameter k, and then randomly generating an element z in the range of f, and then running the "inverting" algorithm I with inputs d, f, and z, the chance that I will successfully invert f at the point z is vanishingly small as a function of k.

Definition: If G is a trap-door permutation generator, we say that $[G(1^k)]$ is a *family of trap-door permutations*.

Definition: We say that f and f^{-1} are *trap-door permutations* if $(d, f, f^{-1}) \in [G(1^k)]$ for some k and trap-door permutation generator G.

---

* For example, any f can be easily inverted at the image of a fixed argument, say 0. In fact, we may consider inverting algorithms that, on inputs x and f, first check whether $x = f(0)$.

VI.B. "Claw-Free" Permutation Pairs

The signature scheme we propose is dependent on the existence of "claw-free" permutation pairs – informally, these are permutations f_0 and f_1 over a common domain for which it is computationally infeasible to find a triple x, y, and z such that $f_0(x) = f_1(y) = z$ (a "claw" – see Figure 1).

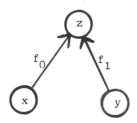

Figure 1. A Claw

Definition: Let G be an algorithm in $\mathcal{RA}$ that on input 1^k, outputs an ordered quintuple $(d, f_0, f_0^{-1}, f_1, f_1^{-1})$ of algorithms. We say that G is a *claw-free permutation pair generator* if there is a polynomial p such that:

(1) Algorithm d always halts within $p(k)$ steps and defines a uniform probability distribution over the finite set $D = [d()]$.

(2) Algorithms f_0, f_0^{-1}, f_1 and f_1^{-1} halt within $p(k)$ steps on any input. Furthermore, the functions $x \mapsto f_0(x)$ and $x \mapsto f_0^{-1}(x)$ are permutations of D which are inverses of each other, as are $x \mapsto f_1(x)$ and $x \mapsto f_1^{-1}(x)$.

(3) For all (claw-making) algorithms $I(\cdot, \cdot, \cdot, \cdot) \in \mathcal{RA}$, for all c and sufficiently large k:

$$\mathbf{P}((d, f_0, f_0^{-1}, f_1, f_1^{-1}) \leftarrow G(1^k); (x, y, z) \leftarrow I(1^k, d, f_0, f_1) : f_0(x) = f_1(y) = z) < k^{-c}.$$

Note: In condition (3) above, x and y need not necessarily belong to D. Thus, it should be hard to find any triplet (x, y, z) such that $f_0(x) = f_1(y) = z$ even when x, y are not in D.

Definition: We say that (d, f_0, f_1) is a *claw-free permutation pair* (or *claw-free pair* for short) if $(d, f_0, f_0^{-1}, f_1, f_1^{-1}) \in [G(1^k)]$ for some k and claw-free permutation pair generator G.

VI.B.1. Claw-Free Permutation Pairs vs. Trapdoor Permutations

In this subsection we clarify the relation between the notions of claw-free permutation pairs and trapdoor permutations, by showing that the existence of the former ones implies the existance of the latter ones. (Since trapdoor permutations are not used in our signature scheme, this subsection can be skipped by the reader without loss of clarity.)

Claim: Let $G \in \mathcal{RA}$ be a claw-free permutation generator. Then there exists a $\bar{G} \in \mathcal{RA}$ which is a trapdoor permutation generator.

Proof: The algorithm $\bar{G}$ is defined as follows on input 1^k: Run G on input 1^k. Say, G outputs the ordered tuple $(d, f_0, f_0^{-1}, f_1, f_1^{-1})$. Then, $\bar{G}$ outputs (d, f_0, f_0^{-1}).

We now show that $\bar{G}$ is a trapdoor permutation generator. Assume for contradiction that it not the case. Namely, there exists a constant $c > 0$ and an inverting algorithm $\bar{I}(\cdot, \cdot, \cdot, \cdot) \in \mathcal{RA}$ such that for infinitely many k:

$$P((d, f_0, f_0^{-1}) \leftarrow \bar{G}(1^k); z \leftarrow d(); y \leftarrow \bar{I}(1^k, d, f_0, z) : f_0(y) = z) > k^{-c}.$$

Note now, that since f_1 is a permutation, algorithms $f_1(d())$ and $d()$ both define the uniform probability distribution over $[d()]$. Thus, for infinitely many k,

$$P((d, f_0, f_0^{-1}, f_1, f_1^{-1}) \leftarrow G(1^k); x \leftarrow d(); z \leftarrow f_1(x); y \leftarrow \bar{I}(1^k, d, f_0, z) : f_1(x) = f_0(y) = z) > k^{-c}.$$

Let $I(\cdot, \cdot, \cdot, \cdot)$ be the following inverting algorithm: On input $1^k, d, f_0,$ and f_1, compute $x \leftarrow d()$, $z \leftarrow f_1(x)$, $y \leftarrow \bar{I}(1^k, d, f_0, z)$, and output (x, y, z).

Then, I is in $\mathcal{RA}$ and for infinitely many k,

$$P((d, f_0, f_0^{-1}, f_1, f_1^{-1}) \leftarrow G(1^k); (x, y, z) \leftarrow I(1^k, d, f_0, f_1) : f_0(x) = f_1(y) = z) > k^{-c}.$$

This contradicts G being a claw-free permutation generator and thus $\bar{G}$ must be a permutation generator.

∎

We note, however, that the the converse to the above claim may be false. For example, the pair of ("RSA") permutations over $Z_n^* = \{1 \leq x \leq n : gcd(x, n) = 1\{$, defined by

$$f_0(x) \equiv x^3 \pmod{n}, \text{ and}$$

$$f_1(x) \equiv x^5 \pmod{n}$$

(where $gcd(\phi(n), 15) = 1$) is not claw-free : since the two functions commute it is easy to create a claw by choosing w at random and then defining $x \equiv f_1(w)$, $y \equiv f_0(w)$, and

$$z \equiv f_0(x) \equiv f_1(y) \equiv w^{15} \pmod{n}.$$

However, it is likely that f_0 and f_1 are trap-door permutations.

In practice, one may want to relax the definition of a claw-free permutation pair generator slightly, to allow the generator to have a very small chance of outputting functions f_0 and f_1 which are not permutations. We do not pursue this line of development in this paper.

VI.C. Claw-free permutations exist if factoring is hard

The assumption of the existence of claw-free pairs is made in this paper in a general manner, independent of any particular number theoretic assumptions. Thus instances of our scheme may be secure even if factoring integers turns out to be easy. However for concretely implementing our scheme the following is suggested.

We first make an assumption about the intractability of factoring, and then exhibit a claw-free permutation pair generator based on the difficulty of factoring.

Notation: Let

$$H_k = \big\{ n = p \cdot q \mid |p| = |q| = k, p \equiv 3 \pmod{8}, q \equiv 7 \pmod{8} \big\}$$

(the set of composite numbers which are the product of two k-bit primes which are both congruent to 3 modulo 4 but not congruent to each other modulo 8), and let $H = \bigcup_k H_k$.

Remark: One way to choose "hard" instances for all known factoring algorithms seems to be to choose k to be large enough and then to choose n randomly from H_k.

These numbers were used in [Wi80] and their wide applicabilty to cryptography was demonstrated by Blum in [Bl82] – hence they are commonly referred to as "Blum integers".

Let Q_n denote the set of quadratic residues $\pmod{n}$. We note that for $n \in H$:
-1 has Jacobi symbol $+1$ but is not in Q_n.
2 has Jacobi symbol -1 (and is not in Q_n).

We also note every $x \in Q_n$ has exactly one square root $y \in Q_n$, but has four square roots $y, -y, w, -w$ altogether. (see [Bl82] for proof). Roots w and $-w$ have Jacobi symbol -1, while y and $-y$ have Jacobi symbol $+1$.

The following assumption about the intractability of factoring is made throughout this subsection.

Intractability Assumption for Factoring (IAF): Let A be a probabilistic polynomial-time (factoring) algorithm. Then for all constants $c > 0$ and sufficiently large k

$$\mathbf{P}\big(n \leftarrow H_k(); x \leftarrow A(n) : x \text{ is a nontrivial divisor of } n \big) < \frac{1}{k^c}$$

(Here we have used the notation $n \leftarrow H_k()$ to denote the operation of selecting an element of H_k uniformly at random.)

Define $f_{0,n}$ and $f_{1,n}$ as follows:

$$f_{0,n}(x) = x^4 \pmod{n}$$

$$f_{1,n}(x) = 4x^4 \pmod{n}.$$

It is easy to prove that $f_{0,n}$ and $f_{1,n}$ are permutations of Q_n when $n \in H$.

Theorem: Under the IAF, the following algorithm G is a claw-free permutation pair generator. On input 1^k, G:
(1) Generates two random primes p and q of length k, where $p \equiv 3 \pmod{8}$ and $q \equiv 7 \pmod{8}$.
(2) Outputs the quintuple

$$(d, f_{0,n}, f_{0,n}^{-1}, f_{1,n}, f_{1,n}^{-1})$$

where
(a) Algorithm d generates elements uniformly at random in Q_n.
(b) Algorithms $f_{0,n}$ and $f_{1,n}$ are as described in the above equations.
(c) Algorithms $f_{0,n}^{-1}$ and $f_{1,n}^{-1}$ are algorithms for the inverse functions (these algorithms make use of p and q).

Proof: We first note that uniformly selecting k-bit guaranteed primes can be accomplished in expected polynomial (in k) time, by the recent work of Goldwasser and

Kilian [GK86], and that asymptotically one-quarter of these will be congruent to 3 (mod 8) (similarly for those congruent to 7 (mod 8)). (In practice, one would use a faster probabilistic primality test such as the one proposed by Solovay and Strassen [SS77] or Rabin [Ra80].)

Let $n \in H$ and $(d, f_{0,n}, f_{0,n}^{-1}, f_{1,n}, f_{1,n}^{-1}) \in [G(1^k)]$. First $f_{0,n}$ and $f_{1,n}$ are permutations. We then only need to show that if there exists a fast algorithm that finds x and y such that $x^4 \equiv 4y^4 \pmod{n}$ (i.e. a claw-creating algorithm) then factoring is easy. Suppose such an x and y have been found. Clearly, if x (or y) is not relatively prime with n, then the $gcd(x, n)$ (or $gcd(y, n)$) is a non-trivial divisor of n. Otherwise, $(x^2)^2 \equiv (2y^2)^2 \pmod{n}$. Since $x^2 \in Q_n$, $y^2 \in Q_n$, $2 \notin Q_n$, we have $2y^2 \notin Q_n$, so that $x^2 \not\equiv \pm 2y^2 \pmod{n}$. Thus $gcd(x^2 \pm 2y^2, n)$ will produce a nontrivial factor of n. ∎

VI.D. An Infinite Set of Pairwise Claw-Free Permutations

For our scheme we need not just claw-free pairs of permutations, but an infinite family of permutations which are pairwise claw-free and generated by a single claw-free pair f_0, f_1.

We define the function $f_i(\cdot)$ for any string $i \in \{0, 1\}^+$ by the equation:

$$f_i(x) = f_{i_0}(f_{i_1}(\ldots(f_{i_{d-1}}(f_{i_d}(x))\ldots)))$$

if $i = i_0 i_1 \ldots i_{d-1} i_d$. (Also, read f_i^{-1} as $(f_i)^{-1}$ so that $f_i^{-1}(f_i(x)) = x$.)

Each f_i is a trap-door permutation: it is easy to compute $f_i(x)$ given f_0, f_1, i, and x, and to compute $f_i^{-1}(x)$ if f_0^{-1} and f_1^{-1} are available. However, given only f_0 and f_1 it should be hard to invert f_i on a random input z, or else f_0 and f_1 do not form a trap-door pair. (By inverting f_i on z one also effectively inverts f_{i_0} on z, where i_0 is the first bit of i.)

This way of generating an infinite family of trap-door permutations was also used in [GMY83].

Looking ahead, we shall see that a user A of our scheme can use the f_i's to perform basic authentication steps as follows. Let us presume that A has published f_0 and f_1 as part of his public key, and has kept their inverses f_0^{-1} and f_1^{-1} secret. If user A is known to have authenticated a string y, then by publishing strings i and x such that

$$f_i(x) = y,$$

he thereby authenticates the new strings i and x.

For this to work, when the signer A reveals $f_i^{-1}(y)$ he should not enable anyone else to compute $f_j^{-1}(y)$ for any other j.

The signer achieves this in our scheme by coding i using a prefix-free mapping $\langle \cdot \rangle$. This prevents an enemy from computing $f_{\langle j \rangle}^{-1}(x)$ from $f_{\langle i \rangle}^{-1}(x)$ in an obvious way since $\langle j \rangle$ is never a prefix of $\langle i \rangle$. The following Lemma 1 shows that this approach is not only necessary but sufficient.

Note: A mapping $\langle \cdot \rangle$ is prefix-free iff for any pair of distinct strings i, j, we have that $\langle i \rangle$ is not a prefix of $\langle j \rangle$. Any prefix-free encoding into binary is usable if it is polynomial-time computable and if the length of x and the length of $\langle x \rangle$ are polynomially related. For concreteness, we suggest coding each 0 as 00, each 1 as 11, and terminating the encoding with 01. One can encode tuples of strings $a_1, \ldots, a_n$ as the string 10 followed by the concatenation of the encodings of $a_1, \ldots, a_n$ (each terminated with 01 as usual), followed by a final occurrence of the string 10. We denote this encoding as $\langle a_1, \ldots, a_n \rangle$.

Lemma 1 essentially says that if (d, f_0, f_1) is a claw-free pair, then it will be hard to find two different strings i and j, and elements x and y such that $f_{<i>}(x) = f_{<j>}(y)$.

Lemma 1: Let $f = (d, f_0, f_1)$ be a claw-free pair, x and y be elements of $[d()]$ and i, j two different binary strings such that $f_{<i>}(x) = f_{<j>}(y)$. Then, there exists an f-claw (x_1, x_2, x_3) where x_1, x_2, x_3 are in $\{f_c(x), f_c(y) : c$ is a prefix of $<i>\}$.

Proof: Let $z = f_{<i>}(x) = f_{<j>}(y)$. Let $<i> = i_0 i_1 \ldots i_a$, $<j> = j_0 j_1 \ldots j_b$. Without loss of generality assume $a \leq b$. Let m denote the smallest natural number such that $i_m \neq j_m$. ($m < a$ as $< \cdot >$ is a prefix-free encoding). If $m = 0$, then trivially $f_{i_m \ldots i_a}(x) = f_{j_m \ldots j_b}(y)$. Otherwise,

$$f_{i_m \ldots i_a}(x) = f_{i_0 \ldots i_{m-1}}^{-1}(z) = f_{j_0 \ldots j_{m-1}}^{-1}(z) = f_{j_m \ldots j_b}(y)$$

Thus, setting $x_1 \leftarrow f_{i_{m+1} \ldots i_a}(x)$, $x_2 \leftarrow f_{j_{m+1} \ldots j_b}(y)$, and $x_3 \leftarrow f_{i_m}(x_1) = f_{j_m}(x_2)$, we obtain an f-claw (x_1, x_2, x_3). ∎

VII. BUILDING BLOCKS FOR SIGNING

In this section we define the basic building blocks needed for describing our signature scheme. In section VIII, we will define what a signature is and how to sign, using the objects and data structures introduced here.

We begin by defining the essential notion of an f-item.

Definition: Let $f = (d_f, f_0, f_1)$ be a claw-free pair. A tuple of strings $(t, r; c_1, \ldots, c_m)$ is an f-*item* if

$$f_{(c_1, \ldots, c_m)}(t) = r$$

Definition: In an f-item $(t, r; c_1, \ldots, c_m)$,
- t is called the *tag* of the item,
- r is called the *root* of the item, and
- the c_i's are the *children* of the item. We note that the children are ordered, so that we can speak of the first child or the second child of the item.

Note that given a claw free pair f and a tuple it is easy to check if the tuple is an f-item by applying the appropriate $f_{(i)}$ to the tag, and checking if the correct root is obtained.

Figure 2 gives a graphic representation of an f-item $(t, r; c_1, c_2)$ with two children and another f-item $(\bar{t}, \bar{r}; \bar{c})$ with one child.

Definition: We say that a sequence of f-items $L_k, L_{k-1}, \ldots, L_1$ is an f-*chain ending at* y if, for $i = 1, \ldots, k - 1$, the root of L_{i+1} is one of the children of L_i and y is the root of L_1. We say the chain *starts at* x if x is one of the children of the item L_k.

For efficiency considerations, our signature scheme will organize a collection of a special type of f-chains in the tree-like structure defined below.

Definition: Let i be a binary string of length k, f a claw free pair, and $Y_i = \{j | j \in \{0, 1\}^*, j \leq i\}$. An f-i-*tree* is a bijection T_i^f between Y_i and a set of f-items such that:
(1) if string $j \in S_i$ has length less than k, then $T_i^f(j)$ is an f-item with exactly two children; otherwise $T_i^f(j)$ has exactly one child. The latter f-items are called *bridge items*.
(2) if c_1 and c_2 are, respectively, the first and second child of $T_i^f(j)$, then c_1 is the root of $T_i^f(j0)$ and c_2 the root of $T_i^f(j1)$.

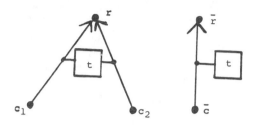

Figure 2. f-items

The *root* of T_i^f is the root of the f-item $T_i^f(\epsilon)$, where ϵ is the empty string. The *nodes* of T_i^f are the children of the f-items $T_i^f(j)$ where $j \in S_i$. The *internal nodes* of T_i^f are the children of the f-items $T_i^f(j)$ where $j \in S_i$ is of length less than k. The *leafs* of T_i^f are the children of f-items $T_i^f(j)$ where $j \in S_i$ is of length k. Node j (or leaf j) is the child of $T_i^f(j)$.

Figure 3 gives a graphic representation of an f-101-tree. (Node and leaf names are shown.)

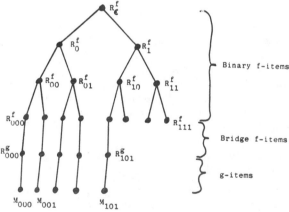

Figure 3. An f-101-tree

VIII. DESCRIPTION OF OUR SIGNATURE SCHEME

VIII.A Message Spaces

The security properties of the new signatures scheme hold for any nonempty message space $M \subset \{0, 1\}^+$.

VIII.B How to Generate Keys

We assume the existence of a claw-free permutation pair generator G.
The key-generation algorithm K runs as follows on inputs 1^k and B:

(1) K runs G twice on input 1^k to secretly and randomly select two quintuples

$$(d_f, f_0, f_0^{-1}, f_1, f_1^{-1}), \text{ and } (d_g, g_0, g_0^{-1}, g_1, g_1^{-1}) \in [G(1^k)].$$

(2) K then randomly selects $R_\epsilon^f \in [d_f()]$.
(3) K outputs a public key consisting of the tuple $(1^k, f, R_\epsilon^f, g, B)$ where $f = (d_f, f_0, f_1)$ and $g = (d_g, g_0, g_1)$.
(4) K outputs a secret key consisting of the quadruple $(f_0^{-1}, f_1^{-1}, g_0^{-1}, g_1^{-1})$.

VIII.C What Is a Signature

A *signature* of M with respect to a public key $(1^k, f, R_\epsilon^f, g, B)$ consists of:

(1) An f-chain of length $b + 1$ starting at R^g and ending at R_ϵ^f, and
(2) A g-item with R^g as its root and M as its only child.

VIII.C HOW TO SIGN

In the remainder of this section we shall presuppose that user A's public key is $PK = (1^k, f, R_\epsilon^f, g, B)$ where $f = (d_f, f_0, f_1)$ and $g = (d_g, g_0, g_1)$. User A's secret key is $SK = (f_0^{-1}, f_1^{-1}, g_0^{-1}, g_1^{-1})$. We shall let D_f denote $[d_f()]$ and similarly let D_g denote $[d_g()]$, the respective domains of the f_i's and the g_i's of user A's public key.

Without loss of generality we make the following assumptions:

- There is a polynomial in k bounding the length of the messages to be signed by user A.
- The outputs of d_f and d_g are strings of length $O(k)$.
- The value of B (the bound on the number of signatures that can be produced) is a power of 2: $B = 2^b$.

Conceptually, user A creates an f-1^b-tree T, which has 2^b leaves. The root of T will be R_ϵ^f. The internal nodes of T are randomly selected elements of D_f. The leaves of T are randomly selected elements of D_g.

Let M_i be the i-th message to be signed by user A. Integer i is represented by a binary string of length b with possible leading 0's.

To sign M_i, user A computes a g-item $G_i = (T_i^g, R_i^g; M_i^g)$ whose root $R_i^g \in D_g$ is the ith leaf of T, and whose only child is the message M_i. He now outputs, as the signature of M_i, G_i and the f-chain in T starting at leaf R_i^g and ending at root R_ϵ^f.

In practice, it will be undesirable for user A to precompute and store all of T. He will instead "grow" T as needed and try to optimize her use of storage and time. This is taken into account by our signing procedure. In what follows, we describe a variation of our signing method that requires the signer to remember just his secret key and his most recently produced signature, in order to produce his next signature.

Assume user A has already signed messages $M_0, M_1, \ldots, M_{i-1}$.

The Signing Procedure (also called SP): The input for this procedure is M_i – the ith message to to be signed.

We presume that the procedure is initialized with the values of the public key PK and the corresponding secret key SK in its local private storage, and that it keeps track of the number of previous messages signed (i.e. the variable $i = i_0 \ldots i_{b-1}$ which is a b-long bit string, which may contain leading 0's), and the most recent signature produced.

To compute a signature for message M_i, user A performs the following steps. Let t to be the length of the longest prefix common to i and $i-1$. (In the case that $i = 0^b$ we set $t = -1$.)

(1) *(Output f-items in common with previous signature.)* He outputs the first t f-items in the stored signature of M_{i-1}.

(2) *(Output new f-items in f-tree.)* For every string $j \in \{i_0 \ldots i_k | k = t, ..., b-2\}$, user A creates and outputs an f-item $F(j)$. He does this in order of increasing length of j. The f-item $F(j)$ is created as follows: Its root, denoted by R_j^f, is the R_ϵ^f from the public key $j = \epsilon$, otherwise it is the i_k-th child of the most recently output item where k is the length of j. The children R_{j0}^f and R_{j1}^f of the f-item with root R_j^f are chosen at random from D_f. The tag T_j^f for the item is computed using the secret trap-door information for inverting f_0 and f_1. Note that the last item produced has R_i^f as one of its children.

(3) *(Output bridge f-item.)* User A next outputs a single f-item with root R_i^f and an only child R_i^g, where R_i^g has been chosen randomly from D_g. The tag T_i^f for this item is computed using the secret trap-door information for inverting f_0 and f_1.

(4) *(Output g-item.)* Finally, user A outputs a g-item with R_i^g as its root and M_i as its only child. The tag T_i^g for this item is computed using the secret trap-door information for inverting g_0 and g_1.

The items output by the above procedure constitute a signature for M_i. Notice that there are many possible signatures (among which A chooses one at random) for each occurrence of each message, but only one signature is actually output.

The reader may verify that the above procedure for producing a signature will have a total running time which is bounded by a polynomial in k and b.

Notice that if A has signed i messages, the function F mapping strings $j \leq i$ to f-items $F(j)$ is an f-i-tree.

VIII.F. How to Verify a Signature

Given A's public key $(d_f, f_0, f_1, R_\epsilon^f, d_g, g_0, g_1, B)$, anyone can easily verify that each item in the signature for M_i is a proper item, and thus can easily check that the set of all the items in the signature (except the last) form an f-chain of length $b+1$ starting at R_i^f and ending at R_ϵ^f, and that the last item in the signature has R_i^g as its root and has M_i as its only child. If these checks are all satisfied, the given signature is accepted as an authentic signature by A of the message M_i.

It is easy to confirm that these operations take time proportional to b times some polynomial in k.

VIII.G. Efficiency of the Proposed Signature Scheme

The time to compute a signature for a message M of length m is is $O(bk)$ f-inversions (i.e. inversions of f_0 or f_1) and $O(m)$ g-inversions. (Another relevant measure of efficiency is "ammortized" time. That is, the time used for producing all possible B signatures divided by B. In ours scheme, the ammortized cost for the f-inversions is $O(k)$. The ammortized cost for the g-inversions is $O(k)$ if the average length of a message is k).

The length of the signature for M is $O(bk+m)$, as M is included as the child of the g-item produced in M's signature. Clearly, if M is known to the signature recepient, the g item need not include M and the length of the signature can be only $O(bk)$ long, which is independent of the length of M and possibly much shorter. The memory required by the signing algorithm is $O(bk)$ since it consists of storing (the f-items in) the most recently produced signature.

IX. PROOF OF SECURITY

Recall that a signature scheme is existentially forgeable if the enemy is able to produce *any* new valid messsage/signature pairs. Also recall that in an adaptive chosen message attack the enemy can repeatedly use the real signer as an "oracle" before attempting to forge a new signature.

We strengthen the definition of existentially forgable to include probabilistic success on part of the forger.

Definition: We say that a signature scheme is ϵ-*existentially forgeable* if it is existentially foregeable with probability ϵ where the probability space includes the random choices of the adaptive chosen message attack, the random choices made by the legal signer in the creation of the public key, and the random choice made by the legal signer in producing signatures.

It is very important to note that the random choices made in creating the public key are included in the probability space; our proof depends critically on this definition. The main theorem of this paper is the following.

Main Theorem. Assuming that claw-free permutation pair generators exist, the signature scheme described in section VIII is not even $\frac{1}{Q(k)}$-existentially forgeable under an adaptive chosen message attack, for all polynomials Q and for all sufficiently large k.

The idea of the the proof will be to assume that there exists an adaptive chosen message attack which enables the enemy to later forge valid signatures, and then derive a contradiction by showing that this attack would enable an enemy to create either an f-claw or a g-claw with sufficiently high probability.

(The details of the proof are omitted in this extended abstract; they will appear in the journal version of this paper.)

X. Variations and Improvements

In this section we describe ways to improve the efficiency of the proposed signature scheme without affecting its security.

X.A Not including the message in the signature

As defined above, the signature for a message M includes a copy of M itself (in the g-item that authenticates M). This is redundant and can be eliminated, since one may reasonably assume that the signature and message are transmitted and stored together. To implement this idea, instead of including the entire g-item in the signature, only its tag is included.

With this modification, the length of the signature becomes only a function of k and B, and is independent of the length of the message being signed. Thus signatures are compact even if the messages are much longer than k.

The length of the signature if the signing variation A is used is just

$$O(b \cdot k).$$

X.B. Using g_i's to sign rather than g_i^{-1}'s.

This variation is of interest if it is substantially easier to compute g_0 or g_1 than to compute their inverses. In this case steps (3) and (4) in the signing procedure can be replaced by:

(3) *(Output g-item.)* User A selects a random $T_i^g \in D_g$, and (using g_0 and g_1) computes the root R_i^g of the g-item $(T_i^g, R_i^g; M_i)$, and outputs this item.

(4) *(Output bridge f-item.)* Using his knowledge of f_0^{-1} and f_1^{-1}, user A outputs an f-item with root R_i^f and an only child R_i^g.

Now each usage of g_0^{-1} or g_1^{-1} has been replaced by a usage of g_0 or g_1.

Although one might be tempted to use this variation using one-way permutations instead of trap-door permutations for the g_i's, this temptation should be resisted, since our proof of security does not hold if this change is made.

X.C Fast iterated square roots

As we saw in section VI.C, if factoring is computationally hard a particular family of trap-door permutations is claw-free. By using these permutations in a straightforward manner, one obtains a particular instance of our signature scheme. Let us discuss its efficiency of this instance. The computation of f_0^{-1}, f_1^{-1}, g_0^{-1}, and g_1^{-1} consists of computing a forth-root modulo a Blum-integer n (more precisely the forth-root that is a quadratic residue). If n is k-bit long, this can be done in $O(k^3)$ steps. Thus the signature of a k-bit message can be computed in time $O(b \cdot k^4)$, or in $O(k^4)$ ammortized time.

This particular instance of our scheme can be improved in a manner suggested in discussions with Oded Goldreich (see [Go86] – we appreciate his permission to quote these results here). The improvement relates to the computation of $f_{\langle y \rangle}^{-1}(x)$ (or $g_{\langle y \rangle}^{-1}(x)$).

We note first of all that taking forth roots modulo n is equivalent to taking u-th powers modulo n, where $u \cdot 4 \equiv 1 \pmod{\phi(n)}$, and where $\phi(n)$ is Euler's phi function. More generally, to find a 4^m-th root w of x modulo n one can raise x to the v-th power modulo n, where $v \equiv u^m \pmod{\phi(n)}$. Computing w by first computing v and then raising x to the v-th power is substantially faster than repeatedly taking square roots.

To apply this observation, we note that the functions f defined in section VI.C. satisfy

$$f_{\langle y \rangle}^{-1}(x) = \left(\frac{x}{4^{rev(\langle y \rangle)}}\right)^{4^{-m}},$$

where "rev" is the operation which reverses strings and interprets the result as an integer, where m is the length of $\langle y \rangle$, and where all operations are performed modulo n. The only computationally difficult portion here is computing a 4^m-th root. Using the observation of the previous paragraph, the computation of such an f-inverse can be performed in time proportional to the cube of the length of n, in the case that messages have the same length k as n. Using these ideas, the signature of a k-bit message can be computed in time $O(b \cdot k^3)$, or in $O(k^3)$ ammortized time.

X.D. "Memoryless" Version of the Proposed Signature Scheme

The concept of a *random function* was introduced by Goldreich, Goldwasser and Micali in [GGM84].

Let I_k denote the set of k-bit integers. Let W_k denote the set of all functions from I_k to I_k, and let $F_k \subseteq W_k$ be a set of functions from I_k to I_k. We say that $F = \bigcup_k F_k$ is a *poly-random* collection if:

(1) Each function in F_k has a unique k bit index associated with it. Furthermore, picking such an index at random (thereby picking an $f \in F_k$ at random) is easy.

(2) There exists a deterministic polynomial time algorithm that given as input as index of a function $f \in F_k$ and an argument x, computes $f(x)$.

(3) No probabilistic polynomial in k time algorithm can "distinguish" between W_k and F_k. Formally, let T be a probabilistic polynomial time algorithm, that on input k and access to an oracle O_f for a function $f : I_k \rightarrow I_k$ outputs 0 or 1. Then, for all T, for all polynomials Q, for all sufficiently large k, the difference between the probability that T outputs 1 on access to an oracle O_f when f was randomly picked in F_k and the probability that T outputs 1 on access to an oracle O_f when f was randomly picked in W_k is less than $1/Q(k)$.

In [GGM84] it was shown how to contruct a poly-random collection assuming the existence of one-way functions. The existence of claw-free permutation pairs is a stronger assumption, and thus implies the existence of a poly-random collection. See section V.D for an implementation of a claw-free family of functions based on factoring and [GGM84] for details on how to contruct a poly-random collection.

Leonid Levin suggested the following use of a poly-random collection in order to reduce the amount of storage that a signer must keep from $O(bk)$ to $O(b)$ bits. His suggestion also eliminates the need to generate new random numbers (e.g. R_i^g) during the signing process.

Let k denote the security parameter. In the secret key generation phase, in addition to computing the secret trap-door pairs (f_0^{-1}, f_1^{-1}), (g_0^{-1}, g_1^{-1}) user A also picks a random function h in a poly-random collection F_k, and keeps h secret. (We assume that $k > b$.) During the signing process, A keeps a counter i to denote the number of times the signing algorithm has been invoked. To sign message M_i, A signs as before, except that (using m to denote the length of j):

- Instead of picking values R_j^f at random from D_f, he *computes* them as $R_j^f = h(0^{k-m}j)$.
- Instead of picking values R_j^g at random from D_g, he *computes* them as $R_j^g = h(1^{k-m}j)$.

We claim that the "memoryless" version of the signature scheme described above enjoys the same security properties as our original scheme. The proof (which we shall not give in detail) is based on the observation that if the memoryless scheme was vulnerable to an adaptive chosen message attack, then it would be possible to efficiently distinguish pseudo-random functions from truly random functions.

A further improvement (due to Oded Goldreich [Go86]) removes even the necessity of remembering the number of previous signatures, by picking the index i for a message M as a random b-bit string. To make this work, the maximum number of signatures that can be produced by an instance of this scheme is limited to $2^{\sqrt{b}}$, so that it is extremely unlikely that two messages would have the same index chosen for them. The security proof can be modified to accomodate these changes. (Note that in the preprocessing step that builds an f-tree, we would now only build a portion of it consisting of $2^{\sqrt{b}}$ randomly chosen paths of length b.)

XI. Open Problems

- It is an open question whether the RSA scheme is universally forgeable under an adaptive chosen message attack.

- Can an encryption scheme be developed for which decryption is provably equivalent to factoring yet for which an adaptive chosen ciphertext attack is of no help to the enemy?

XII. Acknowledgements

We are most grateful for Leonid Levin for his suggestion of how to use random functions in our scheme, in order to (almost) completely eliminate the need of storage in our signature scheme.

We are also very grateful to Oded Goldreich for many valuable suggestions concerning the presentation of these results, and for suggesting the speed-up described in section IX.C.

We are also thankful to Avi Wigderson for helpful suggestions on the presentation of this research.

XIII. References

[BGMR85] Ben-Or, M., O. Goldreich, S. Micali, and R.L. Rivest, "A Fair Protocol for Signing Contracts," *Proc. 12-th ICALP Conference* (Napflion, Greece, July 1985), 43–52.

[Bl82] Blum, M. "Coin Flipping by Telephone," *Proc. IEEE Spring COMPCOM* (1982), 133-137.

[Bl83] Blum, M. "How to Exchange (Secret) Keys" *ACM Trans. Comp. Sys.* 1 (1983), 175–193.

[BD85] Brickell, E., and J. DeLaurentis, "An Attack on a Signature Scheme Proposed by Okamoto and Shiraishi," Proc. CRYPTO 85 (Springer 1986).

[Ch82] Chaum, D. "Blind Signatures and Untraceable Payments," Advance in Cryptography – Proceedings of CRYPTO 82, (Edited by Chaum, D., R. Rivest, and A. Sherman), (Plenum Press, New York 1983).

[De82] Denning, D. CRYPTOGRAPHY AND DATA SECURITY, (Addison Wesley, Reading, Mass., 1982).

[DH76] Diffie, W. and M. E. Hellman, "New Directions in Cryptography", *IEEE Trans. Info. Theory* IT-22 (Nov. 1976), 644-654.

[EAKMM85] Estes, D., L. Adleman, K. Kompella, K. McCurley, and G. Miller, "Breaking the Ong-Schnorr-Shamir Signature Scheme for Quadratic Number Fields," *Proc. CRYPTO 85*, to appear.

[EG84] El-Gamal, T., "A Public Key Cryptosystem and a Signature Scheme Based on Discrete Logarithms", *Proceedings of Crypto 84* (Springer 1985), 10–18.

[EGL82] Even, S., O. Goldreich, and A. Lempel, "A Randomized Protocol for Signing Contracts", *Advances in Cryptology – Proceedings of Crypto 82*, (Plenum Press, New York, 1983), 205-210.

[GGM84] Goldreich, O., Goldwasser, S., and S. Micali, "How to Contruct Random Functions," *Proc. 25th Annual IEEE Symposium on Foundations of Computer Science*, (Florida, November 1984.)

[Go86]   Goldreich, Oded, "Two Remarks Concerning the GMR Signature Scheme," (Manuscript in preparation).

[GK86]   Goldwasser, S., and J. Kilian, "Almost All Primes Can be Quickly Certified," *Proc. 18-th ACM STOC Conference* (Berkely, 1986).

[GM82]   Goldwasser, S., and S. Micali, "Probabilistic Encryption," *JCSS* **28** (April 1984), 270-299.

[GMR84]   Goldwasswer, S., S. Micali, and R. L. Rivest, "A 'Paradoxical' Solution to the Signature Problem," *Proc. 25-th IEEE FOCS Conference* (Singer Island, 1984), 441-448.

[GMY83]   Goldwasser, S., S. Micali, and A. Yao, "Strong Signature Schemes," *Proc. 15th Annual ACM Symposium on Theory of Computing,* (Boston Massachusetts, April 1983), 431-439.

[La79]   Lamport, L. "Constructing Digital Signatures from a One-Way Function," SRI Intl. CSL-98. (Oct. 1979)

[Li81]   Lieberherr, K. "Uniform Complexity and Digital Signatures," *Theoretical Computer Science* **16**,1 (Oct. 1981), 99-110.

[LM78]   Lipton, S., and S. Matyas, "Making the Digital Signature Legal – and Safeguarded," *Data Communications* (Feb. 1978), 41-52.

[Ma79]   Matyas, S. "Digital Signatures – An Overview," *Computer Networks* **3** (April 1979) 87-94.

[MH78]   Merkle, R., and M. Hellman, "Hiding Information and Signatures in Trap-Door Knapsacks," *IEEE Trans. Infor. Theory* IT-24 (Sept. 1978), 525-530.

[Me79]   Merkle, Ralph "Secrecy, Authentication, and Public-Key Systems," Stanford Electrical Engineering Ph.D. Thesis ISL SEL 79-017.

[MM82]   Meyer, C. and S. Matyas, CRYPTOGRAPHY: A NEW DIMENSION IN DATA SECURITY (Wiley, New York, 1982)

[MGR84]   Micali, S., S. Goldwasser, and C. Rackoff, "The Knowledge Complexity of Interactive Proof Systems," Proc. 17th Annual ACM Symposium on Theory of Computing, (Providence, R.I., May 1985), 291-304.

[OS85]   Okamoto, T., and A. Shiraishi, "A Fast Signature Scheme Based on Quadratic Inequalities," Proc. 1985 Symp. on Security and Privacy (Oakland, April 1985).

[OSS84a]   Ong, H., C. Schnorr, and A. Shamir, "An Efficient Signature Scheme Based on Quadratic Equations," *Proc. 16th Annual ACM Symposium on Theory of Computing,* (Washington, D.C., April 1984), 208-217.

[OSS84b]   Ong, H., C. Schnorr, and A. Shamir, "An Efficient Signature Scheme Based on Polynomial Equations," *Proc. CRYPTO 84* (Springer 1985), 37–46.

[Po84]   Pollard, J. "How to Break The 'OSS' Signature Scheme", Private Communication (1984).

[Ra78]   Rabin, Michael, "Digitalized Signatures," In FOUNDATIONS OF SECURE COMPUTATION, (Edited by R. A. DeMillo, D. Dobkin,

A. Jones, and R. Lipton), (Academic Press, New York, 1978), 133-153.

[Ra79] Rabin, Michael. "Digitalized Signatures as Intractable as Factorization," MIT Laboratory for Computer Science Technical Report MIT/LCS/TR-212 (Jan. 1979).

[Ra80] Rabin, Michael. "Probabilistic Algorithms for Testing Primality," *J. Number Theory*, **12** (1980), 128-138.

[RV83] Reif, J. and L. Valiant, "A logarithmic time sort for linear size networks," *Proceedings 15th Annual ACM Symposium on Theory of Computing*, (Boston Massachusetts, April 1983), 10-16.

[RSA78] Rivest, R., A. Shamir, and L. Adleman, "A Method for Obtaining Digital Signatures and Public-Key Cryptosystems," *Comm. of the ACM* (Feb. 1978), 120-126.

[Sh78] Shamir, A., "A Fast Signature Scheme," MIT Laboratory for Computer Science Technical Memo MIT/LCS/TM-107 (July 1978).

[Sh82] Shamir, A., "A Polynomial Time Algorithm for Breaking the Basic Merkle-Hellman Cryptosystem," *Proc. 23rd Annual IEEE FOCS Conference* (Nov. 1982), 145-152.

[SS77] Solovay, R., and V. Strassen, "A Fast Monte-Carlo Test for Primality," *SIAM J. Computing*, **6** (1977), 84-85.

[Tu84] Tulpan, Y., "Fast Cryptanalysis of a Fast Signature System," Master's Thesis in Applied Mathematics, Weizmann Institute. (1984)

[Wi80] Williams, H. C., "A Modification of the RSA Public-Key Cryptosystem," *IEEE Trans. Info. Theory* **IT-26** (Nov. 1980), 726-729.

[Yu79] Yuval, G., "How to Swindle Rabin," *Cryptologia* **3** (July 1979), 187-189.

Are problems having a polynomial time upper

bound actually thought to be feasible ?

Akeo ADACHI

Science Institute, IBM Japan Ltd.

5-19 Sanban-cho, Chiyoda-ku, Tpkyo 102

and

Takumi KASAI

Dept. of Computer Science

Univ. of Electro-communications

1-5-1 Chofugaoka, Chofu-shi, Tokyo 182

Abstract   An indexing Turing machine is introduced as a simple and very strong computation model that simulates multi-tape Turing machines and random access machines effectively. In fact we show that $T(n)$ time bounded random access machines under logarithmic cost criterion can be simulated by indexing Turing machines in $O(T(n)\log T(n))$ time. We can also show that $T(n)$ time bounded multi-tape Turing machines can be simulated by indexing Turing machines in $O(T(n)\log T(n))$ time. In this paper, we proved a lower bound of $(2k + 1)$ -pebble game problem is n^k. This is a concrete problem which has a polynomial time lower bound, but is considered to be infeasible.

1.Introduction

It is one of the significant points in complexity theory to find concrete polynomial lower bounds with a rigid degree of the polynomial. It was shown that for each $\varepsilon > 0, k > 0, k$ -pebble game problem cannot be solved in $O(n^{(k-1)/2-\varepsilon})$ time on single-tape Turing machines [1, 2], and lower bounds for several games have been obtained on single-tape Turing machines by using k -pebble games.   From the fact that $T(n)$ time bounded multi-tape Turing machines can be simulated by single-tape Turing machines in $O(T^2(n))$ time and $T(n)$ time bounded random access machines can be simulated by multi-tape Turing machines in $O(T^2(n))$ time, we can get lower bounds of the k -pebble game problem on multi-tape Turing machines and random access machines as

DISCRETE ALGORITHMS AND
COMPLEXITY

311

$O(n^{(k-1)/4})$ time and $O(n^{(k-1)/8})$ time , respectively. However, these results cannot be considered as better lower bounds on multi-tape Turing machines or random access machines. These come from the rough relations between single-tape Turing machines and multi-tape Turing machines [5], and multi-tape Turing machines and random access machines [6].

In this paper, we introduce indexing Turing machines (ITM), and show that $T(n)$ time bounded random access machines under logarithmic cost criterion can be simulated by ITM in $O(T(n)\log T(n))$ time. We can also show that $T(n)$ time bounded multi-tape Turing machines can be simulated by ITM in $O(T(n)\log T(n))$ time. As is mentioned, ITM is a simple and very strong model of machines that can simulate multi-tape Turing machines and random access machines effectively. Thus lower bounds on ITM gives better lower bounds on multi-tape Turing machines and random access machines.

In fact, we show that the k -pebble game problem cannot be solved in $O(n^{(k-1)/2-\varepsilon})$ time on ITM for any $\varepsilon > 0$. Thus a lower bound of the k -pebble game problem is $O(n^{(k-1)/2})$ time both on multi-tape Turing machines and random access machines.

2. Preliminaries

(i) Indexing Turing Machines

An indexing Turing machine is a Turing machine which has a main tape and two auxiliary tapes, one is called the index tape and one is called the work tape, each of these tapes has the left end marker in the left-most cell of the tape as is depicted in Fig.2.1. The read/write head position of the main tape is directed by the content of the index tape. The work tape is used to modify the content of the index tape.

Whenever the content of the index tape is changed, the tape head of the main tape jumps to the position indicated by the index tape.

The tape symbols written on the index and the work tape are #, 0, 1, and blank$B$. The symbol # is written only in the left-most position on the tape, and no symbol except blank can be written on the right to a blank symbol B. A configuration is a six tuple $C = (q, u, h, i, j, w)$, where q is a state, u is the content of the main tape, h denotes the position of the index tape, i denotes the content of the index tape, j denotes the position of the work tape, and w is the content of the work tape. A surface configuration of C is a six tuple $C' = (q, a, h, b, j, d)$, where a is a character in the position on the main tape indicated by the content of the index tape (i.e., the i th character of the input) b denotes the h th character on the index tape, and d denotes the j th character on the work tape.

Note that a surface configuration has enough information for determinig the next move of M. The accepting surface configuration is a surface configuration with the state q being an accepting state.

(ii) Random Access Machines

A random access machine has a countable number of registers $X_0, X_1, \ldots$, and X_0 is called the accumulator. Here we consider a RAM under logarithmic cost criterion.

Let $\lg n$ be defined as follows:

$$\lg n = \begin{cases} \lceil \log n \rceil, & \text{if } n \geq 2 \\ 1, & \text{otherwise} \end{cases}$$

Instructions and their execution time (costs) are defined in Table 2.1, where i and $c(i)$ denote the register number and the content of the register i, respectively. Let $\Sigma = \{a_1, \ldots, a_k\}$.

Given an input $a_{i_1} \ldots a_{i_n}$ in Σ^*, the RAM starts running with $i_1, \ldots, i_n$ setting on register $1, \ldots, n$ and other registers zero.

A RAM accepts an input x if the content of the accumulator is zero when the RAM terminates, otherwise rejects.

(iii) k -pebble game problem [3]

A k -pebble game is a quadruple $G = (X, R, S, t)$ where

(1) X is a finite set of nodes.

(2) $R \subset \{(x, y, z) \mid x, y, z \in X, x \neq y, y \neq z, z \neq x\}$ is called a set of rules,

(3) S is a subset of X; the number of nodes in S is called the rank of G,

(4) t is a node in X, called the terminal node.

A pebble game of rank k is simply called k-pebble game.

A pebble game is played by two players, P_1 and P_2, who alternately move pebbles on the pebble game, with P_1 playing first.

At the begining of the pebble game, pebbles are placed on all nodes of S.

If $(x, y, z) \in R$, and pebbles are placed on x, y, but not on z, then the pebble on x can be moved to z. The winner is the player who puts a pebble on the terminal node or makes the other player unable to move. A k -pebble game problem is the problem to determine whether the first player has a forced-win in k -pebble game.

(iv) Two-person game [1]

A two-person game G is a triple $G = (X, E, s)$, where:

(1) X is a finite set, an element of X is called a position,

(2) E is a subset of $X \times X$, an element of E is called a rule, we write $x \to y$ for an element (x, y) of E,

(3) s, in X, is called the starting position.

At the begining of the game, the first player is in position s. If $(x, y) \in E$ for any $x, y \in E$, then a player in his turn may move the position x to the position y.

The winner is the player who makes the other player unable to move.

3. Results

Theorem 1. Let a language A be accepted by a RAM in time $T(n)$. Then there exists an ITM M accepting the language A such that

(1) M is $O(T(n)\log T(n))$ time bounded,

(2) The space bound of the main tape of M is $O(T(n)\log T(n))$,

(3) The space bound of auxiliary tapes is $O(\log T(n))$.

Proof. The main tape of ITM is divided into 4 tracks, which is depicted as Fig.3.1. Track 1 holds contents of the registers that have been used. Track 2 holds the positions of the registers on track 1 , and has the data as linked list structure, each of which, called the node, is the form of;

j

link (j)	link (j)	entry (j)

Let the binary representation of integer i be $i = i_1 i_2 \ldots i_k$.

Suppose that the register i was used. Then there exists integers $j_1, j_2, \ldots, j_k$, such that

(1) $j_1 = \text{IFIRST}, \quad j_2 = \text{link} i_1(j_1), \quad j_3 = \text{link} i_2(j_2), \quad \ldots, \quad j_k = \text{link} i_{k-1}(j_{k-1}), \quad e = \text{entry}(j_k)$.

(2) The content of the register i is stored on the first track begining from the position e.

The position e is called the entry of the register i. Track 3 is used for four fields called as IFIRST, ITOP, DTOP, and TEMP. IFIRST contains the position of the list head on the track 2. The content of the ITOP is the position of the right-most cell used on the second track. DTOP contains the position of the right-most cell used on the first track. TEMP field is used for storing the content of register i temporarily when indirect addressing is used. ACC on track 4 is the content of the accumulator.

We consider here the simulation of STORE i and LOAD* i by an indexing Turing machine M.

Simulation of STORE i

M stores the content of ACC into the cells begining from the cell indicated by DTOP, then M modifies the list structure such that the entry of the register i points to the DTOP, and modifies the content of DTOP.

Simulation of LOAD*i

M scans the list on the second track and M finds the entry of register i. M copies the content of the register i to TEMP by character-wise way.

Let the entry of the register i be e and the content of the register i be j. Copying into TEMP is performed by at most $O(|e| \times |j|)$ steps, where $|e|$ and $|j|$ denotes the length of strings e and j. M scans over the list and if finds the corresponding entry to j, M copies the content to ACC, and if M does not find the entry, M sets zero to ACC.

We show that the ITM takes at most $O(T \log T)$ time for the simulation of T time bounded RAM under logarithmic cost criterion.

Then there exists a constant d that satifies the followings:

(1)   the value of $DTOP \leq T$,

(2)   the value of $ITOP \leq T \log T$,

(3)   the time required to simulate $\leq d T \log T$.

In logarithmic cost criterion, the cost of performing each instruction on RAM is proportional to the length of data moved. Since DTOP is at most the total length of data moved, (1) holds. Since the length of each node is at most $\log T(n)$, (2) holds. Finally, for finding the entry of each register i, ITM searches the linked list on track 2 in $O(\log T)$ steps. Thus (3) holds.

Theorem 2. Let A be a language accepted in $T(n)$ time by a multi-tape Turing machine. Then there exists an ITM M that accepts A such that

(1) M is $O(T(n) \log T(n))$ time bounded,

(2) The main tape of M is $T(n) \log T(n)$ space bounded,

(3) The auxiliary tapes of M are $\lceil \log T(n) \rceil$ space bounded.

Sketch of the proof. Assume that the multi-tape Turing machine M_1 has the configuration as Fig.3.2. We construct an ITM M_2 with a main tape of $(k + 1)$ tracks as Fig.3.3. The head position of each tape of M_1 is written on the $(k + 1)$ th track of the main tape of M_2. M_2 copies i_j to the index tape, and then the i_j th symbol of the track j is stored in the finite control of M_2. After M_2 has scanned all the symbols indicated by $i_j (1 \leq j \leq k)$, M_2 has enough information to simulate one move of M_1. Since the length of each i_j is $log T(n)$, each move of M_1 is simulated in $O(log T(n))$ time. Thus M_1 is simulated by M_2 in $O(T(n)log T(n))$ time.

Let ITM (T(n)) be the set of languages accepted by ITM M $= (Q, \Sigma, \Gamma, \delta, q, b, F)$ which satisfies the following conditions:

(1) M is $T(n)$ time bounded,

(2) the main tape of M is $T(n)$ space bounded,

(3) the auxiliary tapes are $\rceil log T(n) \lceil$ space bounded.

    Theorem 3. $(2k + 1)$ -pebble game problem $\notin$ ITM $(n^{k-\varepsilon})$.

    Outline of the proof. Let L be an arbitrary element of ITM (n^k). Let L be a subset of Σ^*. For any $x = x_0 x_1 \ldots x_{n-1} (x_i \in \Sigma)$, it suffices to show that we can construct $(2k + 1)$-pebble game G_x such that;

(1) $x \in L$ iff the first player has a forced-win in G_x.

(2) the construction of G_x is performed in time $O(n \log n)$ from M and x.

We construct a two-person game G_x' for given $x = x_0 x_1 \ldots x_{n-1} (x_i \in \Sigma)$ such that $x \in L$ if and only if the first player has a forced-win in G_x'.

Let $G_x' = (X \cup \{\$,s\}, E, s)$.

X consists of positions:

$< t, i, C, \ell >$, $< t, i, a, \ell >$, $< t, h, b, \ell >'$, $< t, j, d, \ell >''$, where $0 < t, i < n^k$, C is a surface configuration, $\ell \in \{0, 1, 2\}$, $0 \leq h, j \leq k log n$, and $b, d \in \{\#, 0, 1, B\}$.

ℓ is an auxiliary parameter to distinguish which player's position it is. If ℓ is 0 or 2, the position belongs to the first player, otherwise to the second player.

The necessary and sufficient condition for the first player to have a forced-win at any position $< , , ,0 >$ described by the following table :

position	the position for the first player to have a forced-win
$< t, i, C, 0 >$	at time t, the content of the index tape is i, and the surface configuration is C
$< t, i, a, 0 >$	at time t, the i-th character on the main tape is, a
$< t, h, b, 0 \overset{\prime}{>}$	at time t, the h-th character on the index tape is, b
$< t, j, d, 0 \overset{\prime\prime}{>}$	at time t, the j-th character on the work tape is, d

$ denotes the distinguished position. There is no rule to move this position to any other position. Thus a player who has this position loses the game. E, the set of rules, is defined as follows:

1. For each t, i $(0 \le t, i \le n^k)$ and each accepting surface configuration C, E contains

$$s \to \; < t, i, C, 1 >.$$

These are the first rules the first player selects.

2. Rules for position $< t, i, C, 1 >$.

For each t, i $(0 \le t, i \le n^k)$ and each surface configuration $C = (q, a, h, j, d)$, E contains

2.1 $< t, i, C, 1 > \; \to \; < t, i, C, 0 >,$

2.2 $< t, i, C, 1 > \; \to \; < t, i, a, 0 >,$

2.3 $< t, i, C, 1 > \; \to \; < t, j, d, 0 >'',$

2.4 $< t, i, C, 1 > \; \to \; < t, h, b, 0 >',$

2.5 Let the binary representation of i be $i_w \ldots i_2 i_1$.

For each r $(1 \le r \le w)$, E contains

$$< t, i, C, 1 > \; \to \; < t, r, i_r, 0 >'.$$

Assume that the second player has the position $< t, i, C, 1 >$. Rules are constructed such that the second player has a forced-win at position $< t, i, C, 1 >$ if the content of the index tape at time t is not i, or the surface configuration at time t is not C. The second player has a forced-win, by the rule 2.2 if the i th character of the main tape is not a, by rule 2.3 if the j th character of the index tape is not d, by rule 2.4 if the h th character character of the work tape is not b, by rule 2.5 if the content of the index tape is not i, respectively.

3. Rules for position $< t, i, C, 0 >$.

For each t, i, i' $(0 < t < n^k, 0 \le i, i' < n^k)$ and surface configurations C, C' such that $C' \vdash C$, E contains

$$< t, i, C, 0 > \ \rightarrow \ < t - 1, i', C', 1 >.$$

4. Rules for position $< t, i, a, 1 >$.

For each t, i, a $(0 < t < n^k, 0 \leq i < n^k, a \in \Gamma)$ and surface configuration C', E contains the followings:

4.1 Assume that M executes a move with writing symbol a in the i th position on the main tape at surface configuration C'. Then E contains

$$< t, i, a, 0 > \ \rightarrow \ < t - 1, i, C', 1 >.$$

4.2 $< t, i, a, 0 > \ \rightarrow \ < t, i, a, 1 >.$

4.3 $< t, i, a, 1 > \ \rightarrow \ < t - 1, i, a, 0 >.$

4.4 $< t, i, a, 1 > \ \rightarrow \ < t, i, a, 2 >.$

4.5 For each i such that $i \neq i', 0 \leq i' < n^k$, E contains

$$< t, i, a, 2 > \ \rightarrow \ < t - 1, i', C', 1 >.$$

Assume that the first player has a position $< t, i, a, 0 >$ and assume the i th character of the main tape is a. If the i th character a of the main tape is changed at time $t - 1$ by M, the first player selects the surface configuration C' of time $t - 1$. Thus the first player applies rule 4.1. If the content of the index tape at time $t - 1$ is not a, the first player selects rule 4.2. Then the second player only has the way of selecting either rule 4.3 or 4.4.

If the second player selected rule 4.3, the i th character of the main tape at time $t - 1$ is a. Thus the first player has a forced-win at the position. If the second player selected rule 4.4, the first player selects the content of the index tape, $i'(i' \neq i)$ and surface configuration C' at time $t - 1$, that is, selects rule 4.5.

If the i th character of the main tape at time t is not a, the first player loses the game at the position no matter what rule he/she selects.

5. Rules for position $< t, h, b, 1 >'$.

For each t, i', h, b such that $0 \leq t, i' < n^k, 0 \leq h < k \log n, b \in \{\#, 0, 1, B\}$ and surface configuration $C' = (q', a', h', b', j', d')$, E contains the following rules:

5.1 Assume that M executes a move with writing symbol b in the h th position on the work tape at surface configuration C' (thus $h' = h$). Then E contains

$$< t, h, b, 0 >' \ \rightarrow \ < t - 1, i', C', 1 >.$$

5.2 $< t, h, b, 0 >' \ \rightarrow \ < t, h, b, 1 >'.$

5.3 $< t, h, b, 1 >' \ \rightarrow \ < t - 1, h, b, 0 >'.$

5.4 $< t, h, b, 1 >' \ \rightarrow \ < t, h, b, 2 >'.$

5.5 If $h' \neq h$, E contains

$$< t, h, b, 2 >' \; \rightarrow \; < t - 1, i', C', 1 > .$$

6. Rules for position $< t, j, d, 1 >''$ are similar to that of 5. So we omit them.

7. Rules for $t = 0$.

7.1 $< 0, i, x, 0 > \; \rightarrow \; \$, \quad 0 \leq i < n.$

7.2 $< 0, i, B, 0 > \; \rightarrow \; \$, \quad n \leq i < n^k.$

7.3 $< 0, h, B, 0 >' \; \rightarrow \; \$, \quad 1 \leq h < k \log n.$

7.4 $< 0, 0, \#, 0 >' \; \rightarrow \; \$.$

7.5 $< 0, j, B, 0 >'' \; \rightarrow \; \$, \quad 1 \leq h < k \log n.$

7.6 $< 0, 0, \#, 0 >'' \; \rightarrow \; \$.$

7.7 $< 0, 0, (q_0, x_0, 0, \#, 0, \#), 0 > \; \rightarrow \; \$.$

There is no rule to move the position \$ to any other position. If the first player moves a position to \$ position, the second player loses the game.

Obviously from the construction, $x \in L$ if and only if the first player has a forced-win in G_x'.

Total number of positions in G_x' is more than $n^{2k}\log n$. therefore, the construction of G_x' is at least $n^{2k}\log n$ time.

Thus we construct a $(2k + 1)$ -pebble game G_x from two-person game G_x' which satisfies the following conditions:

(1) G_x' if and only if the first player has a forced-win in G_x,

(2) G_x is constructed from M and x in $O(n \log n)$ time.

We describe here only the essential points of the construction since this is very similar to the one in [2].

Positions for counting t and i made the total number of positions large in G_x'. Thus we introduce in G_x two counters, TCOUNTER and ICOUNTER, representing t and i, respectively. k pebbles are used for each counter.

Let $s = \lceil \log n \rceil$, $m = 2^s$.

We provide nodes $T_{\ell, j}$ and $I_{\ell, j}$ $(1 \leq \ell \leq k, 0 \leq j < m)$, respectively for TCOUNTER and ICOUNTER.   Let i be   an   integer   such   that $0 \leq i < m^k$,   that   is, $i = i_1 + i_2 m + \cdots + i_k m^{k-1}, 0 \leq i_\ell < m, 1 \leq \ell \leq k.$

k pebbles are placed on nodes

$$I_{1, i_1}, I_{2, i_2}, \dots, I_{k, i_k}$$

If we let the binary representation of i_u, the u th digit of i, be $j_s j_{s-1} \dots j_2 j_1$, j_v is the $((u-1)s + v)$ th bit of the representation of i.

In this construction, we suppose the number i is written on the index tape with the least significant bit of the binary representation at the leftmost cell to the right of the left end marker, $\#$. Let the current contents of TCOUNTER and ICOUNTER be t and i, respectively.

In addition to $2k$ pebbles for two counters, one pebble is placed on one of the following nodes:

$< C, \ell >$, $< a, \ell >$, $< h, b, \ell >'$, $< j, d, \ell >''$.

These nodes are corresponding to the following positions in G_x', respectively:

$< t, i, C, \ell >$, $< t, i, a, \ell >$, $< t, h, b, \ell >'$, $< t, j, d, \ell >''$.

Now we simulate rule 2.5 in G_x'. We use auxiliary nodes of the following forms in G_x:

$< r, 0 >$, $< r, 1 >$, $1 \leq r \leq k \times s$.

G_x contains the following rules for each surface configuration C and r $(1 \leq r \leq k \times s)$:

(1) $(< C, 1 >, *, < r, 0 >)$,

(2) $(< r, 0 >, *, < r, 1 >)$,

where $*$ denotes an arbitrary node. Let $r = (u-1)s + v$ such that $1 \leq u \leq k, 1 \leq v \leq s$, and j be integer such that $0 \leq j < m$.

Let the binary representation i be $j_s \dots j_1$. For these u, v, r, i, j, G_x contains

(3) $(< r, 1 >, I_{u,j}, < r, j_v, 0 >)$.

Assume that the current content of TCOUNTER and ICOUNTER be t and i, respectively.

Assume that a pebble is placed on node $< C, 1 >$, and it is the second player's turn. At the time, the second player selects an r such that $1 \leq r \leq k \times s$, and then moves the pebble on node $< C, 1 >$ to node $< r, 0 >$ by rule (1).

The first player, in his turn, moves the pebble on $< r, 0 >$ to $< r, 1 >$ by rule (2).

Let $r = (u-1)s + v$. Assume that a pebble is placed on $I_{u,j}$. Then the r th bit of the binary representation of i is j_v.

Thus the second player moves the pebble on $< r, 1 >$ to $< r, j_v, 0 >$.

Simulation is performed with similar way for other rules. The number of nodes introduced is $O(n)$, and G_x is constructed in $O(n \log n)$ time.

Concluding Remarks

We showed that indexing Turing machines simulate $T(n)$ time bounded random access machines under logarithmic cost criterion in $O(T(n)\log T(n))$ time. And also we showed that for an arbitrary multi-tape Turing machine that accepts a language A in $T(n)$ time, there exists an ITM that accepts A in $O(T(n))$ time. Therefore if a problem is known to be unsolvable in $T(n)$ time on ITM we can know the problem is not solved in $T(n)/\log T(n)$ time in practice since random access machines are regarded as a model of actual computing devices.

Consider a 51-pebble game problem with 100 nodes. Then at least $100^{25} \times c$ time is required to solve whether the first player has a "forced win" in the game. Assume that one step of the fastest machine is executed in one nano- second.

$$100^{25} \, nsec = 10^{50} \, nsec = 10^{47} \, \mu sec = 10^{44} \, msec = 10^{41} \, sec$$

$$10^{41} / 10^{12} \, sec = 10^{29} \, tera\text{-sec}$$

Since one tera second equals to 32,000 year,

$$10^{29} \, tera\text{-sec} = 10^{29} / 32 \times 10^{3} \, tera\text{-sec} = 10^{26} / 32 > 10^{24} \, year$$

Since 2×10^{8} year equals to one $gala$-year (the sun goes around the center of the Galaxy for 2×10^{8} years. [7])

$$10^{24} \, year \, (\, = 10^{24} / (2 \times 10^{8})) > 10^{15} \, gala\text{-year}$$

Thus the time required to decide whether the first player has a "forced win" is the time required for the sun to go around the center of our Galaxy 10^{15} times. Is this amount of time thought to be feasible ?

As it was cleared, we cannot say the 51-pebble game problem is feasible even if it belongs to the class P.

Even the 31-pebble game problem requires

$$1 \, tera\text{-sec} = 32,000 \, year$$

We hope we can obtain the concrete lower bounds on more general problems in P, other than game problems.

References

[1] A. Adachi, S. Iwata, and T. Kasai, Low Level Complexity for Combinatorial Games, proc. ACM Symp. on Theory of Computing, Milwaukee, 1981.

[2] A. Adachi, S. Iwata, and T. Kasai, Some Combinatorial Game Problems Require $\Omega(n^k)$ Time, JACM, Vol.31,No.2, 1984.

[3] T. Kasai, A. Adachi, and S. Iwata, Classes of Pebble Games and Complete Problems, SIAM J. on comput., Vol.8, No.4, 1979.

[4] A. Aho, J. Hopcroft, and J. Ullman, The Design and Analysis of Computer Algorithms, Addison-Wesley, Reading, Mass., 1974.

[5] J. Hartmanis, and R. Stearns, On the Computational Complexity of Algorithms, Trans. Amer. Math. Soc. 117(1965).

[6] S. Cook, and R. Reckhow, Time Bounded Random Access Machines, JCSS 7, 1973.

[7] I. Asimov, Adding a Dimension, Doubleday & Co. Inc., 1964.

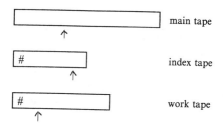

Fig. 2.1 Tapes of an indexing Turing machine

LOAD i	lg c(i)
LOAD* i	lg c(i) + lg c(c(i))
STORE i	lg c(0)
STORE* i	lg c(0) + lg c(i)
SETC i	1
JZERO k	1
ADD i	lg c(0) + lg c(i)
SUB i	lg c(0) + c(i)

Table 2.1 Instruction set on RAM

		DTOP	ITOP		
					track 1
	#					#				track 2
IFIRST		ITOP		DTOP		TEMP			track 3
ACC					track 4

Fig. 3.1 Structure of the main tape

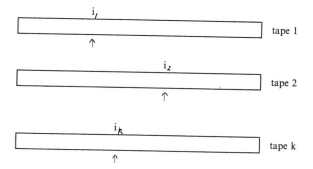

Fig. 3.2 Tapes of multi-tape Turing macine M

Fig 3.3 Tapes of indexing Turing machine M

On Probability that a Randomly Selected Set Has

Some complexity-Theoretical Property

Kojiro Kobayashi

Department of Information Sciences

Tokyo Institute of Technology

O-okayama, Meguro-ku, Tokyo 152, Japan

Abstract. Let p be the probability that a randomly selected set is NP-hard under the polynomial time Turing reducibility and let p^A be the value of p that is relativized with respect to an oracle set A. We construct oracle sets A_1, A_2 such that $p^{A_1} = 0$ and $P^{A_2} \neq NP^{A_2} \wedge p^{A_2} = 1$. This implies that (1) to prove $p = 1$ or (2) to prove $p = 0$ under the assumption $P \neq NP$ is impossible by a method that relativizes.

We also show similar results for some other pairs of complexity classes.

1. Introduction

One interesting problem in the theory of complexity of computation is what is the probability that a randomly selected set L of words has some complexity-theoretical property such as NP-completeness. Here, by "randomly

DISCRETE ALGORITHMS AND
COMPLEXITY

325

selected" we mean that a set L of words is selected from the class of all subsets of $\{0,1\}^*$ in such a way that, for each word x, whether x is included in L or not is determined independently and that the probability of inclusion is 1/2.

For each class C of sets of words in $\{0,1\}^*$, let $\mu(C)$ (or simply μC) denote the probability that a randomly selected set L is in C (when that probability is defined.) Then, the problem we are interested in is what is the probability $\mu\{L \mid Q(L)\}$ for complexity-theoretical properties $Q(L)$ on L.

For example, let us consider the probability $\mu\{L \mid L$ is NP-complete (under the polynomial time Turing reducibility)}. The class of all NP-complete sets in $\{0,1\}^*$ is countably infinite. Hence, the probability is 0.

Then, what is the probability $\mu\{L \mid L$ is NP-hard (under the polynomial time Turing reducibility)}? If L is NP-hard and $(L - L') \cup (L' - L)$ is finite, then L' is NP-hard. From this follows that the above probability is either 0 or 1 (the "0-1 law" of the theory of probability).

At present, we do not know which of 0, 1 is the correct value of the probability. If we could prove that the probability is 0, it means that we have proved $P \neq NP$. Hence, a reasonable goal would be to prove one of the following statements:

$$\mu\{L \mid L \text{ is NP-hard}\} = 1,$$

$$P \neq NP \implies \mu\{L \mid L \text{ is NP-hard}\} = 0,$$

or equivalently,

$$\mu\{L \mid NP \subseteq P^L\} = 1,$$

$$P \neq NP \implies \mu\{L \mid NP \subseteq P^L\} = 0.$$

However, even this goal seems to be very difficult. In the present paper, we show that to prove one of the above statements by a method that relativizes is impossible. That is, we prove that there exist oracle sets A_1, A_2 such that

$$\mu\{L \mid NP^{A_1} \subseteq P^{A_1,L}\} = 0,$$

$$P^{A_2} \neq NP^{A_2} \wedge \mu\{L \mid NP^{A_2} \subseteq P^{A_2,L}\} = 1.$$

We also show similar results for some other pairs of complexity classes.

2. Preliminaries

The definitions of Turing machines (TM's for short), their time and space complexity, complexity classes P, NP, PSpace etc. and their relativizations P^A, NP^A, $PSpace^A$ etc. are the standard ones. As for the definitions of space bounded oracle Turing machines, we assume that the lengths of oracle tapes are also bounded. We also assume that the underlying alphabet is the fixed alphabet $\{0,1\}$. Let $\{0,1\}^n$, $\{0,1\}^{\geq n}$, $\{0,1\}^{\leq n}$ denote the sets $\{u \in \{0,1\}^* \mid |u| = n\}$, $\{u \in \{0,1\}^* \mid |u| \geq n\}$, $\{u \in \{0,1\}^* \mid |u| \leq n\}$ respectively.

For a set A ($\subseteq \{0,1\}^*$) and an oracle TM M, let $L^A(M)$ denote the set of input words in $\{0,1\}^*$ accepted by M with the oracle set A. For sets A_1, A_2 ($\subseteq \{0,1\}^*$), let $L^{A_1,A_2}(M)$ denote $L^{A_1 \oplus A_2}(M)$, let P^{A_1,A_2} denote $P^{A_1 \oplus A_2}$, and similarly for other classes. Here, $A_1 \oplus A_2$ denotes the set $\{0x \mid x \in A_1\} \cup \{1x \mid x \in A_2\}$.

For the classes ZPP, R, BPP, PP that are defined by polynomial time probabilistic Turing machines and their relativizations, we refer the readers to [3, 4]. Inclusion relations $P \subseteq ZPP$, $ZPP \subseteq R \subseteq BPP$, $ZPP \subseteq coR \subseteq BPP$, $BPP \subseteq PP \subseteq PSpace$, $R \subseteq NP \subseteq PP$, $coR \subseteq coNP \subseteq PP$ among these classes are well-known.

Bennett and Gill ([3]) proved

$$\mu\{L \mid P^L = ZPP^L = R^L = coR^L = BPP^L\} = 1.$$

Their proof can be easily relativized to show

$$\mu\{L \mid P^{A,L} = ZPP^{A,L} = R^{A,L} = coR^{A,L} = BPP^{A,L}\} = 1$$

for any set A.

3. Main results

First we prove three theorems.

Theorem 3.1.   There exists an oracle set A such that $\mu\{L \mid coNP^A \subseteq NP^{A,L}\} = 0$.

Proof. Let M_0, M_1, ... be an enumeration of all polynomial time bounded oracle nondeterministic TM's. We may assume that the running time of M_i is bounded by n^i. For a set A, let $L_1(A)$ denote the set $\{0^m \mid \forall x [|x| = m \Rightarrow x \notin A]\}$ in $coNP^A$.

We construct a set A such that $\mu\{L \mid L_1(A) = L^{A,L}(M_i)\} = 0$ for any i. From this follows the theorem because

$$\mu\{L \mid coNP^A \subseteq NP^{A,L}\}$$

$$\leq \mu\{L \mid L_1(A) \in NP^{A,L}\}$$

$$= \mu\{L \mid \exists i \ [L_1(A) = L^{A,L}(M_i)]\}$$

$$\leq \sum_{i=0}^{\infty} \mu\{L \mid L_1(A) = L^{A,L}(M_i)\}$$

$$= 0.$$

Let w_0, w_1, w_2, ... be an enumeration of all words in $\{0,1\}^*$. For each $u = a_0 a_1 \ldots a_{m-1} \in \{0,1\}^*$ (each a_i is 0 or 1), let

$C_u = \{L \subseteq \{0,1\}^* \mid$ for each i $(0 \leq i \leq m-1)$, w_i is in

L or not according as a_i is 1 or 0$\}$.

Note that $\mu(C_u) = 1/2^{|u|}$ ($|u|$ denotes the length of a word u).

We construct the desired oracle set A in steps. We maintain sets A', A", W_0, W_1, ... The set A' (or A" respectively) is the set of words which we have decided to include in A (or exclude from A respectively). The desired set A is the limit set of A'. The set W_i is the set of words u such that we have completed diagonalization with respect to M_i and sets in C_u. That is, at any step we have

$(\forall B) \ [A' \subseteq B \wedge A" \cap B = \emptyset$

$$\Rightarrow (\forall i) \ (\forall u \in W_i) \ (\forall L \in C_u) \ [L_1(B) \neq L^{B,L}(M_i)]].$$

At the beginning of the construction, A', A", W_0, W_1, ... are all empty.

Let m_0, m_1, m_2, ... be a sequence of nonnegative integers such that, for any nonnegative integer m there exist infinitely many i such that $m_i = m$. The construction starts with step 0.

(Step j) Let $i = m_j$, let n be a value such that $(A' \cup A") \cap \{0,1\}^n = \emptyset$ and $n^i/2^n \leq 1/2$, and let k be a value such that w_0, w_1, ... , w_{k-1} contain all the words in $\{0,1\}^{\leq n^i}$.

Let u_0, u_1, $\ldots$, u_{s-1} be the words of length k that are not extensions of words in W_i.

For each t ($0 \leq t \leq$ s-1), let L_t be an arbitrary set in C_{u_t}. Let us consider the computation of M_i that is given 0^n as the input and A' $\oplus$ L_t as the oracle set ($0 \leq t \leq$ s-1). Note that, for each t, whether M_i accepts 0^n or not with the oracle set A' $\oplus$ L_t does not depend on the selection of L_t from C_{u_t}. Let U (or V respectively) be the set of t ($0 \leq t \leq$ s-1) such that M_i accepts 0^n with the oracle set A' $\oplus$ L_t (or does not accept 0^n, respectively).

(Case 1) Suppose that $|U| \leq |V|$ ($|U|$ and $|V|$ denote the cardinalities of U and V respectively). Then, we add

(1) all words u_t for t $\in$ V to W_i,

(2) all words in $\{0,1\}^n$ to A", and

(3) all the words in $\{0,1\}^* - (\{0,1\}^n \cup A' \cup A")$ that were queried in some computation for the input 0^n for some oracle set A' $\oplus$ L_t, t $\in$ V, to A".

Note that $0^n \in L_1(A)$ and $0^n \notin L^{A,L}(M_i)$ for the resulting set A and any L $\in$ C_{u_t}, t $\in$ V. Moreover, if W_i ', W_i " denote the set W_i at the beginning and at the end of this step respectively, we have

$$\mu(\, 2^{\{0,1\}^*} - \bigvee \{C_{u_t} \mid t \in W_i"\} \,)$$

$$= \mu(\, \bigvee_{t \in U} C_{u_t} \,)$$

$$= |U| \, / \, 2^k$$

$$\leq (1/2) \, (|U| + |V|) \, / \, 2^k$$

$$= (1/2) \, \mu(\, 2^{\{0,1\}^*} - \bigvee \{C_{u_t} \mid t \in W_i'\} \,).$$

Here, $2^{\{0,1\}^*}$ denotes the class of all subsets of $\{0,1\}^*$.

(Case 2) Suppose that $|U| > |V|$. For each $t \in U$ we select one accepting computation path of M_i that is given 0^n as the input and $A' \oplus L_t$ as the oracle set. We consider the following $|U|$ row 2^n column matrix. The rows correspond to elements of U and the columns correspond to words in $\{0,1\}^n$. The component at the row for t ($\in U$) and the column for z ($|z| = n$) is 1 if the selected computation of M_i for the oracle set $A' \oplus L_t$ queries z, and 0 otherwise.

On each row, at most n^i components are 1, and consequently at most $|U| \, n^i$ components are 1 in the matrix. Hence there exists z_0 ($|z_0| = n$) such that at most $|U| \, n^i / 2^n$ components are 1 on the column for z_0. Let U' (or U'' respectively) denote the set of t ($\in U$) such that the component at the row for t and the column for z_0 is 1 (or 0 respectively).

Then, we add

(1) all words u_t for $t \in U''$ to W_i,

(2) z_0 to A', and

(3) all the words in $\{0,1\}^* - (A' \cup A'')$ that were queried in the selected computations for the input 0^n for some oracle set $A \oplus L_t$, $t \in U''$, to A''.

Note that $0^n \notin L_1(A)$ and $0^n \in L^{A,L}(M_i)$ for the resulting set A and any $L \in C_{u_t}$, $t \in U''$. In this case, we have

$$
\mu(\, 2^{\{0,1\}^*} - \bigcup \{C_{u_t} \mid t \in W_i''\} \,)
$$

$$
= \mu(\bigcup_{t \in U' \cup V} C_{u_t})
$$

$$
= (|U'| + |V|) / 2^k
$$

$$
\leq (|U| \, n^i / 2^n + |V|) / 2^k
$$

$$\leq (|U|/2 + |V|) / 2^k$$

$$< (|U|/2 + |V|) / 2^k + (1/4) (|U| - |V|) / 2^k$$

$$= (3/4) (|U| + |V|) / 2^k$$

$$= (3/4) \mu(\bigvee_{t \in U \cup V} C_{u_t})$$

$$= (3/4) \mu(2^{\{0,1\}^*} - \bigvee \{C_{u_t} \mid t \in W_i'\}).$$

(End of Step j)

In both of Case 1 and Case 2, the measure of the class of sets L for which we have not completed diagonalization with respect to M_i is decreased by the factor of either 1/2 (Case 1) or 3/4 (Case 2). Moreover, in the entire construction, each M_i is selected infinitely often. Hence we have $\mu\{L \mid L_1(A) = L^{A,L}(M_i)\} = 0$. □

Theorem 3.2. There exists an oracle set A such that $coNP^A \neq NP^A \wedge PSpace^A \subseteq BPP^A$.

Proof. We use the idea used by Baker, Gill and Solovay ([1]) to construct an oracle set A such that $P^A \neq NP^A \wedge coNP^A = NP^A$.

Let M_0, M_1, ... be an enumeration of all polynomial time bounded nondeterministic oracle TM's. We may assume that the running time of M_i is bounded by n^i. Let $L_1(A)$ denote the set in $coNP^A$ introduced in the proof of Theorem 3.1. We construct A in such a way that $\forall i [L_1(A) \neq L^A(M_i)]$. This guarantees $L_1(A) \notin NP^A$, and consequently $coNP^A \neq NP^A$. In the construction process, an index i will be canceled when we have achieved $L_1(A) \neq L^A(M_i)$.

Let N_0, N_1, ... be an enumeration of all polynomial

space bounded deterministic oracle TM's. We may assume that the tape space used by N_i (including that of the oracle tape) is bounded by n^i.

For an oracle TM M, let $d(M) \in \{0,1\}^*$ be some natural representation of the structure of M, and for words u, v, w $\in$ $\{0,1\}^*$, let $\langle u, v, w \rangle \in \{0,1\}^*$ be some natural representation of the triple u, v, w. For a set A ($\subseteq$ $\{0,1\}^*$), let K(A) be defined by

$$K(A) = \{\langle d(N_i), x, 0^{|x|^i} \rangle \mid i \geq 0, x \in \{0,1\}^*,$$
$$N_i \text{ accepts } x \text{ within space bound } |x|^i \text{ with the}$$
$$\text{oracle set A}\}.$$

Note that, if the representation $\langle u, v, w \rangle$ satisfies $|w| \leq |\langle u, v, w \rangle|$, then whether y is in K(A) or not is completely determined by whether z is in A or not for words z such that $|z| \leq |y|$.

We construct A in such a way that, for each y $\in$ $\{0,1\}^*$,

$$\left.\begin{array}{l} y \in K(A) \implies \dfrac{|\{ z \mid |y| = |z|, yz \in A \}|}{2^{|y|}} > \dfrac{3}{4}, \\[4mm] y \notin K(A) \implies \dfrac{|\{ z \mid |y| = |z|, yz \in A \}|}{2^{|y|}} < \dfrac{1}{4}. \end{array}\right\} \quad (*)$$

This will guarantee K(A) $\in$ BPP^A, and consequently PSpace^A $\subseteq$ BPP^A. (Note that PSpace^A = $\{L^A(N_i) \mid i \geq 0\}$ and that $L^A(N_i) \leq_m^P K(A)$ for any i by the definition of K(A).)

The construction starts with A' = A" = $\emptyset$. In Step j, all words in $\{0,1\}^j$ and some words in $\{0,1\}^{\geq j+1}$ are added to A' or A". Hence, at the beginning of Step j we have $\{0,1\}^{\leq j-1} \subseteq$ A' $\cup$ A". The desired set A is the limit set of

A'.

(Step 2m) In this step, we add each word in $\{0,1\}^{2m} - (A'$ $\cup$ A") either to A' or to A" so that, at the end of the step we have

$$y \in K(A') \implies \frac{|\{ z \mid |z| = m, yz \in A' \}|}{2^m} > \frac{3}{4},$$

$$\left. y \notin K(A') \implies \frac{|\{ z \mid |z| = m, yz \in A' \}|}{2^m} < \frac{1}{4} \right\} \quad (**)$$

for any y in $\{0,1\}^m$, and consequently the previously mentioned conditions $(*)$ are satisfied for A. This is possible because we have $|(A' \cup A") \cap \{0,1\}^{2m}| < (1/8) \, 2^m$ at the beginning of this step. This will be shown later.

(Step 2m + 1) If either $(A' \cup A") \cap \{0,1\}^{2m+1} \neq \emptyset$ or there is no uncanceled index i less than log m, we add all words in $\{0,1\}^{2m+1} - (A' \cup A")$ to A' and proceed to the next step. Otherwise, let i be the least of the uncanceled indexes.

Suppose that there exists a set B in $\{0,1\}^{\geq 2m+2} - (A' \cup A")$ such that M_i accepts 0^{2m+1} with the oracle set $A' \cup B$. Then, (1) select one such B, (2) select one computation path that accepts 0^{2m+1} for this B, (3) select one word w of length 2m + 1 that was not queried in the selected computation path, (4) add w to A', (5) add all the words in $\{0,1\}^{2m+1}$ other than w to A", (6) add all the words in B that were queried in the selected computation path to A', and (7) add all the words in $\{0,1\}^{\geq 2m+2} - (A' \cup A" \cup B)$ that were queried in the selected computation path to A". The selection of w in (3) is possible because

$(2m+1)^i$ < $(2m+1)^{\log m}$ ≤ 2^{2m+1}. We have 0^{2m+1} ∉ $L_1(A)$ and 0^{2m+1} ∈ $L^A(M_i)$.

If there exist no such set B, then we add all the words in $\{0,1\}^{2m+1}$ to A". In this case we have 0^{2m+1} ∈ $L_1(A)$, and also 0^{2m+1} ∉ $L^A(M_i)$ (0^{2m+1} ∈ $L^A(M_i)$ will contradict the assumption that there is no such set B.)

The condition mentioned at Step 2m is satisfied because, at the beginning of Step 2m, we have

$$|(A' \cup A'') \cap \{0,1\}^{2m}|$$
$$\leq \sum_{k=0}^{m-1} (2k + 1)^{\log k}$$
$$\leq m (2m - 1)^{\log m}$$
$$< (1/8) \, 2^m$$

It is easy to see that each index i is ultimately canceled. Hence, we have $L_1(A) \neq L^A(M_i)$ for each i. □

Theorem 3.3. There exists an oracle set A such that $coR^A \neq R^A$.

Proof. We construct A in such a way that, for each m, $|A \cap \{0,1\}^m| / 2^m$ is either greater than 1/2 or is 0. Hence we have $L_1(A) = \{0^m \mid \forall x \; [|x| = m \Rightarrow x \notin A]\} \in coR^A$. We achieve $\forall i \; [$ " M_i is an R-machine with A " $\Rightarrow L_1(A) \neq L^A(M_i)]$ by diagonalization. The construction is straightforward and we will omit the details. □

As for Theorem 3.3, the following stronger result is obtained in [2] using a more elaborate construction: there exists an oracle set A such that coR^A contains an R^A-immune set.

	PP	NP	BPP	R	ZPP	P
PSpace	?	$\circ^{(1)}$	$\circ^{(1)}$	$\circ^{(1)}$	$\circ^{(1)}$	$\circ^{(1)}$
PP	/	$\circ^{(1)}$	$\circ^{(1)}$	$\circ^{(1)}$	$\circ^{(1)}$	$\circ^{(1)}$
NP	/	/	$\circ^{(1)}$	$\circ^{(1)}$	$\circ^{(1)}$	$\circ^{(1)}$
coNP	/	$\circ^{(1)}$	$\circ^{(1)}$	$\circ^{(1)}$	$\circ^{(1)}$	$\circ^{(1)}$
BPP	/	$\times^{(2)}$	/	$\times^{(2)}$	$\times^{(2)}$	$\times^{(2)}$
R	/	/	/	/	$\times^{(2)}$	$\times^{(2)}$
coR	/	$\times^{(2)}$	/	$\times^{(2)}$	$\times^{(2)}$	$\times^{(2)}$
ZPP	/	/	/	/	/	$\times^{(2)}$

Table I

Table I summarizes our results of the form "there exists A such that $\mu\{L \mid C_1{}^A \subseteq C_2{}^{A,L}\} = 0$" and Table II summarizes our results of the form "there exists A such that $C_1{}^A \neq C_2{}^A \land \mu\{L \mid C_1{}^A \subseteq C_2{}^{A,L}\} = 1$." In the tables, a symbol o (or × respectively) at the row C_1 and the column C_2 means the existence (or nonexistence respectively) of such A for the pair (C_1, C_2). Pairs (C_1, C_2) such that $C_1{}^A$ $\subseteq C_2{}^A$ is evident are not interesting and we exclude these pairs from our consideration. Pairs with slash symbols are such pairs.

All of these results (except for $o^{(5)}$) follow from Theorems 3.1 - 3.3, the closure property of P, ZPP, BPP, PP, PSpace with respect to the operation of

	PP	NP	BPP	R	ZPP	P
PSpace	?	○$^{(3)}$	?	○$^{(3)}$	○$^{(3)}$	○$^{(3)}$
PP	/	○$^{(3)}$	?	○$^{(3)}$	○$^{(3)}$	○$^{(3)}$
NP	/	/	○$^{(3)}$	?	○$^{(3)}$	○$^{(3)}$
coNP	/	○$^{(3)}$	○$^{(3)}$	○$^{(3)}$	○$^{(3)}$	○$^{(3)}$
BPP	/	○$^{(3)}$	/	○$^{(4)}$	○$^{(4)}$	○$^{(4)}$
R	/	/	/	/	○$^{(4)}$	○$^{(4)}$
coR	/	○$^{(4)}$	/	○$^{(4)}$	○$^{(4)}$	○$^{(4)}$
ZPP	/	/	/	/	/	○$^{(5)}$

Table II

complementation, and (the relativized and the nonrelativized versions of) the result by Bennett and Gill ([3]) mentioned at the end of Section 2.

Existence for o$^{(1)}$ follows from Theorem 3.1. Let A be the set of the theorem. Then, for example, we have

$$\mu\{L \mid NP^A \subseteq BPP^{A,L}\} \leq \mu\{L \mid NP^A \subseteq P^{A,L} \lor P^{A,L} \neq BPP^{A,L}\}$$
$$\leq \mu\{L \mid NP^A \subseteq P^{A,L}\} + \mu\{L \mid P^{A,L} \neq BPP^{A,L}\}$$
$$= \mu\{L \mid NP^A \subseteq P^{A,L}\} \leq \mu\{L \mid coNP^A \subseteq NP^{A,L}\} = 0.$$

The proofs for other pairs with o$^{(1)}$ are similar.

Nonexistence for ×$^{(2)}$ follows from the relativized version of the result by Bennett and Gill.

Existence for o$^{(3)}$ follows from Theorem 3.2. Let A be the set of the corollary. Then, for example, we have $P^A \neq$

$coNP^A$ and

$$\mu\{L \mid coNP^A \subseteq P^{A,L}\} \geq \mu\{L \mid PSpace^A \subseteq P^{A,L}\}$$

$$\geq \mu\{L \mid PSpace^A \subseteq BPP^{A,L} \wedge P^{A,L} = BPP^{A,L}\}$$

$$\geq \mu\{L \mid PSpace^A \subseteq BPP^{A,L}\} + \mu\{L \mid P^{A,L} = BPP^{A,L}\} - 1$$

$$= \mu\{L \mid PSpace^A \subseteq BPP^{A,L}\} \geq \mu\{L \mid PSpace^A \subseteq BPP^A\} = 1.$$

The proofs for other pairs with $o^{(3)}$ are similar.

For the ten pairs (C_1, C_2) with $o^{(4)}$ and $o^{(5)}$, we have $\mu\{L \mid C_1^A \subseteq C_2^{A,L}\} = 1$ for any A by the nonrelativized version of the result by Bennett and Gill. Hence, existence of the desired A is equivalent to existence of A such that $C_1^A \neq C_2^A$. Therefore, existence follows from Theorem 3.3 for $o^{(4)}$. As for $o^{(5)}$, it follows from existence of A such that $P^A \neq R^A = NP^A = coNP^A$ shown in [5]. Note that, for these ten pairs, we already know the correct answer $\mu\{L \mid C_1 \subseteq C_2^L\} = 1$ to the original problem by the nonrelativized version of the result by Bennett and Gill.

The following corollary shows that even the statement

$$coNP \neq NP \implies \mu\{L \mid NP \subseteq P^L\} = 0$$

that is weaker than the statement

$$P \neq NP \implies \mu\{L \mid NP \subseteq P^L\} = 0$$

cannot be proved by a method that relativizes.

Corollary 3.4.   There exists an oracle set A such that $coNP^A \neq NP^A \wedge \mu\{L \mid NP^A \subseteq P^{A,L}\} = 1$.

Proof.   The result follows from Theorem 3.2. $\square$

Acknowledgments

The author would like to thank Mr. Osamu Watanabe for helpful discussions.

References

[1] T. Baker, J. Gill and R. Solovay, Relativizations of the P =? NP question, SIAM J. Comput. 4 (1975) 431-442.

[2] J. L. Balcazar and D. Russo, Immunity and simplicity in relativizations of probabilistic complexity classes, manuscript.

[3] C. H. Bennett and J. Gill, Relative to a random oracle A, $P^A \neq NP^A \neq coNP^A$ with probability 1, SIAM J. Comput. 10 (1981) 96-113.

[4] J. Gill, Computational complexity of probabilistic Turing machines, SIAM J. Comput. 6 (1977) 675-695.

[5] C. Rackoff, Relativized questions involving probabilistic algorithms, J. Assoc. Comput. Mach. 29 (1982) 261-268.

Ranking Rooted Trees, and a Graceful Application

Herbert S. Wilf*
Department of Mathematics
University of Pennsylvania
Philadelphia, PA 19104

Nancy A. Yoshimura†
Department of Computer and Information Science
University of Pennsylvania
Philadelphia, PA 19104

Abstract

We define an ordering on the set of all rooted trees of a fixed number of vertices that leads to fast ranking and unranking algorithms. An application to the graceful labeling problem is given, which shows how the method can eliminate repeated isomorphism testing.

Key Words: rooted trees, free trees, ranking, unranking, graceful labeling

A.M.S. subject classifications: 05A17, 05C05, 05C30, 68E10, 94C15

Date: March, 1986

* Research supported in part by the U. S. Office of Naval Research
† This work is a portion of a dissertation to be submitted to the faculties of the University of Pennsylvania in partial fulfillment of the requirements for the degree of Doctor of Philosophy

341

1. Introduction

A *listing* algorithm for a certain family $\mathcal{F}$ of objects is a procedure that will, on demand, produce a list $\mathcal{L}$ of all of those objects. Such an algorithm, of course, implies a certain ordering on the elements of $\mathcal{F}$.

A *ranking* algorithm for $\mathcal{F}$ takes as input an object ω of $\mathcal{F}$ and produces an integer $r = r(\omega)$ in the range $0 \le r \le |\mathcal{F}| - 1$. The integer r gives the position of the object ω in the list $\mathcal{L}$, where $r = 0$ corresponds to the first object on the list, etc.

An *unranking* algorithm accepts an integer r as input, and produces the object of rank r on the list $\mathcal{L}$.

Many ranking, unranking and listing algorithms for various families of objects in various orderings are known. See [7] for some early algorithms, [8] for a number of examples, and [9], [10] for a unified theory that covers a number of important cases.

In this paper we will discuss the ordering, ranking and unranking of the set of rooted and free trees of a given number of vertices. This family is not covered by the theory in [9]. The immediate motivation for doing this research was the utility of such an algorithm for a computation relating to the famous 'graceful labeling problem' for trees.

In the next section we describe the linear ordering that will be used in the algorithms, and in section 3 we present the algorithms themselves. In section 4 we describe the application to the graceful labeling question. In a sequel we will give a number of generalizations of these ideas.

2. Preliminaries

2.1 Ordering partitions of integers

To order trees we will first have to say how we order partitions of integers. We write a partition of the integer n in the form

$$\pi : n = \overbrace{k_1 + k_1 + \cdots + k_1}^{q_1 \text{ times}} + \cdots + \overbrace{k_p + k_p + \cdots + k_p}^{q_p \text{ times}}$$
$$\stackrel{\text{def}}{=} k_1^{q_1} \oplus k_2^{q_2} \oplus \cdots \oplus k_p^{q_p}$$

where $k_1 > k_2 > \cdots > k_p$ and $q_i > 0 \, (\forall i)$. We order partitions reverse lexicographically according to the 'words' $k_1 k_1 \cdots k_p$, and we write $\pi' \prec \pi''$ in that ordering.

2.2 Ordering rooted trees

If T is a rooted tree of n vertices, then by its *root partition* we mean the partition $\pi = \pi(T)$ of the integer $n - 1$ that is induced by the sizes of the root subtrees of T. If T and T' are two rooted trees, and if $\pi(T) \prec \pi(T')$ then T precedes T' in our ordering of trees, and we write $T \prec T'$.

It remains to discuss the ordering of rooted trees with a common root partition. Let T, T' be two rooted trees with root partition π. Recursively compute the ranks, as trees of k_1 vertices, of the q_1 subtrees of size k_1 in T. Arrange these ranks in nondecreasing order in a vector **v**. Then compute the ranks of the subtrees of the next size k_2 similarly, and append them to **v**, etc., obtaining a complete vector $\mathbf{v}(T)$, and in the same way, $\mathbf{v}(T')$. Say that T precedes T', and write $T \prec T'$, if $\mathbf{v}(T) < \mathbf{v}(T')$ in the usual lexicographic order on the words **v**.

In Fig. 1 we show the 9 rooted trees on 5 vertices arranged in the order just described, along with their root partitions.

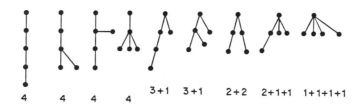

$$4 \qquad 4 \qquad 4 \qquad 4 \qquad 3+1 \quad 3+1 \quad 2+2 \quad 2+1+1 \quad 1+1+1+1$$

Fig. 1: The rooted trees on 5 vertices

Another notation will be useful for describing rooted trees. Let ω_i be the number of vertices in the ith largest root-subtree of T. Then we can describe T by the array of $(\omega : \rho)$, where ω is the size of a root subtree and ρ is the rank of that subtree among all trees of its size. We write this as

$$T = (\omega_1 : \rho_1) \otimes (\omega_2 : \rho_2) \otimes \cdots \otimes (\omega_p : \rho_p)$$

where the ω's have been written in nonincreasing order and the ρ's corresponding to equal ω's are in nondecreasing order. Fig. 2 shows an example of this notation.

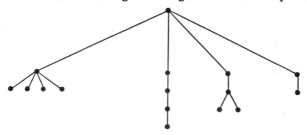

$$T = (5 : 8) \otimes (4 : 0) \otimes (4 : 1) \otimes (2 : 0)$$

Fig. 2: A rooted tree and its (subtree size, rank) coding

2.3 Some useful counting sequences

Here we will introduce three counting functions that will be useful in the sequel.

First, t_n will be the number of rooted trees with n vertices. It satisfies the well known recurrence

$$t_n = \frac{1}{(n-1)} \sum_{j,d \geq 1} d \cdot t_{n-jd} \cdot t_d \quad (n \geq 2) \tag{1}$$

together with the starting values $t_n = 0 \, (\forall n \leq 0); t_1 = 1$.

Next, let $a(n, k)$ be the number of rooted trees with $n + 1$ vertices whose root subtrees have at most k vertices each. Then ($e.g.$ [3])

$$a(n, k) = \frac{1}{n} \sum_{i, d \geq 1} a(n - id, k) d a(d - 1, k) \qquad (2)$$

holds, together with the starting values $a(i, 0) = 0 \, (\forall i > 0)$ and $a(i, j) = t_{i+1} \, (j \geq i)$.

Finally, let $c(n, k, q)$ be the number of rooted trees with $n + 1$ vertices such that there are at least $q + 1$ root subtrees of exactly k vertices and none have more than k vertices. Then the c's can be explicitly expressed in terms of the a's by

$$c(n, k, q) = a(n, k) - a(n, k - 1) - \sum_{i=1}^{q} \binom{i + t_k - 1}{i} a(n - ik, k - 1). \qquad (3)$$

3. Ranking rooted trees

Let T be a rooted tree of $n + 1$ vertices. We will now compute its rank, in the ordering described above, among all rooted trees of $n + 1$ vertices. First we will find the number of rooted trees whose root partitions precede that of T. Then we will determine the relative rank of T among all rooted trees with its root partition $\pi(T)$. The sum of these will be the desired rank of T.

We will let $rank(T)$ be the rank of T among all rooted trees of $n + 1$ vertices; $prec(\pi(T))$ be the number of rooted trees of $n + 1$ vertices whose root partitions strictly precede $\pi(T)$; and $relrank(T)$ be the relative rank of T among all rooted trees whose root partition is $\pi(T)$. Hence $rank(T) = prec(\pi(T)) + relrank(T)$.

3.1 Computing $prec(\pi(T))$

One of the pleasant surprises that we encountered in doing this work was that $prec(\pi(T))$ can be computed rapidly.

We will split the partitions that precede $\pi(T)$ into three classes and deal separately with each class. Let

$$\pi(T) = k_1^{q_1} \oplus k_2^{q_2} \oplus \cdots \oplus k_p^{q_p}. \qquad (4)$$

Then the partitions

$$\pi' = k'^{q'_1}_1 \oplus k'^{q'_2}_2 \oplus \cdots \oplus k'^{q'_r}_r$$

that precede $\pi(T)$ are of one of the following three kinds:

1^0 $k'_1 > k_1$: there are exactly $t_{n+1} - a(n, k_1)$ trees of this kind;

2^0 $k'_1 = k_1, q'_1 > q_1$: there are exactly $c(n, k_1, q_1)$ such trees;

3^0 $k'_1 = k_1, q'_1 = q_1$: we will count these trees recursively.

Indeed, the number of trees whose root partitions are of type 3^0 is

$$prec(\pi(T)) - prec(\pi^*)$$

where π^* is the first partition of n in which k_1 occurs q_1 times. We will prove

Lemma 1. *The number of rooted trees of type 3^0 above is*

$$prec(\pi(T)) - prec(\pi^*) = \binom{q_1 + t_{k_1} - 1}{q_1}(prec(\tilde{\pi}(t)) - prec(\pi^* - k_1^{q_1})). \quad (5)$$

where $\tilde{\pi}(T) = \pi(T) - k_1^{q_1}$.

Proof: Observe that

    (a) there are exactly $\binom{q_1 + t_{k_1} - 1}{q_1}$ ways to select q_1 rooted trees of k_1 vertices each, with repetition allowed, from the t_{k_1} possible such rooted trees, and

    (b) $prec(\tilde{\pi}(t)) - prec(\pi^* - k_1^{q_1})$ is the number of rooted trees of $n + 1 - q_1 k_1$ vertices whose root partition precedes $\tilde{\pi}(t)$ and whose largest root subtree is of size $< k_1$. ∎

    Next, it is clear that

$$prec(\pi^* - k_1{}^{q_1}) = t_{n-k_1 q_1 + 1} - a(n - k_1 q_1, k_1 - 1)$$

since both sides enumerate the trees of $n + 1 - k_1 q_1$ vertices whose largest root subtree has size $\geq k_1$.

    This completes the count of trees of type 3^0 above, and by combining the numbers of trees of each of the three types we obtain

Theorem 1. *The number of rooted trees of $n + 1$ vertices whose root partitions precede $\pi(T)$ is*

$$prec(\pi(T)) = \binom{q_1 + t_{k_1} - 1}{q_1}\{prec(\tilde{\pi}(T)) - t_{n-k_1 q_1 + 1} + a(n - k_1 q_1, k_1 - 1)\} \\ + c(n, k_1, q_1) + t_{n+1} - a(n, k_1) \quad (6)$$

where $\tilde{\pi}(T) = \pi(T) - k_1{}^{q_1}$. ∎

    The complexity of the algorithm for determining *prec* can be described as follows. If n is given, we first tabulate the binomial coefficients, and the quantities shown in equations (1)-(3) above. This can be done in time $O(n^2 \log n)$. Now if we are given a tree T to rank, we first need to discover its root partition, and this costs $O(n)$ time. After that, the recursive computation shown in Theorem 1 requires a time $O(p)$, where p is the number of *distinct* parts in the root partition of T, and therefore is surely $O(\sqrt{n})$.

    Therefore, to compute $prec(\pi(T))$ there is a preprocessing charge of $O(n^2 \log n)$ followed by a linear time cost per tree of n vertices that is ranked.

3.2 Computing $relrank(T)$

    Next we consider the problem of computing the relative rank of a rooted tree T among all rooted trees that have the same partition $\pi = \pi(T)$.

    Among the root subtrees of T of largest size ω, let $(\omega : \rho)$ be a subtree of least rank ρ. Suppose we delete from T exactly one copy of the subtree $(\omega : \rho)$, thereby obtaining a tree T'. We want to determine $\Delta r = relrank(T) - relrank(T')$.

Clearly Δr is the excess of the number of trees that precede T, among those of root partition $\pi(T)$, over the number that precede T' among those of partition $\pi(T')$. The trees that precede T are of two kinds:

(a) those whose root subtree of lowest rank among those of largest size is an $(\omega : \rho)$ or

(b) those whose root subtree of lowest rank among those of largest size is an $(\omega : \rho')$ with $\rho' < \rho$.

Since every tree of type (a) above is obtained by adjoining to some $T'' \prec T'$ an $(\omega : \rho)$, it follows that there are exactly $relrank(T')$ trees of the kind (a) above. Hence the change in relative rank, Δr, is equal to the number of trees of the form (b) above.

To count them, fix a $\rho' < \rho$. We count the predecessors of T whose root subtree of lowest rank, among those of largest size, has rank *exactly* ρ'.

Such trees are constructed as follows. Begin with $(\omega : \rho')$. Then choose $\mu(\omega) - 1$ more root subtrees of size ω from the $t_\omega - \rho' - 1$ trees of ω vertices whose ranks are $> \rho'$. There are

$$\binom{t_\omega - \rho' + \mu(\omega) - 3}{\mu(\omega) - 1}$$

ways to do this. If we sum over all $\rho' < \rho$ we find that the subtrees of largest size ω can be chosen in

$$\binom{t_\omega + \mu(\omega) - 2}{\mu(\omega)} - \binom{t_\omega + \mu(\omega) - 2 - \rho}{\mu(\omega)} \tag{7}$$

ways. Having made these choices we may complete the tree in any way at all except that the root partition must continue to agree with $\pi(T)$. There are exactly

$$\prod_{\omega' < \omega} \binom{t_{\omega'} + \mu(\omega') - 1}{\mu(\omega')} \tag{8}$$

ways to complete the tree subject to that restriction. The desired change in rank, Δr, is therefore given by the product of the two quantities (7), (8), and we have

$$relrank(T) = relrank(T') + \Delta r \tag{9}$$

as a recursive computation of the relative rank of a rooted tree T.

3.3 The complete algorithm

We can now state the complete ranking algorithm by piecing together the two procedures *prec* and *relrank* that we have just discussed. Interestingly, the result is a pair of procedures that call each other repeatedly with smaller and smaller arguments (trees).

```
function rank(T, n);
begin
  compute root partition π(T);
  prec(π(T));
  {from Theorem 1 above}
  rank := prec + relrank(T, n)
end.
function relrank(T, n);
begin
  for each root subtree Tᵢ of T do
  begin
    n' := |V(Tᵢ)|;
    ρᵢ := rank(Tᵢ, n')
  end
  ρ := min{ρᵢ|Tᵢ is of maximal size};
  relrank:= right side of equation (9) above
end.
```

The same operations can be carried out on free (unrooted, unlabeled) trees by using the centroid(s). This will be discussed in a sequel.

4. Graceful trees

Let T be a tree of n vertices. A *graceful labeling* of T is an assignment of labels $\lambda(v) \in \{1, 2, \ldots, n\}$ to the vertices v of T in such a way that

$$\{|\lambda(u) - \lambda(v)| \ ((u, v) \in E(T))\} = \{1, 2, \ldots, n - 1\}.$$

It has been conjectured that every tree has a graceful labeling ('all trees are graceful'), and this has been proved for various special kinds of trees and small values of n (≤ 16).

We want to compute, for small n, not only whether or not trees have graceful labelings, but *the number* of different graceful labelings that each of them has. Consider the following triangular tableau.

$$(1, n)$$
$$(1, n - 1), (2, n)$$
$$(1, n - 2), (2, n - 1), (3, n)$$
$$\cdots \qquad \cdots \qquad \cdots$$
$$(1, 2), (2, 3), (3, 4), \cdots, (n - 1, n)$$

Every graceful labeling of a tree of n vertices will have the edges of the tree labeled with $n - 1$ pairs of labels, one taken from each row of the tableau above.

Conversely, however, it is not true that each choice of a set of pairs, one from each row, corresponds to a graceful labeling of some tree.

Our calculation did a backtrack search of the tableau, choosing a pair from each of the first k rows and attempting to choose another one from the $(k+1)^{st}$ row without creating any circuits. Whenever the computation successfully chooses a pair from the last row, a complete graceful labeling of *some* tree has been constructed. We next want to find the underlying free tree and augment its 'score' by 1, since we have now found one more of its graceful labelings.

It is at this moment that our ranking algorithm is used. We find the rank r of the free tree whose graceful labeling has just been discovered, and we augment the rth counter by 1 unit.

We ran this program to find all graceful labelings of all trees of ≤ 10 vertices and tabulated the frequencies with which the various free trees occur.[*] Obviously the tree with the fewest graceful labelings (it has 2) is the star $K_{1,n}$. In Fig. 3 we show the free trees of each size ≤ 10 that have the greatest numbers of graceful labelings.

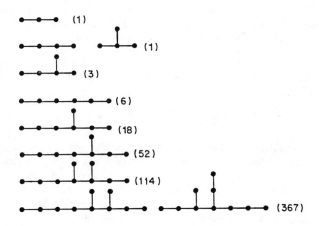

Fig. 3: Free trees with the greatest numbers of graceful labelings

Here are some questions that we have not been able to answer.

First, the trees in Fig. 3 are all 'identity trees' (have only the trivial automorphism). Is there some good reason why nontrivial automorphisms should cut down on the number of graceful labelings?

Next, define a *graceful permutation* as a permutation $\sigma \in S_n$ such that

$$\{|\sigma(i) - \sigma(i-1)| \ (i = 2,\ldots,n)\} = \{1,2,\ldots,n-1\}.$$

---

[*] Detailed printouts available upon request.

These permutations correspond to graceful labelings of paths (see also [6]). The numbers $f(n)$ of graceful permutations of $[n]$, for $n = 3, \ldots, 10$ are 4, 4, 8, 24, 32, 40, 120, 296. In general, what is $f(n)$? If that is too hard, what is the asymptotic behavior of $f(n)$? In particular, what can be said about $\lim f(n)^{1/n}$?

References

1. T. Beyer and S. M. Hedetniemi, Constant time generation of rooted trees, *SIAM J. Comput.* **9** (1980), 706-712.

2. R. A. Wright, B. Richmond, A. Odlyzko and B. D. McKay, Constant time generation of free trees

3. H. S. Wilf, The uniform selection of free trees, *J. Algorithms* **2**, (1981) 204-207.

4. D. E. Knuth, *The art of computer programming, Vol. I: Fundamental Algorithms*, Addison-Wesley, Reading MA, 1973.

5. G. Ringel, *Theory of Graphs and its Applications*, Problem 25, Proc. Int. Symp. Smolenice (1964), 162.

6. A. Rosa, Labeling snakes, *Ars Combinatoria* **3** (1977), 67-74.

7. D. H. Lehmer, The machine tools of combinatorics, in Applied Combinatorial Mathematics, E. Beckenbach, ed., John Wiley, New York, 1964.

8. A. Nijenhuis and H. S. Wilf, Combinatorial Algorithms, 2nd Ed., Academic Press, New York, 1978.

9. H. S. Wilf, A unified setting for sequencing, ranking and random selection algorithms for combinatorial objects, Adv. Math. **24** (1977), 281-291.

10. H. S. Wilf, A unified setting for selection algorithms (II), Ann. Discr. Math. **2** (1978), 135-148.

Dynamic Search in Graphs

F. R. K. Chung

Bell Communications Research
Morristown, New Jersey 07960

R. L. Graham

Bell Laboratories
Murray Hill, New Jersey 07974

M. E. Saks

Bell Communications Research
Morristown, New Jersey 07960

ABSTRACT

Suppose G is a fixed finite connected graph and for any two vertices x and y in G, $d_G(x,y)$ denotes the distance in G between x and y, i.e., the number of edges in a shortest path connecting x and y. Given an infinite sequence $Q = (q_1, q_2, ...)$ of vertices in G, suppose we would like to find another sequence $P = P_Q = (p_0, p_1, ...)$ of vertices so that the quantity

$$v(P) = \lim_{N \to \infty} \sup \frac{1}{N} \left[\sum_{i=1}^{N} (d(p_{i-1}, p_i) + d(p_i, q_i)) \right]$$

is as small as possible. This question represents a general formulation of a class of problems arising in self-adjusting data structures.

In this paper we will investigate this and a number of related graph searching problems, such as requiring p_n to be chosen before q_{n+i}, $i \geq k$, is known, and show how a number of interesting structural and algorithmic concepts from graph theory come together rather naturally, e.g., isometric embedding, Steiner points in graphs, retracts, diameters and linear programming.

DISCRETE ALGORITHMS AND
COMPLEXITY

351

Dynamic Search in Graphs

F. R. K. Chung

Bell Communications Research
Morristown, New Jersey 07960

R. L. Graham

Bell Laboratories
Murray Hill, New Jersey 07974

M. E. Saks

Bell Communications Research
Morristown, New Jersey 07960

Introduction and Background

In a *sequential search* file, a set of records is arranged in a linear list $L = (\ell_1, \ell_2, ...)$. When a record ρ is requested, the list L is searched from the first entry ℓ_1 of L and consecutive entries are probed until the the requested record ρ is found. If ρ occupies the ith position in L, the cost of this access will be i. Such a model of sequential search has long been in use and has an extensive literature (see [31,32,42]).

It is not difficult to show that if the access frequencies for the requests are known then the *best* list L_{OPT}, i.e., one for which the average access cost is as small as possible, is formed by arranging the records in order of decreasing frequency. However, it may happen that the access frequencies are not known a priori, and that in general the average cost per access can be decreased by rearranging the list from time to time. A number of different such self-adjusting schemes have been investigated in the literature. These include "move-to-front" [12,31,32], "transport" [42], "more-ahead-k" [9,10], "k-in-a-row" [21,29] and "k-in-a-batch" [21]. Various analyses of these and other schemes, both mathematical and experimental, can be found in [8,9,10].

However, a fundamental question still remains unresolved, namely, what is the *optimal* self-adjusting algorithm. By this we mean an algorithm which results in the *least* cost per access for any sequence of requests. In contrast to the earlier situation of a *static* list L_{OPT}, we now allow *dynamically changing* lists. However to change a list L to some other list L' entails a *cost*. The cost measure we will use for our analysis is just the *minimum number of transpositions* needed to transform L to L'. Thus, in our model, each probe costs 1 and each transposition costs 1. (We will discuss the possibility of different weightings at the end of the paper.) In order to fix ideas, let us examine a simple special case, namely, the case in which we have just *three* records, say, a, b and c. We are given some arbitrary sequence $Q = \{q_1, q_2, ...\}$ with $q_i \in \{a,b,c\}$. We are required to produce a sequence of lists $L_0, L_1, L_2, \ldots$, each L_i being some permutation of $\{a,b,c\}$, where we choose without loss of generality $L_0 = (a,b,c)$. For $i = 1,2,3, \ldots$, the cost associated with the ith request q_i is the *sum* of the cost of transforming list L_{i-1} to list L_i, and the cost of finding record q_i in list L_i (i.e., 1, 2 or 3 depending on whether q_i is the first, second or third entry in L_i).

We can model this process in terms of moving a *pebble* π on a graph G, in this case consisting of a 6-cycle C_6, labelled as shown in Fig. 1.

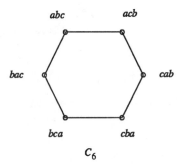

Figure 1

In fact, this is just the graph formed by taking the set of six permutations of $\{a,b,c\}$ as its vertex set, and placing an edge between two vertices if the corresponding permutations differ by a single transposition.

Let d denote the usual (path-metric) distance on this graph, where if X, $Y \subseteq V = \{a,b,c\}$ then $d(X,Y): = \min\{d(x,y): x \in X, y \in Y\}$. Any sequence of lists $L_0, L_1, L_2, \ldots$ can be regarded as successive positions occupied by the pebble π, starting from the initial vertex $L_0 = (a,b,c)$ (which are identify with vertex abc, etc.). Partition the vertex set V into three sets: $V_a = \{abc, acb\}$, $V_b = \{bac, bcd\}$ and $V_c = \{cab, cba\}$. Thus, for the request sequence $Q = (q_1, q_2, \ldots)$ and the "pebble sequence" $P = (L_0, L_1, L_2, \ldots)$, the cost of the i^{the} access is just

(1) $$c_i(Q,P) = d(L_{i-1}, L_i) + d(V_{q_i}, L_i) + 1,$$

where the term $+1$ comes from the fact that the cost of probing the list L_i to find the record q_i is *one more* than the distance of (vertex) L_i to the corresponding set V_{q_i}. One goal might be, given Q, to determine P so that

$$c(Q,P): = \limsup_{N \to \infty} \frac{1}{N} \sum_{i=1}^{N} c_i(Q,P)$$

is minimized. Other possible objectives will be mentioned in subsequent sections.

It was shown by Tarjan and Wei [45] that the following algorithm achieves this desired minimum value for this case. Suppose $L_i = abc$ (without loss of generality) and $Q_{i+1} = (q_{i+1}, q_{i+2}, q_{i+3}, \ldots)$ is the current request sequence seen after i steps. To form the list L_{i+1} move b in front of a only if two b's occur in Q_{i+1} *before* one a occurs. Similarly, move c in front of a only if two c's occur before one a occurs, and do the same for b and c. Thus, the relative order of *each* pair in $\{a,b,c\}$ for L_{i+1} is determined, which thereby determines L_{i+1}.

This same technique gives an algorithm for generating an optimal sequence of lists in the case of *two* records, in which L_{i+1} can be determined by only knowing the next *two* symbols q_{i+1} and q_{i+2}. This is in contrast to this algorithm for the case of *three* records which may require unbounded look-ahead. In fact, already for the case of *four* or more records, the corresponding questions appear to be substantially more difficult and optimal list selection algorithms are not currently known. One problem with the preceding approach for the use of four records is that the adjoining graph G_{24} of lists now has 24 vertices and has a certain amount of structure (see Fig. 2).

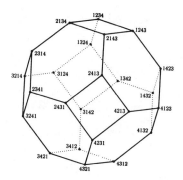

Figure 2

Our approach in this paper will be to focus on these generic questions with two changes: (1) We will consider *all* connected graphs G rather than just those arising from permutations of an n-set; (2) The requests will always consist of *single* vertices of G rather than more general *subsets* of vertices.

It will be seen that for this problem we can say a fair amount, although we are still far from having a complete understanding even here.

Moving pebbles on graphs. We now give a more precise formulation of our problem. For a given connected graph $G = (V,E)$, let $d = d_G$ denote the usual (path-metric) distance on G, i.e., for $x,y \in V$, $d(x,y)$ is equal to the minimum number of edges in any path between x and y. For a *request* sequence $Q = (q_1, q_2, ...)$ and a *pebbling* sequence $P = (p_0, p_1, p_2, ...)$, with q_i, $p_j \in V$, define

$$c_N(Q,P) = \sum_{i=1}^{N} (d(p_{i-1},p_i) + d(p_i,q_i)),$$

$$\bar{c}(Q,P) = \limsup_{N \to \infty} \frac{1}{N} c_N(Q,P),$$

(2)

$$\bar{c}(Q) = \inf_P \bar{c}(Q,P),$$

$$\lambda(G) = \sup_Q \bar{c}(Q),$$

We call $\lambda(G)$ the *search value* of G. We currently know of no polynomial-time algorithm for determining $\lambda(G)$. Note that we have normalized c_N by omitting the automatic +1 term occurring in (1).

Let us call the sequence P Q-*optimal* if

$$\sup_N (c_N(Q,P) - c_N(Q,\hat{P}))$$

is bounded for all pebbling sequences $\hat{P}$. For any Q, Q-optimal sequences always exist, as the following argument shows. Let Q_k denote the finite request sequence $(q_1,q_2,\ldots,q_k)$ and suppose $P_k = (p_{k0},p_{k1},\ldots,p_{kk})$ denotes an *optimal* pebbling sequence for Q_k. That is, P_k minimizes

$$c_k(Q_k,P_k) = \sum_{i=1}^{k} (d(p_{kj-1}, p_{kj}) + d(p_{kj}, q_i))$$

over all possible pebbling sequences of length $k+1$. Define an infinite pebbling sequence $P^* = (p_0^*, p_1^*,\ldots)$ using the König infinity lemma, so that any initial segment $P_m^* = (p_0^*, p_1^*, \ldots, p_m^*)$ occurs as an initial segment of infinitely many of the P_k. However, for any $i \leq k$, if $P_k(i)$ denotes the initial segment $(p_{k0}, p_{k,1}, \ldots, p_{kj})$ then

(3) $c_i(Q_i, P_k(i)) - c_i(Q_i, P_i) \le$ diam (G)

where diam (G) denotes the *diameter* of G. This follows from the observation that

if (3) did not hold then the first $i+1$ terms of P_k would be replaced by P_i, thereby

forming a pebbling sequence $\hat{P}_k$ with

$$c_k(Q_k, \hat{P}_k) < c_k(Q_k, P_k) \, ,$$

which contradicts the definition of P_k.

For a finite request sequence $Q_k = (q_1, \ldots, q_k)$, we can characterize an

optimal pebbling sequence $P_k = (p_0, p_1, \ldots, p_k)$ in other terms as follows.

Consider the tree $S(Q, P)$ shown in Fig. 3.

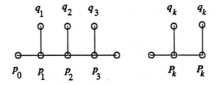

$S(Q,P)$

Figure 3

Such a graph is often called a *caterpillar*, with *leaves* $p_0, q_1, q_2, \ldots, q_k$ and

internal vertices $p_1, p_2, \ldots, p_k$. Since P_k is optimal for Q_k then we must have for

all i,

(4) $$d(p_{i-1}, p_i) + d(p_i, q_i) + d(p_i, p_{i+1})$$

$$\leq d(p_{i-1}, x) + d(x, q_i) + d(x, p_{i+1})$$

for all vertices $x \in G$ (otherwise, replacing p_i by x would decrease $c_k(Q_k, P_k)$).

Such a point p_i is called a *Steiner point* for the set $\{p_{i-1}, q_i, p_{i+1}\}$. The set of all

such Steiner points will be denoted by $S(p_{i-1}, q_i, p_{i+1})$. Thus,

$p_i \in S(p_{i-1}, q_i, p_{i+1})$ for $1 \leq i < k$. We will call the corresponding caterpillar a

Steiner minimal caterpillar for Q.

The windex of G. An algorithm A which produces a Q-optimal pebbling sequence

$A(Q)$ for each request sequence Q will be said to be an *optimal* algorithm for G.

It can happen that an algorithm A can produce Q-optimal algorithms even though

at any time only a finite portion of Q can be seen by A.

Definition. A graph G is said to have *windex* k, written $wx(G) = k$, if there is an

optimal algorithm A for G with the property that A always determines p_i with

only knowledge of q_j for $j < i + k$.

If there is no such k for G, we write $wx(G) = \infty$. The name windex, a

shortened form of window index, refers to the fact that one can think of A as

having a window through which exactly k future request symbols of Q can be seen.

In this section we discuss various elementary properties of the windex function.

In studying graphs with windex k it is useful to consider the process as a game

between two players, Red and Blue. At the ith step of the game:

(a)   Red selects the $(i+k)^{\text{th}}$ request vertex q_{i+k};

(b)   Blue then selects the ith pebble vertex p_i and pays Red the amount

$$d_G(p_{i-1}, p_i) + d_G(p_i, q_i) .$$

The initial choices of p_0 and $q_1, \ldots, q_k$ can be made arbitrarily.

Of course, the object of Blue is to minimize the amount paid to Red, whereas Red would like to maximize this amount.

Lemma 1. For any nontrivial graph G, $\omega x(G) \geq 2$.

Proof: Let $\{u, v\}$ be some edge of G and suppose Blue has available only a window of length 1, i.e., at the ith step Blue can only see q_{i+1}. Suppose $p_i = u$ and Blue sees $q_{i+1} = v$. If Blue elects to move the pebble π to v, i.e., selects $p_{i+1} = v$, then Blue pays 1 and Red can select $q_{i+2} = u$, reversing the preceding situation. Blue pays (possibly) even more if some $p_i \notin \{u, v\}$ is selected. On the other hand, if Blue choose $p_{i+1} = u$ then Blue pays 1 and Red can select $q_{i+2} = v$, duplicating the preceding situation. Thus, in any case, Red can choose the request sequence so that Blue pays at least 1 unit per request. However, for any sequence $Q = \{q_1, q_2, \ldots, q_N\}$ with all $q_i \in \{u, v\}$, Blue never has to pay more than $\frac{1}{2}N + \text{diam}(G)$, by just going to and staying at the more frequently occurring symbol. Thus, we must have $\omega x(G) \geq 2$. ∎

Lemma 2. If T is any nontrivial tree then $\omega x(T) = 2$.

Proof: By Lemma 1, it suffices to show $\omega x(T) \leq 2$. Suppose the pebble is at p_i, Blue sees q_{i+1} q_{i+2} and wants to determine p_{i+1}. We know that p_{i+1} should be a Steiner point of $\{p_i, q_{i+1}, p_{i+2}\}$ (although p_{i+2} is not yet determined). However, since T is a tree, $S(p_i, q_{i+1}, p_{i+2})$ will always consist of a unique vertex, which in fact, is just the same as the Steiner point $S(p_i, q_{i+1}, q_{i+2})$. Thus, Blue can construct a Q-optimal sequence using a window of length 2, and the proof is completed. ∎

Lemma 3. For the complete graph K_n on n vertices, $\omega x(K_n) = n$.

Proof: We first show that $\omega x(K_n) > n-1$. Let $V = \{v_1, \ldots, v_n\}$ and suppose (without loss of generality) $p_i = v_i$ and a length $n-1$ window shows $q_{i+1} = v_2, q_{i+2} = v_3, \ldots, q_{i+n-1} = v_n$. If $q_{i+n} = v_1$ then π should stay at v_1 (since otherwise Red is paying more than is necessary for this segment). On the other hand, if $q_{i+n} = v_2$ then π should move to v_2 (otherwise Red again pays too much). Thus, $\omega x(K_n) > n-1$.

In the other direction, it is not difficult to prove by induction that the following algorithm with a window of length n is optimal: choose p_{i+1} to be the *first repeated vertex* in the sequence $p_i, q_{i+1}, q_{i+2}, \ldots, q_{i+n}$. This shows that $\omega x(G) \le n$. ∎

For two graphs G and H, the *product* of G and H, denoted by $G \square H$, is defined to be the graph with vertex set $\{(u,v): v \in V(G), v \in V(H)\}$ and having as edges all pairs $\{(u,v), (u',v')\}$ where either $u = u'$ and $(v,v') \in E(H)$ or $v = v'$ and $(u,u') \in E(G)$. It is easy to check that

$$d_{G \square H}((u,v), (u',v')) = d_G(u,u') + d_H(v,v') .$$

Lemma 4.

$$\omega x (G \,\square\, H) = \max \{\omega x (G)), \omega x (H)\}$$

Proof: Let $(q_1,q'_1), (q_2,q'_2),...$ be a request sequence in $G \,\square\, H$. Suppose $p_0,p_1,p_2,...$ forms an optimal pebbling sequence for $q_1,q_2,...$ in G, and $p'_0,p'_1,p'_2,...$ forms an optimal pebbling sequence for $q'_1,q'_2,...$ in H. It is straightforward to check that in fact $(p_0,p'_0), (p_1,p'_1), (p_2,p'_2),...$ forms an optimal pebbling sequence for $(q_1,q'_1), (q_2,q'_2),...$ in $G \,\square\, H$. Thus,

$$\omega x (G \,\square\, H) \leq \max \{\omega x (G), \omega x (H)\} \ .$$

The reverse inequality is immediate and the lemma is proved. ∎

By the n-cube Q_n we mean the graph $K_2 \,\square\, K_2 \,\square\, \cdots \,\square\, K_2$ (n factors). As an immediate corollary of Lemma 4, we have

(5) $\omega x (Q_n) = 2 \ .$

Suppose G and H are graphs sharing exactly one common vertex v. Let $G \overset{v}{\cup} H$ denote the union of G and H.

Lemma 5.

$$\omega x (G \overset{v}{\cup} H) = \max \{\omega x (G), \omega x (H)\}$$

Proof: Let $Q = (q_1,q_2,...)$ be a request sequence in $G \overset{v}{\cup} H$. We will construct an optimal pebbling sequence $P = (p_0,p_1,p_2,...)$ inductively. Let k denote the maximum of $\omega x (G)$ and $\omega x (H)$. We will define p_i using only knowledge of

$Q_k = (q_{i+1}, \ldots, q_{i+k})$. Without loss of generality we may assume $p_{i-1} \in V(G)$.

Suppose either q_i or q_{i+1} is in $V(G)$. It then easily follows that $S(p_{i-1}, q_i, p_{i+1})$ must be contained in $V(G)$. Form $Q_k{}'$ from Q_k by replacing each q_j in $V(H)$ by v. Now use $Q_k{}'$ to determine an optimal choice (in G) for p_i. On the other hand, if both q_i and q_{i+1} are in $V(H)$ then form Q''_k from Q_k by replacing each q_j in $V(G)$ by v_1 and use Q_k'' to determine an optimal choice (in H) for p_i. In either case, we have managed to determine one more internal vertex in a Steiner minimal caterpillar for Q, using a window of length k. ∎

Note that Lemma 2 is just a consequence of Lemmas 5 and 3 (with $n = 2$). Using the preceding results we can construct large families of graphs having windex 2. These include not only trees, n-cubes and grids but various types of recursive combinations of these (using products and unions).

However, it turns out that *induced* or even *isometric* subgraphs of windex 2 graphs may not themselves have windex 2. A simple example is the 6-cycle C_6, an isometric subgraph of Q_3, which happens to have infinite windex.

We next recall a concept from topology which will be very relevant to our study of the windex of a graph.

Definition. A subgraph H of G is called a *retract* of G if there is a mapping from $V(G)$ to $V(H)$ which preserves edges, i.e., which maps adjacent vertices in G to adjacent vertices in H. Similarly, H is called a *weak retract* of G if there is a mapping from $V(G)$ to $V(H)$ such that adjacent vertices in G are mapped to either adjacent vertices or a single vertex in H.

Lemma 6. If H is a weak retract of G then

$$\omega x(H) \le \omega x(G) \ .$$

Proof: For a request sequence $Q = (q_1, q_2, \ldots, q_N)$ in H, let a corresponding optimal pebbling sequence in G be denoted by $P = (p_0, p_1, p_2, \ldots, p_N)$. Let $f: V(H) \to V(G)$ be a mapping making H a weak retract of G, and consider the pebbling sequence $f(P) = (f(p_0), f(p_1), f(p_2), \ldots, f(p_N))$ in H.

Clearly,

$$c_N(Q, f(P)) \le c_N(Q, P) \ .$$

Thus, we may restrict our search for a Q-optimal pebbling sequence to the subgraph H. Thus, if $\omega x(H) \ge k$ then $\omega(G) \ge k$ as well. This proves the lemma. ∎

We conclude this section with several examples of graphs having infinite windex.

Lemma 7. Let $K_{2,3}$ denote the complete bipartite graph on vertex sets of sizes two and three. Then

$$\omega x(K_{2,3}) = \infty \ .$$

Proof: Let the vertex sets of $K_{2,3}$ be denoted by $\{x_1, x_2\}$ and $\{y_1, y_2, y_3\}$, where the edges of $K_{2,3}$ are exactly all the pairs $\{x_i, y_j\}$. Suppose $\omega x(K_{2,3}) = k < \infty$. Consider a request sequence formed by repeating the sequence $(y_1 y_2 y_3)^* z$ where $(y_1 y_2 y_3)^*$ means that the string $y_1 y_2 y_3$ is repeated so that it has length greater than $k+10$, and z is either x_1 or x_2. When Blue sees the window with (just) an initial segment of $(y_1y_2y_3)^*$ visible, there are several options for the pebble π. If π is moved to x_1 then this is not optimal if z were to be x_2. Similarly, if π is moved to x_2 then this is not optimal if z were to be x_1. On the other hand, to move to (or stay at) any of the y_i is also suboptimal since Blue pays at least 4 for each occurrence of the three requests $y_1y_2y_3$ with this strategy, which costs more than moving to some x_i right away. We can repeat this process infinitely often in a request sequence Q, causing Blue to pay an unbounded amount more than N for the first N requests. However, an Q-optimal pebbling sequence P^* satisfies $c_N(Q,P^*) \leq N+2$. Thus, $\omega x(K_{23}) > k$. Since k was arbitrary, the lemma is proved. ∎

Lemma 8. For the 5-cycle C_5, $\omega x(C_5) = \infty$.

Proof: Let $V(C_5) = \{0,1,2,3,4\}$ and suppose $\omega x(C_5) = k < \infty$. Consider a request sequence Q formed by concatenating subsequences of the form $S = 002414(24130)^* z$ where z is either 0 or 2. The block 24130 is repeated ω times where $5\omega > k$. Let $p_0, p_1, p_2, \ldots$ denote the (purported) optimal pebbling sequence. We may assume $p_0 = p_1 = 0$ without increasing the cost. If $p_5 \neq 0$ or 4, z could be chosen to be 0. The total cost of accessing S is at least $6(\omega+1)$, *one more* than the optimal cost of $6(\omega+1) - 1$ achieved by choosing $p_5 = 0$ or 4. On the other hand, if $p_5 = 0$ or 4 then z could be chosen to be 2. In this case, the total cost Blue pays is at least $6(\omega+1) + 1$, again which is one more than the optimal cost. Thus, as in the previous lemma, $\omega x(C_5) > k$ for any k, and the proof is complete. ∎

Graphs of windex 2. In this section we will characterize the class of graphs having windex 2. A consequence of this characterization will be a polynomial-time algorithm for deciding if $\omega x (G) = 2$.

Before we state the main theorem we need a definition. A graph G is called a *median* graph if for any three distinct vertices a, b and c of G, there is a unique vertex of G which lies simultaneously on shortest paths joining a and b, a and c, and b and c. Median graphs arise naturally in the study of ordered sets and discrete distributive lattices, and have an extensive literature (cf. [3,4,5,6,28,33,34,35,36]). We say that G has the *unique Steiner point property* if $S(a,b,c)$ contains exactly one element.

Theorem 1. For a (nontrivial) connected graph G, the following four statements are equivalent:

(a) $\omega x (G) = 2$;

(b) G has the unique Steiner point property;

(c) G is a median graph;

(d) G is a retract of Q_n for some n.

Proof: First, observe that the implication $(d) \Rightarrow (a)$ is an immediate consequence of Lemmas 1 and 6, and equation (5). We also point out that the equivalence of (c) and (d) has been proved by H. J. Bandelt [7]. We will prove $(a) \Rightarrow (b) \Rightarrow (c)$.

Before beginning, we need several definitions. For vertices u and v in G, a shortest path joining u and v is called a (u,v)-path. Let $SP(u,v)$ denote the union of all vertices on all (u,v)-paths.

Proof of $(a) \Rightarrow (b)$: Suppose $\omega x(G) = 2$. Let a,b and c be three distinct vertices in G having two distinct Steiner points, say s and s'. Furthermore, among all such triples, choose a,b and c so that $t = d(a,s) + d(b,s) + d(c,s)$ is as small as possible. First, consider a request subsequence $aabczz$ where z is either s or s'. Let the corresponding pebbling sequence be denoted by $p_0, p_1, p_2, \dots$ Thus, we must have $p_1 = a = p_2$ and the window shows b,c. Without loss of generality we can assume $p_3 \ne s'$. Take $z = s'$. The Steiner minimal caterpillar for the sequence b,c,s',s' with $p_2 = a$ has length t. Then $d(p_4, s')$ must be 0, i.e., $p_4 = s'$, if $\omega x(G)$ is to be 2. Since we assumed $p_3 \ne s'$, and since it must be *some* Steiner point for $\{a,b,c\}$ then we can assume without loss of generality that $p_3 = s$. Therefore, $d(s,s') + d(s',c) = d(s,c)$, and so, s' is on an (s,c)-path. By the minimality assumption in choosing $\{a,b,c\}$ we must have $c = s'$, since otherwise would could have chosen the set $\{a,b,s'\}$.

For this set, since

$$d(a,s') + d(b,s') + d(c,s') = t = d(a,s) + d(b,s) + d(c,s)$$
$$= d(a,s) + d(b,s) + d(s,s') + d(s',c)$$

then

$$d(a,s') + d(b,s') = d(a,s) + d(b,s) + d(s',s) = t'.$$

But s is a Steiner point of $\{a,b,s\}$ which then implies that s' also is a Steiner point of $\{a,b,s'\}$. Thus, we can conclude that $c = s'$ must be a Steiner point of $\{a,b,c\}$. By symmetry, a and b must also be Steiner points of $\{a,b,c\}$.

Now, in the request subsequence $aabczz$, suppose $z = a$. Then it follows that $p_1 = a = p_2$, and also $p_5 = p_4 = a$, and therefore $p_3 = a$. However, if $z = b$ then the same argument forces $p_5 = p_4 = p_3 = b$. Since $a \neq b$ then we have a contradiction. This shows $(a) \Rightarrow (b)$.

Proof of $(b) \Rightarrow (c)$: Suppose G has the unique Steiner point property. We will show that for any three distinct vertices a, b and c, the unique Steiner point s in fact satisfies

$$s = SP(a,b) \cap SP(a,c) \cap SP(b,c)$$

By symmetry, it will be enough to show that

$$s \in SP(a,b) .$$

Suppose $s \notin SP(a,b)$. Let $t \in SP(a,b)$ so that $d(s,t) = i > 0$ is as small as possible. Let $t = u_0, u_1, \ldots, u_i = s$ be a (t,s)-path.

Claim 1. $d(a,u_1) = d(a,t) + 1$.

Proof: Since $|d(a,u_1) - d(a,t)| \leq 1$ then $d(a,u_1)$ is either $d(a,t) - 1$, $d(a,t)$ or $d(a,t) + 1$. However, if $d(a,u_1) = d(a,t) - 1$ then $u_1 \in SP(a,b)$ which implies $d(s,SP(a,b)) < i$, a contradiction. Also, if $d(a,u) = d(a,t)$ then the Steiner minimal tree for the three vertices a, t and u_1 has length $d(a,t) + 1$, and there are two possible Steiner points, t and u_1, which achieve this minimum total length. This is also impossible, so the claim is proved.

Claim 2. $d(a,u_j) = d(a,t) + j$ for $j \leq i$.

Proof: The claim holds for $j = 0$ and $j = 1$. Suppose that for some j with $2 \leq j \leq i$ the claim holds for all $j' < j$. Since $|d(a,u_j) - d(a,u_{j-1})| \leq 1$ then $d(a,u_j)$ is either $d(a,u_{j-1}) - 1$, $d(a,u_{j-1})$ or $d(a,u_{j-1}) + 1$.

Case 1. Suppose $d(a,u_j) = d(a,u_{j-1}) - 1$. Consider the set $\{a,u_{j-2},u_j\}$, and let ω denote the length of its Steiner minimal tree. Clearly

$$d(a,u_{j-2}) \leq \omega \leq d(a,u_{j-2}) + 2 \ .$$

If $\omega = d(a,u_{j-2})$ then u_j is on a (a,u_{j-2})-path which implies $d(a,u_j) = d(a,u_{j-1}) - 1 = d(a,u_{j-2})$ by induction, which is impossible. On the other hand, if $\omega = d(a,u_{j-2}) + 2$ then there would have to be at least two Steiner points, namely u_{j-2} and u_j, which is a contradiction.

Thus, we must have $\omega = d(a,u_{j-2}) + 1$. Let s' denote the (unique) Steiner point of the set $\{a,u_{j-2},u_j\}$. It is easily checked that $d(s',u_j) = d(s',u_{j-2}) = 1$ and $d(a,s') = d(a,u_{j-2}) - 1 = d(a,t) + j - 3$. This implies $d(s',SP(a,b)) = j - 1$ and that s' is on an (s,t)-path. However, by induction we have $d(a,s') = d(a,t) + j - 1$, which contradicts the preceding equation. Thus, Case 1 cannot occur.

Case 2. Suppose $d(a,u_j) = d(a,u_{j-1})$. Therefore, the Steiner minimal tree for the set $\{a,u_j,u_{j-1}\}$ has length $d(a,u_j) + 1$, and furthermore, there are two Steiner points u_{j-1} and u_j, which is impossible. Thus, Case 2 cannot occur, and we are left with one possibility, namely

$$d(a,u_j) = d(a,u_{j-1}) + 1 = d(a,t) + j$$

which proves Claim 2.

In the same way we can prove that

$$d(b,u_i) = d(b,t) + i$$

Therefore,

$$d(a,s) + d(b,s) = d(a,t) + d(b,t) + 2i$$
$$= d(a,t) + d(b,t) + d(t,s) + i .$$

Since s is a Steiner point for $\{a,b,c\}$ and therefore, also for $\{a,b,s\}$, then we have $i = 0$, i.e., $s \in P(a,b)$, a contradiction. This complete the proof of the theorem. ∎

We next give an alternative characterization of graphs of windex 2. This will lead to an efficient algorithm for determining if $\omega x(G) = 2$. First, we need a definition. For two (connected) graphs G and H, we say that G can be *isometrically embedded* into H if there is a map $\phi: V(G) \to V(H)$ such that for all $u,v \in V(G)$,

$$d_G(u,v) = d_H(\phi(u), \phi(v)).$$

Various aspects of isometric embeddings can be found in [1,2,14,15,17,18,19,20]. Suppose G is isometrically embeddable into the n-cube Q_n. Thus, each vertex v of G is associated with a binary n-tuple $\phi(v) = (v_1, \ldots, v_n) \in V(Q_n)$. For three vertices $\bar{a} = (a_1, \ldots, a_n)$, $\bar{b} = (b_1, \ldots, b_n)$ and $\bar{c} = (c_1, \ldots, c_n)$ of H, define the *majority* vertex $M(\bar{a}, \bar{b}, \bar{c}) = (m_1, \ldots, m_n)$ of H by choosing for each i, $m_i = z_i$ where *at least two* of the values a_i, b_i, c_i are equal to z_i. Let us call a subset $X \subseteq V(H)$, *majority-closed* if for any $x, y, z \in X$, $M(x, y, z) \in X$.

Theorem 2. A (nontrivial) graph G has windex 2 if and only if G can be isometrically embedded into some Q_n, say by the map ϕ, and $\phi(V(G))$ is majority-closed.

Proof: Suppose $\phi: V(G) \rightarrow V(Q_n)$ is an isometric embedding of G into Q_n, and $\phi(V(G))$ is majority-closed. It is easy to see that for any three distinct vertices $\bar{a}$, $\bar{b}$, $\bar{c}$ of Q_n, $M(\bar{a}, \bar{b}, \bar{c})$ is their unique Steiner point. Thus, since ϕ preserves distances then for any three distinct vertices a, b, c of G, $\phi^{-1}(M(\phi(a), \phi(b), \phi(c)))$ is their unique Steiner point in G. Therefore, by Theorem 1, $\omega x(G) = 2$.

In the other direction, suppose $\omega x(G) = 2$. By Theorem 1, G is a retract of Q_n for some r. Thus, for vertices u, v of G, $d_G(u, v) \leq d_{Q_n}(u, v)$. Since (by the definition of retract) G is a subgraph of Q_n then $d_G(u, v) \geq d_{Q_n}(u, v)$. Therefore, $d_G(u, v) = d_{Q_n}(u, v)$, i.e., G is isometrically embeddable in Q_n. Also from Theorem 1, we know that G is a median graph. For three vertices a, b and c of Q_n, the unique vertex in $SP(a, b) \cap SP(a, c) \cap SP(b, c)$ is exactly $M(a, b, c)$. This implies that G is also closed under M. This proves Theorem 2. ∎

Theorem 3. If G has n vertices then "$\omega x(G) = 2$?" can be tested in $O(n^4)$ steps.

Proof: By a result in [20.5], any n-vertex subgraph of a Q_n can have at most $c\,n\log n$ edges (for a fixed small c). First, check to verify that this holds for G. Next, compute a list of the distances between all pairs of vertices in G. This can be done in $O(ne)$ steps. Then use the decomposition algorithm given in [18] to determine whether (and, if so, how) G can be isometrically embedded into some Q_n. This requires $O(e^2)$ steps. Finally, in $O(n^4)$ steps, determine if G is closed under the majority function M. Since $e = O(n\log n)$ then this algorithm requires at most $O(n^4)$ steps, as required. ∎

We point out here that the following generalization for graphs of windex k has been proved by F. R. K. Chung and M. E. Saks and will appear elsewhere.

Theorem   A graph G has $\omega x(G) \leq k$ if and only if G is a retract of $K_k \,\square\, K_k \,\square\, \cdots \,\square\, K_k$, ($n$ factors) for some n.

The search value of a graph. Recall that for request sequences $Q = (q_1, q_2, \ldots)$ and pebbling sequences $P = (p_0, p_1, p_2, \ldots)$ we have defined the *search value* $\lambda(G)$ of G to be:

$$\lambda(G) = \sup_{Q} \inf_{P} \limsup_{N \to \infty} \frac{1}{N} \sum_{i=1}^{N} (d(p_{i-1}, p_i) + d(p_i, q_i))$$

In this section we will discuss several results relating to $\lambda(G)$. As we remarked earlier, however, we do not currently know of a polynomial time algorithm for determining $\lambda(G)$. It can be shown however ([43]) that $\lambda(G)$ is always rational. It is not difficult to show that

$$\lambda(G \overset{v}{\cup} H) = \max\{\lambda(G), \lambda(H)\},$$

$$\lambda(G \square H) = \lambda(G) + \lambda(H)$$

For any graph G, if we choose $Q = (u, v, u, v, u, v, ...)$ where $d(u, v) = \text{diam}(G)$ then we obtain

$$\lambda(G) \geq \frac{1}{2}\text{diam}(G)$$

On the other hand, let $\text{rad}(G)$ denote the *radius* of G, defined by

$$\text{rad}(G) = \inf_{u} \sup_{v} d(u, v) .$$

Let c denote a vertex in the *center* of G, i.e., such that

$$\sup_{v} d(c, v) = \text{rad}(G).$$

By choosing $P = (c, c, c, ...)$ then we have

$$\lambda(G) \leq \text{rad}(G)$$

This proves the following.

Lemma 9.

$$\frac{1}{2}\text{diam}(G) \leq \lambda(G) \leq \text{rad}(G) \leq \text{diam}(G) .$$

It turns out that for *trees*, the lower bound in Lemma 9 is tight.

Lemma 10. If T is a tree then

$$\lambda(T) = \frac{1}{2}\text{diam}(T)$$

Proof: For any tree T,

$$2 \operatorname{rad}(T) - 1 \le \operatorname{diam}(T) \le 2 \operatorname{rad}(T) .$$

If $\operatorname{diam}(T) = 2 \operatorname{rad}(T)$ then the desired conclusion follows by Lemma 9. So, suppose $\operatorname{diam}(T) = 2 \operatorname{rad}(T) - 1$. Thus, T has *two* centers c_1 and c_2, joined by an edge. It is easy to see that by moving the pebble on the set $\{c_1, c_2\}$ appropriately (and, of course, a window of length 2 is enough here) we can bound the cost per request by $\frac{1}{2}(2 \operatorname{rad}(T) - 1) = \frac{1}{2} \operatorname{diam}(T)$ This proves the lemma. ∎

We next consider cycles C_n. As is often the case in graph theory, *even* cycles are somewhat easier to deal with than *odd* cycles.

Lemma 11.

$$(i) \quad \lambda(C_{2m}) = \frac{m}{2};$$

$$(ii) \quad \lambda(C_{2m+1}) = \frac{m(m+1)}{2m+1}.$$

Proof (i): By Lemma 9 we have

$$\lambda(C_{2m}) \ge \frac{1}{2} \operatorname{diam}(C_{2m}) = \frac{m}{2} .$$

We will show the reverse inequality by using a pebbling strategy which does not move the pebble! For any finite request sequence $Q_N = (q_1, q_2, \ldots, q_N)$, let $Q_N(v)$ denote the number of q_i equal to v, where v is a vertex of C_{2m}. Thus, $\sum_v Q_N(v) = N$. The cost per request $\bar{c}(v)$ of staying at a vertex v, i.e., selecting

$P = (v,v,v, \ldots, v)$ is

$$\bar{c}(v) = \frac{1}{N} \sum_u Q_N(v)d(u,v)$$

where u ranges over all vertices of C_{2m}. The average of $\bar{c}(v)$ over all v is just

$$\frac{1}{2m} \sum_v \bar{c}(v) = \frac{1}{2mN} \sum_v \sum_u Q_N(v)d(u,v)$$

$$= \frac{1}{2mN} \sum_v Q_N(v) \sum_u d(u,v)$$

$$= \frac{1}{2m} \sum_u d(u,v) = \frac{m}{2}$$

Thus, for *some* vertex v^*, $\bar{c}(v^*) \leq \frac{m}{2}$. Therefore, $\lambda(C_{2m}) \leq \frac{m}{2}$ as required.

(ii): An averaging argument similar to that used in the proof of *(i)* shows that

$$\lambda(C_{2m+1}) \leq \frac{1}{2m+1} \sum_u d(u,v) = \frac{m(m+1)}{2m+1} \ .$$

To prove the reverse inequality, we will use a request sequence of the form

$$Q = (0, m+1, m+2, 2, m+3,...)$$

where we take for $V(C_{2m+1})$ the set of integers modulo $(2m+1)$. Thus, consecutive requests q_i, q_{i+1} in Q always satisfy

$$d(q_i, q_{i+1}) = m = \text{diam}(C_{2m+1})$$

A straightforward (but slightly messy) analysis of this choice shows that *the cost the pebbler must pay for any $2m+1$ requests is always at least $m(m+1)$*, no matter where the pebble happens to be at the start of the request sequence. This then shows that $\lambda(C_{2m+1}) \geq \dfrac{m(m+1)}{2m+1}$ and the proof of the lemma is complete. ∎

We can apply the preceding averaging argument to general graphs G and obtain a bound $\lambda_{LP}(G)$ on $\lambda(G)$, which we call the *linear programming* bound, which is usually quite good for small graphs. It is obtained as follows. As before, for a finite request sequence $Q_N = (q_1, q_2, \ldots, q_N)$, let $Q_N(v)$ denote the number of occurrences of v in Q_N. The cost per request of staying at v is just

$$\bar{c}(v) = \frac{1}{N} \sum_u Q_N(v) d(u,v)$$

$$= \sum_u \frac{1}{N} Q_N(v) d(u,v)$$

$$= \sum_u \alpha(v) d(u,v)$$

where $\alpha(v) = \dfrac{1}{N} Q_N(v)$. Suppose we now consider the linear program:

$$\sum_u x(v) d(u,v) - z \geq 0, \quad v \in V(G)$$

$$\sum_v x(v) = 1, \quad x(v) \geq 0,$$

maximize z .

Denote the maximum value of z by $\lambda_{LP}(G)$. Thus, if $\lambda > \lambda_{LP}(G)$ and $x(v) = \alpha(v)$ satisfy $\sum_v x(v) = 1$ then for at least one vertex v_0,

$$\bar{c}(v_0) = \sum_u \alpha(v_0)\, d(u,v_0)$$

$$= \sum_u x(v_0)\, d(u,v_0) < \lambda_{LP}(G)$$

so that keeping the pebble π at v_0 results in a cost per request of less than $\lambda_{LP}(G)$. Therefore,

$$\lambda(G) \leq \lambda_{LP}(G)\,.$$

Although as we have remarked earlier this bound is usually rather good for small graphs, for "most" graphs it is off by a factor of 2! This follows from the following observation of Joel Spencer. For a fixed ρ, $0 < \rho < 1$, consider the random graph $G_\rho(n)$ on n vertices formed by selecting each potential edge independently with probability ρ. Thus, almost certainly, $\deg(v) = (1+o(1))\rho n$ and $d(u,v) \leq 2$ for all vertices u,v of $G_\rho(n)$. We can bound $\lambda_{LP}(G_\rho(n))$ by choosing all $x(v) = \dfrac{1}{n}$ in the linear program, giving

$$\lambda_{LP}(G_\rho(n)) \geq (1+o(1))(\rho n \cdot 1 + (1-\rho)n \cdot 2) \cdot \frac{1}{n}$$

$$= 2 - \rho + o(1)$$

However, for any fixed k, if n is sufficiently large then $G_\rho(n)$ almost certainly has the property that for any k vertices $q_1, \ldots, q_k$, there is some vertex p with $d(p,q_i) = 1$ for $1 \leq i \leq k$. Thus, the pebbler can partition the request sequence Q into consecutive blocks of length k, say $B_1, B_2, \ldots$ For each B_j, the pebble π is moved a distance of at most 2 to a vertex adjacent to *all* vertices in B_j, resulting in a cost per request of at most $\dfrac{1}{k}(2 + k \cdot 1) = 1 + \dfrac{2}{k}$. Since k can be taken arbitrarily large then $\lambda(G_\rho(n)) = 1$.

A specific example in which this behavior can be demonstrated can be constructed as follows. Let $S = PG(3,F)$ denote projective 3-space over the field $F = GF(5)$ (cf. [3], [5]). Thus, S has 156 points and 156 planes, with each plane containing 31 points and each point lying in 13 planes. To each point $s \in S$ we can associate a plane $s^\perp$, consisting of all $t \in S$ orthogonal to s, i.e., with $s \cdot t = 0$. Our graph G^* will have $V(G^*) = S$ and edges $\{u,v\}$ where $u \in v^\perp$ (and loops $\{u,u\}$ are deleted). Then G^* has maximum degree 13 and diameter 2. Thus,

$$\lambda_{LP}(G^*) \geq \frac{1}{156}(31 + 124 \cdot 2) = \frac{279}{156}$$

by choosing all $x(v) = \frac{1}{156}$. On the other hand, since any three points lie in *some* plane, we can always choose a pebbling sequence P (by partitioning Q into blocks of length 3 as described earlier) which has cost per request of at most $5/3$. Since $5/3 < 279/156$ then

$$\lambda(G^*) < \lambda_{LP}(G^*)$$

It would be interesting to find small graphs for which this holds.

The linear programming bound can be strengthened by allowing π to have more mobility in the following way. For a fixed integer k, we will partition Q into blocks of length k. The pebble will only be moved at the beginning of each block, and will remain fixed for all requests from the block. The bound we get by this strategy corresponds to the solution of the following *integer* programming problem:

$$\sum_u a(v)d(u,v) - z_k, \quad v \in V(G),$$

$$\sum_v a(v) = k, \quad a(v)\text{-nonnegative integers,}$$

$$\text{maximize} \quad (z_k + \text{diam}(G))/k$$

The maximum value of $(z_k + \text{diam}\,G)/k$ is denoted by $\lambda_{I_k}(G)$. It is clear that

$$\lambda(G) \le \inf_k \lambda_{I_k}(G) := \lambda_I(G) \le \lambda_{LP}(G)$$

Observe that for the random graph $G_\rho(n)$,

$$\lambda_I(G_\rho(n)) \to 1 \quad \text{as} \quad n \to \infty.$$

Concluding remarks. There are numerous questions concerning dynamic search on graphs which currently remain unanswered. We will close by discussing these and some related issues.

(i) *Is there a polynomial-time algorithm for computing $\lambda(G)$?* The algorithm of Saks [43] runs in time $O(n^n)$ where G has n vertices.

(ii) We have already mentioned that it can be shown that $\lambda(G)$ is always *rational. What is*

$$q(n) = \max\{q : \lambda(G) = P/q, \ G \text{ has } n \text{ vertices}\}?$$

It seems likely that $q(n)$ can grow exponentially with n. If C_5^+ denotes the graph formed by adding one chord to a 5-cycle then it is not hard to show that $\lambda(C_5^+) = 7/6$, thus giving an example showing $q(5) > 5$ (this can be easily generalized to show that $q(n) > n$).

(iii)   In all of the examples we have seen thus far, request sequences

$Q = (q_1, q_2, ...)$ which achieve $\bar{c}(Q) = \lambda(G)$ have had the property that

$$d(q_i, q_{i+1}) = \text{diam}(G) ,$$

i.e., consecutive requests are as far away from each other as possible. While there is a certain intuitive justification for this property, it can sometimes fail to produce the extremal Q, as the following example shows. Let G_{11} denote the graph shown in Fig. 4.

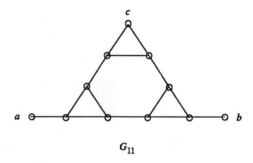

G_{11}

Figure 4

It is easy to see that if Q has for all i

$$d(q_i, q_{i+1}) = 5 = \text{diam}(G_{11})$$

then $\bar{c}(Q) = 5/2$ (since $d(x,y) = 5 \Rightarrow \{x,y\} = \{a,b\}$). On the other hand, it can be checked that $\lambda(G_{11}) = 8/3$ and this is achieved by $Q = (a,b,c,a,b,c,...)$. We remark that G_{11} also occurred as a counterexample in [11].

In this connection, the following question arises. For a (connected) graph G, define $\Delta(G)$, the *diameter graph* of G, by defining $V(\Delta(G)) = V(G)$ and $\{v,v'\}$ is an edge of $\Delta(G)$ provided $d_G(v,v') = \text{diam}(G)$. *Which graphs H occur as $\Delta(G)$ for some G?* In fact, it can be shown that *all* graphs H occur as (connected components of) diameter graphs. Typically, $\text{diam}(G)$ contains many components.

(iv)   *The λ-windex of G.* We will define $\omega x_\lambda(G)$, the λ-*windex* of G, in the same way that $\omega x(G)$ was defined, except that only Q-optimal algorithms with $\bar{c}(Q) = \lambda(G)$ must be produced (using a window of length $\omega x_\lambda(G)$). All of the questions for $\omega x(G)$ can also be asked for $\omega x_\lambda(G)$. These are not the same functions as shown, for example, by the graph $K_{2,3}$. As we have seen, $\omega x(K_{2,3}) = \infty$. However, $\lambda(K_{2,3}) = 1$ and it is not difficult to show that $\omega x_\lambda(K_{2,3}) = 2$.

Another such example is given by the graph P_{2n}, a path with $2n$ vertices. Here, $\omega x(P_{2n}) = 2$ while $\omega x_\lambda(P_{2n}) = 1$. *Is there a structural characterization of graphs G with $\omega x_\lambda(G) = k$?*

(v)   Of course, our choice to charge the same cost for moving the pebble across one edge as for having the pebble location p_i "miss" the requested vertex q_i by a distance of 1, was arbitrary (it is in some sense the simplest choice).

One could more generally define for some $\alpha > 0$,

$$C_N(Q,P) = \sum_{i=1}^{N} \left(d(p_{i-1}, p_i) + \alpha d(p_i, q_i) \right) .$$

What are the analogues of the preceding results for $\alpha \neq 1$?

REFERENCES

[1]   P. Assouad, Un espace hypermétrique non plongeable dans un espace L', C. R. Acad. Sci. Paris, 285 (ser A) (1977), 361-363.

[2]   P. Assouad and C. Delorme, Graphs plongeables dans L', C. R. Acad. Sci. Paris 291 (1980), 369-372.

[3]   S. P. Avann, Metric ternary distributive semi-lattices. Proc. Amer. Math. Soc. 12 (1961), 407-414.

[4]   H. J. Bandelt, Free generalized Boolean extensions as iterated Sholander extensions. Algebra Universalis (to appear).

[5]   H. J. Bandelt and J. Hedlíková, Median algebras. Discrete Math. (to appear).

[6]   H. J. Bandelt and H. M. Mulder, Infinite median graphs, $(0,2)$-graphs, and hypercubes. J. Graph Theory (to appear).

[7]   H. J. Bandelt, Retracts of hypercubes, preprint.

[8]   J. L. Bentley, C. C. McGeoch, Worst-case analyses of self-organizing sequential search heuristics, Communication of ACM (to appear).

[9]   J. R. Bitner, Heuristics that dynamically alter data structure to reduce their access time, Ph.D. Thesis, Univ. of Illinois, (1976).

[10]   J. R. Bitner, Heuristics that dynamically organize data structures, SIAM J.

Comp. 8 (1979), 82-110.

[11] F. R. K. Chung, J. Cohen and R. L. Graham, Pursuit-evasion in graphs (to appear).

[12] F. R. K. Chung, D. J. Hajela and P. Seymour, Self-organizing sequential search and Hilbert's inequality, Proc. 17th Symposium on Theory of Computing (1985), 217-223.

[13] P. Dembowski, Finite Geometries, Springer-Verlag, New York, 1968.

[14] A. K. Dewdney, The embedding dimension of a graph, Ars Combinatoria 9 (1980), 77-90.

[15] D. Z. Djoković, Distance preserving subgraphs of hypercubes, J. Comb. Th. (B) 14 (1973), 263-267.

[16] D. Duffus and I. Rival, Graphs orientable as distributive lattices, Proc. Amer. Math. Soc. (to appear).

[17] R. L. Graham, On isometric embeddings of graphs in Proc. Waterloo Univ. Silver Jubilee).

[18] R. L. Graham and P. M. Winkler, On isometric embeddings of graphs Transactions Amer. Math. Soc. 288 (1985), 527-539.

[19] R. L. Graham and H. O. Pollak, On the addressing problem for loop switching, Bell Sys. Tech. Jour., 50 (1971), 2495-2519.

[20] R. L. Graham and H. O. Pollak, On embedding graphs in squashed cubes,

Graph Theory and Applications, in Lecture Notes in Math. No. 303, Springer-Verlag, New York, 1972, 99-110.

[20.5] R. L. Graham, On primitive graphs and optimal vertex assignments, NY Acad. Sci. 175 (1970), 170-186.

[21] G. Gonnet, J. I. Munro and H. Suwanda, Toward self-organizing sequential search heuristics, Proc. 20th IEEE Symp. Foundations Computer-Science, (1979), 169-174.

[22] E. Evans, Median lattices and convex subalgebras, Colloq. Math. Soc. János Bolyai, 29 Universal algebra (1982), 225-240.

[23] M. Hall, Jr., Combinatorial Theory, Blasidell Pub. Co, Waltham, Ma 1967.

[24] P. Hell, Rétractions de graphes, Ph.D. thesis, Université de Montréal, 1972.

[25] P. Hell, Absolute planar retracts and the four color conjecture. J. Combinatorial Theory 17 (1974), 5-10.

[26] P. Hell, Absolute retracts in graphs, Springer-Verlag, New York, Lecture Notes Math. 406 (1974), 291-301.

[27] P. Hell, Graph retractions. Colloq. Intern. Teorie Combinatorie II, Roma, 1976, 263-268.

[28] J. R. Isbell, Median algebra. Trans. Amer. Math. Soc. 260 (1980), 319-362.

[29] Y. C. Kan and S. M. Ross, Optimal list order under partial memory constraints, J. Appl. Prob. 17 (1980), 1004-1015.

[30] N. Karmarkar, A new polynomial-time algorithm for linear programming, Combinatorica, v. 4 (1984), 373-395.

[31] D. E. Knuth, The Art of Computer Programming Vol. 3, Sorting and Searching, Addison-Wesley, Reading MA (1973), 398-399.

[32] J. McCabe, On serial file with relocatable records, Oper. Res. 12 (1965), 609-618.

[33] H. M. Mulder, The structure of median graphs. Discrete Math. 24 (1978), 197-204.

[34] H. M. Mulder, n-Cubes and median graphs. J. Graph Theory 4 (1980), 107-110.

[35] H. M. Mulder and A. Schrijver, Median graphs and Helly hypergraphs. Discrete Math. 25 (1979), 41-50.

[36] L. Nebeský, Median graphs. Comment. Math. Univ. Carolinae 12 (1971), 317-325.

[37] J. Nieminen, Join-semilattices and simple graphic algebras. Math. Nachr. 77 (1977), 87-91.

[38] R. Nowakowski and I. Rival, Fixed-edge theorem for graphs with loops. J. Graph Theory 3 (1979), 339-350.

[39] R. Nowakowski and I. Rival, On a class of isometric subgraphs of a graph. Combinatorica 2 (1982), 79-90.

[40] R. Nowakowski and I. Rival, The smallest graph variety containing all paths. Discrete Math. 43 (1983), 223-234.

[41] R. Nowakowski and P. Winkler, Vertex-to-vertex pursuit in a graph. Discrete Math. (to appear).

[42] R. Rivest, On self-organizing sequential search heuristics, CACM 19 (1976), 63-67.

[43] M. Saks (personal communication).

[44] R. E. Tarjan, Amortized computational complexity, SIAM J. Alg. Disc. Math. (to appear).

[45] R. E. Tarjan and V. Wei, (personal communication).

A Leaf-Size Hierarchy of Two-Dimensional Alternating Turing Machines

Katsushi Inoue,

Itsuo Takanami

Department of Electronics

Faculty of Engineering

Yamaguchi University

Ube, 755 Japan

and

Juraj Hromkovič

Department of Theoretical

Cybernetics

Comenius University

842 15 Bratislava

Czechoslovakia

Abstract. This paper introduces a simple, natural complexity measure for space bounded two-dimensional alternating Turing machines, called "leaf-size", and provides a hierarchy of complexity classes based on leaf-size bounded computations. Specifically, we show that for any positive integer $k \geq 1$ and for any two functions $L:N \to N$ and $L':N \to N$ such that (1) L is a two-dimensionally space-constructible function such that $L(m)^{k+1} \leq m$ ($m \geq 1$), (2) $\lim_{m \to \infty} L(m)L'(m)^k/\log m = 0$, and (3) $\lim_{m \to \infty} L'(m)/L(m) = 0$, $L(m)$ space bounded and $L(m)^k$ leaf-size bounded two-dimensional alternating Turing machines are more powerful than $L(m)$ space bounded and $L'(m)^k$ leaf-size bounded two-dimensional alternating Turing machines.

DISCRETE ALGORITHMS AND
COMPLEXITY

389

1. Introduction

Alternating Turing machines were introduced in [1] as a generalization of nondeterministic Turing machines and as a mechanism to model parallel computation. In papers [1-10], investigations of alternating machines have been continued. It seems to us, however, that there are many problems about alternating machines to be solved in the future.

In [6,9,10], we introduced a two-dimensional alternating Turing machine (2-ATM), and gave several properties of this machine. This paper continues the investigation of fundamental properties of 2-ATM's whose input tapes are restricted to square ones. In particular, we shall introduce a simple , natural complexity measure for 2-ATM's, called "leaf-size", and provide a hierarchy of complexity classes based on leaf-size bounded computations. Specifically, we show that for any positive integer $k \geq 1$ and for any two functions $L:N \to N$ and $L'':N \to N$ such that (1) L is a two-dimensionally space constructible function such that $L(m)^{k+1} \leq m$ $(m \geq 1)$, (2) $\lim_{m \to \infty} L(m)L'(m)^k/\log m = 0$, and (3) $\lim_{m \to \infty} L'(m)/L(m) = 0$, $L(m)$ space bounded and $L(m)^k$ leaf-size bounded two-dimensional alternating Turing machines are more powerful than $L(m)$ space bounded and $L'(m)^k$ leaf-size bounded two-dimensional alternating Turing machines. Leaf-size is a useful abstraction which provides a spectrum of complexity classes intermediate between nondeterminism and full alternation. The concept of leaf-size bounded computations have already been introduced in [6,7]. The similar concepts were introduced in [5, 8].

2. Preliminaries

Definition 2.1. Let Σ be a finite set of symbols. A two-dimensional tape over Σ is a two-dimensional rectangular array of elements of Σ.

The set of all two-dimensional tapes over Σ is denoted by $\Sigma^{(2)}$. Given a tape x in $\Sigma^{(2)}$, we let $\ell_1(x)$ be the number of rows of x and $\ell_2(x)$ be the number of columns of x. If $1 \leq i \leq \ell_1(x)$ and $1 \leq j \leq \ell_2(x)$, we let $x(i,j)$ denote the symbol in x with coordinates (i,j). Further, we define

$$x[(i,j),(i',j')],$$

only when $1 \leq i \leq i' \leq \ell_1(x)$ and $1 \leq j \leq j' \leq \ell_2(x)$, as the two-dimensional tape z satisfying the following:

(i) $\ell_1(z)=i'-i+1$ and $\ell_2(z)=j'-j+1$;

(ii) for each k, r $(1 \leq k \leq \ell_1(z), 1 \leq r \leq \ell_2(z))$, $z(k,r)=x(k+i-1,r+j-1)$.

We now recall a two-dimensional alternating Turing machine introduced in [6].

Definition 2.2. A two-dimensional alternating Turing machine (2-ATM) is a seven-tuple $M=(Q,q_0,U,F,\Sigma,\Gamma,\delta)$, where

(1) Q is a finite set of states,

(2) $q_0 \in Q$ is the initial state,

(3) $U \subseteq Q$ is the set of universal states,

(4) $F \subseteq Q$ is the set of accepting states,

(5) Σ is a finite input alphabet ($\# \notin \Sigma$ is the boundary symbol),

(6) Γ is a finite storage tape alphabet ($B \in \Gamma$ is the blank symbol),

(7) $\delta \subseteq (Q \times (\Sigma \cup \{\#\}) \times \Gamma) \times (Q \times (\Gamma-\{B\}) \times \{left,right,up,down,no\ move\} \times \{left ,right,no\ move\})$ is the next move relation.

A state q in Q-U is said to be existential. As shown in Fig.1, the machine M has a read-only (rectangular) input tape with boundary symbols "#" and one semi-infinite storage tape, initially blank. Of course, M has a finite control, an input head, and a storage tape head. A position is assigned to each cell of the read-only input tape and to each cell of the storage tape, as shown in Fig.1. A step of M consists of reading one symbol from each tape, writing a symbol on the storage tape, moving the input and storage heads in specified directions, and entering a new state, in accordance with the next move relation δ. Note that the machine cannot write the blank symbol. If the input head falls off the input tape, or if the storage head falls off the storage tape (by moving left) then the ma-

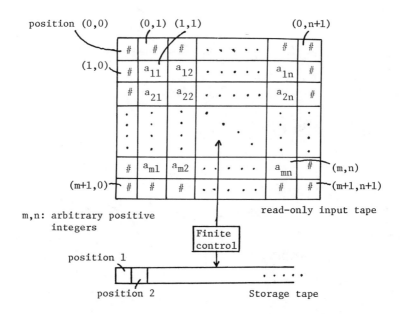

Fig.1.   Two-dimensional alternating Turing machine

chine can make no further move.

Definition 2.3.   An instantaneous description (ID) of a 2-ATM $M=(Q,q_0,U,$ $F,\Sigma,\Gamma,\delta)$ is an element of

$$\Sigma^{(2)} \times (N \cup \{0\})^2 \times S_M,$$

where $S_M = Q \times (\Gamma-\{B\})^* \times N$, and N denotes the set of all positive integers.

The first component of an ID $I=(x,(i,j),(q,\alpha,k))$[1] represents the input to M. The second component (i,j) of I represents the input head position. The third component (q,α,k) of I represents the state of the finite control, nonblank contents of the storage tape, and the storage-head position. An element of S_M is called a storage state of M. If q is the state associated with an ID I, then I is said to be universal (existential, accepting) ID

---

[1]We note that $0 \leq i \leq \ell_1(x)+1$, $0 \leq j \leq \ell_2(x)+1$, and $1 \leq k \leq |\alpha|+1$, where for any string w, $|w|$ denotes the length of w (with $|\lambda|=0$, where λ is the null string).

if q is a universal (existential, accepting) state. The _initial_ ID of M

on x is

$$I_M(x)=(x,(1,1),(q_0,\lambda,1)).$$

We write $I\vdash_{\overline{M}} I'$ and say I' is a _successor_ of I if an ID I' follows from

an ID I in one step of M. A _computation tree of M_ is a finite, nonempty

labeled tree with the properties

(1) each node π of the tree is labeled with an ID $\ell(\pi)$,

(2) if π is an internal node (a nonleaf) of the tree, $\ell(\pi)$ is universal

and $\{I \mid \ell(\pi)\vdash_{\overline{M}} I\}=\{I_1,\ldots,I_k\}$, then π has exactly k children $\rho_1,\ldots,$

ρ_k such that $\ell(\rho_i)=I_i$,

(3) if π is an internal node of the tree and $\ell(\pi)$ is existential, then

π has exactly one child ρ such that $\ell(\pi)\vdash_{\overline{M}} \ell(\rho)$.

A _computation tree of M on an input x_ is a computation tree of M whose

root is labeled with $I_M(x)$. An _accepting computation tree of M on x_ is a

computation tree of M on x whose leaves are all labeled with accepting

ID's. We say that M _accepts_ x if there is an accepting computation tree of

M on input x. Define

$$T(M)=\{x\in \Sigma^{(2)} \mid M \text{ accepts } x\}.$$

In this paper, we are mainly concerned with a 2-ATM whose input tapes are

restricted to square ones. We denote such a 2-ATM by 2-ATM^S.

Let $L:N\to N$ be a function with one variable m. With each 2-ATM^S M we asso-

ciate a space complexity function SPACE which takes ID's to natural num-

bers. That is, for each ID $I=(x,(i,j),(q,\alpha,k))$, let SPACE(I)=$|\alpha|$. We say

that M is _L(m) space bounded_ if for all m and for all x with $\ell_1(x)=\ell_2(x)=$

m, if x is accepted by M, then there is an accepting computation tree of M

on x such that for each node π of the tree, SPACE($\ell(\pi)$)$\leq$L(m).

We next present a simple, natural complexity measure for 2-ATM^S's, called

leaf-size [6]. Leaf-size, in a sense, reflects the number of processors

which run in parallel in reading a given input.

Definition 2.4. Let $Z:N \to N$ be a function with one variable m. For each finite tree t, let LEAF(t) denote the leaf-size of t (i.e., the number of leaves of t). We say that a 2-ATM^S M is $\underline{Z(m) \text{ leaf-size bounded}}$ if, for each m and for each input x with $\ell_1(x)=\ell_2(x)=m$, each computation tree t of M on x is such that LEAF(t)$\leq$Z(m).

By 2-ATM^S(L(m),Z(m)) we denote a simultaneously L(m) space bounded and Z(m) leaf-size bounded 2-ATM^S. Define

$$\mathcal{L}[2\text{-ATM}^S(L(m),Z(m))] = \{T \mid T=T(M) \text{ for some 2-ATM}^S(L(m),Z(m)) \text{ M}\}.$$

We need the following concepts in the next section.

Definition 2.5. A two-dimensional $\underline{\text{deterministic}}$ Turing machine [11] is a 2-ATM whose ID's each have at most one successor. A function $L:N \to N$ is $\underline{\text{two-dimensionally space constructible}}$ if there is a two-dimensional deterministic Turing machine M such that

(1) for each m$\geq$1 and for each input tape x with $\ell_1(x)=\ell_2(x)=m$, M uses at most L(m) cells of the storage tape,

(2) for each m$\geq$1, there exists some input tape x with $\ell_1(x)=\ell_2(x)=m$ on which M halts after its read-write head has marked off exactly L(m) cells of the storage tape, and

(3) for each m$\geq$1, when given any input tape x with $\ell_1(x)=\ell_2(x)=m$, M never halts without marking off exactly L(m) cells of the storage tape.

(In this case, we say that M $\underline{\text{constructs}}$ the function L.)

Definition 2.6. Let Σ_1, Σ_2 be finite sets of symbols. A $\underline{\text{projection}}$ is a mapping $\bar{\tau}:\Sigma_1^{(2)} \to \Sigma_2^{(2)}$ which is obtained by extending a mapping $\tau:\Sigma_1 \to \Sigma_2$ as follows: $\bar{\tau}(x)=x'$ (i) $\ell_k(x)=\ell_k(x')$ for each k=1,2, and (ii) $\tau(x(i,j))=x'(i,j)$ for each $(i,j)\in \{(i,j) \mid 1\leq i\leq\ell_1(x) \text{ and } 1\leq j\leq\ell_2(x)\}$.

3.Results

This section investigates a hierarchical property of the powers of space bounded 2-ATM^S's based on leaf-size bounded computations. Specifically, we show that $\mathcal{L}[2\text{-}ATM^S(L(m),L'(m)^k)] \subsetneqq \mathcal{L}[2\text{-}ATM^S(L(m),L(m)^k)]$ for any positive integer $k \geq 1$ and for any two functions L and L' such that (i) L is a two-dimensionally space-constructible function such that $L(m)^{k+1} \leq m$ ($m \geq 1$), (ii) $\lim_{m \to \infty} L(m)L'(m)^k/\log m = 0$, and (iii) $\lim_{m \to \infty} L'(m)/L(m) = 0$.

We first give several preliminaries to get the desired result. Let Σ be a finite alphabet. For each $m \geq 2$ and each $1 \leq n \leq m-1$, an <u>(m,n)-chunk</u> over Σ is a pattern x over Σ as shown in Fig.2., where $x_1 \in \Sigma^{(2)}$, $x_2 \in \Sigma^{(2)}$, $\ell_1(x_1)$ $= m-1$, $\ell_2(x_1) = n$, $\ell_1(x_2) = m$, and $\ell_2(x_2) = m-n$. (Below, "(m,n)-chunk" means an (m,n)-chunk over Σ.) Let M be a $2\text{-}ATM^S(\ell,z)$. Note that if the numbers of states and storage-tape symbols of M are s and t, respectively, then the number of possible storage states of M is $s\ell t^\ell$. Let Σ be the input alphabet of M, and let $\#$ be the boundary symbol of M. For any (m,n)-chunk x, we denote by $x(\#)$ the pattern (obtained from x by surrounding x with $\#$'s) as shown in Fig.3. Below we assume without loss of generality that for any (m,n)-chunk ($m \geq 2$, $1 \leq n \leq m-1$), M has the following property [2]:

(A) M enters or exits the pattern $x(\#)$ only at the face designated by the bold line in Fig.3, and M never enters an accepting state in $x(\#)$.

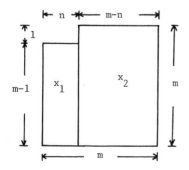
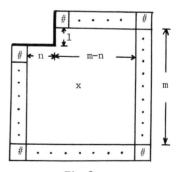

Fig.2. (m,n)-chunk.   Fig.3.

---

[2] Note that for any $2\text{-}ATM^S(\ell,z)$ M', we can construct a $2\text{-}ATM^S(\ell,z)$ M with the property (A) such that $T(M)=T(M')$.

Then the number of entrance points to $x(\#)$ for M is n+3. We suppose that these entrance points are numbered 1,2,...,n+3 as shown in Fig.4. For each (m,n)-chunk x, an ID of M on $x(\#)$ is of the form

$$(x(\#),(p,(q,\alpha,k))),$$

where p represents the position of the head of M on $x(\#)$, and (q,α,k) represents a storage state of M. The second component $(p,(q,\alpha,k))$ of an ID $I=(x(\#),(p,(q,\alpha,k)))$ is called the <u>configuration component</u> of I. For convenience sake, for each i $(1{\le}i{\le}n+3)$, let the position of the cell confronted with entrance point i of $x(\#)$ be "i". (See Fig.4.) Further, as shown in Fig.5, we consider n+2 virtual cells (confronted with $x(\#)$) designated

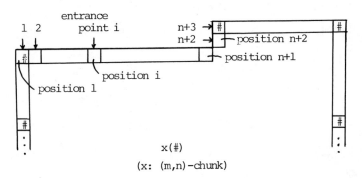

Fig.4. Entrance points to $x(\#)$ and positioning of the cells of $x(\#)$.

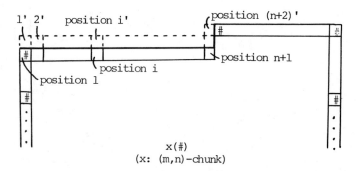

Fig.5. Virtual cells of $x(\#)$ and positioning of virtual cells.

by dotted line squares, and we assign positions $1',2',...,n',(n+1)',(n+2)'$
to these virtual cells. We include these positions in the set of positions
of the head of M on $x(\#)$.

An ID $I=(x(\#),(p,(q,\alpha,k)))$ is said to be <u>universal</u> (<u>existential</u>) if q is
a universal (existential) state. For any two ID's I and I' of M on $x(\#)$,
we write $I\vdash_M I'$ and say I' is a <u>successor</u> of I if I' follows from I in one
step of M on $x(\#)$. Note that for any ID $I=(x(\#),(p,(q,\alpha,k)))$, where x is
an (m,n)-chunk, such that $p \in \{1',2',...,n',(n+1)',(n+2)'\}$(i.e., p is a
virtual position), I has no successor.

A <u>computation tree of M on $x(\#)$</u> is a finite, nonempty labeled tree with
the properties

(1) each node π of the tree is labeled with an ID, $\ell(\pi)$, of M on $x(\#)$,

(2) if π is an internal node (a nonleaf) of the tree and $\ell(\pi)$ is univer-
    sal and $\{I \mid \ell(\pi)\vdash_M I\}=\{I_1,I_2,...,I_k\}$, then π has exactly k children
    $\rho_1,...,\rho_k$ such that $\ell(\rho_i)=I_i$,

(3) if π is an internal node of the tree and $\ell(\pi)$ is existential, then
    π has exactly one child ρ such that $\ell(\pi)\vdash_M \ell(\rho)$.

A <u>prominent computation tree</u> of M on an (m,n)-chunk x is a computation
tree of M on $x(\#)$ with the properties

(1) the root node is labeled with an ID of the form $(x(\#),(i,(q,\alpha,k)))$,
    where $1\le i\le n+3$ (i.e., the root node is labeled with an ID of M just
    after M entered the pattern $x(\#)$ from some entrance point i),

(2) each leaf node is labeled either

    (a) with an ID of the form $(x(\#),(j,(q,\alpha,k)))$, where $j \in \{1',2',...;$
        $(n+2)'\}$ (i.e., an ID of M just after M exited the pattern $x(\#)$),

or (b) with an ID I such that starting from the ID I, M never reaches a
        universal ID which has two or more successors, and M never exits
        $x(\#)$.

(A leaf node labeled with an ID of type (b) above is called a <u>looping leaf</u>
<u>node</u>. A leaf node labeled with an ID of type (a) above is called <u>normal</u>.)

Let $C=\{c_1,c_2,\ldots,c_u\}$ be the set of possible storage states of M, where u= $s\ell t^{\ell}$. For each prominent computation tree t of M on an (m,n)-chunk, let the <u>leaf configuration set</u> of t (denoted by LCS(t)) be a "multi-set" of elements of $\{1',2',\ldots,(n+2)'\}\times C\cup\{L\}$ (where L is a new symbol) defined as follows:

(1) For each normal leaf node π of t, LCS(t) contains the configuration component of $\ell(\pi)$;

(2) For each looping leaf node of t, LCS(t) contains the symbol L;

(3) LCS(t) does not contain any element other than elements described in (1) and (2) above.

(Note that for any prominent computation tree t of M, $|\text{LCS}(t)|\leq z$, since M is z leaf-size bounded.)[3]

For each (m,n)-chunk x and for each $(i,c)\in\{1,2,\ldots,n+3\}\times C$, let

$$M_{(i,c)}(x)=\{\text{LCS}(t)\mid t \text{ is a prominent computation tree of M on x}$$
$$\text{whose root is labeled with the ID } (x(\#),(i,c))\}.$$

Let x, y be two (m,n)-chunks. We say that x and y are <u>M-equivalent</u> if for each $(i,c)\in\{1,2,\ldots,n+3\}\times C$, $M_{(i,c)}(x)=M_{(i,c)}(y)$. For any (m,n)-chunk x and for any tape $v\in\Sigma^{(2)}$ with $\ell_1(v)=1$ and $\ell_2(v)=n$, let x[v] be the tape in $\Sigma^{(2)}$ consisting of v and x as shown in Fig.6.

The following lemma means that M cannot distinguish between two (m,n)-chunks which are M-equivalent.

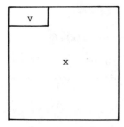

Fig.6. x[v]

---

[3]For any set S, $|S|$ denotes the number of elements of S.

<u>Lemma 3.1</u>. Let M be a 2-ATM^S(ℓ,z) with the property (A) described before, and Σ be the input alphabet of M. Let x and y be M-equivalent (m,n)-chunks over Σ (m$\geq$2, 1$\leq$n$\leq$m-1). Then, for any tape $v \in \Sigma^{(2)}$ with ℓ_1(v)=1 and ℓ_2(v)=n, x[v] is accepted by M if and only if y[v] is accepted by M.

Proof. "If part": We assume that y[v] is accepted by M. Then there exists an accepting computation tree t of M on y[v] such that LEAF(t) (i.e., the number of leaves of t) $\leq$ z. Since x and y are M-equivalent, we can construct from t an accepting computation tree t' of M on x[v] such that LEAF(t')=LEAF(t)$\leq$z. Therefore, x[v] is accepted by M.

"Only if part": Analogous to "If part". Q.E.D.

Clearly, M-equivalence is an equivalence relation on (m,n)-chunks, and we get the following lemma.

<u>Lemma 3.2</u>. Let M be a 2-ATM^S(ℓ,z) with the property (A) described before, and Σ be the input alphabet of M. Further, let s and t be the numbers of states and storage tape symbols of M, respectively, and let u=sℓt$^\ell$. Then there are at most

$$(2^{b^{z+1}})^d$$

M-equivalence classes of (m,n)-chunks over Σ, where b=(n+2)u+1 and d=(n+3)u.

Proof. The lemma follows from the observation that

(1) $|\{1,2,\ldots,n+3\} \times C|$=(n+3)u=d (where C is the set of possible storage states of M), and

(2) the number of possible leaf configuration sets of prominent computation trees of M on (m,n)-chunks is bounded by
$$b+b^2+\ldots+b^z \leq b^{z+1} \text{ (where b=(n+2)u+1)}$$
since M is z leaf-size bounded. Q.E.D.

We are now ready to prove the main theorem.

<u>Theorem 3.1.</u> Let $k \geq 1$ be a positive integer. Let $L:N \to N$ and $L':N \to N$ be any

functions such that (1) L is a two-dimensionally space-constructible fun-

ction such that $L(m)^{k+1} \leq m$ $(m \geq 1)$, (2) $\lim_{m \to \infty} L(m)L'(m)^k / \log m = 0$, and (3)

$\lim_{m \to \infty} L'(m)/L(m) = 0$. Then there is a set in $\mathcal{L}[2\text{-ATM}^S(L(m),L(m)^k)]$, but not

in $\mathcal{L}[2\text{-ATM}^S(L(m),L'(m)^k)]$.

Proof. Let M be a two-dimensional deterministic Turing machine which

constructs the function L. Let $T_k[L,M]$ be the following set, which depends

on k, L, and M.

$\quad T_k[L,M] = \{ x \in (\Sigma \times \{0,1\})^{(2)} \mid \; ^{\exists}m \geq 2 [\ell_1(x) = \ell_2(x) = m$ & (when the tape $\bar{h}_1(x)$

$\qquad$ is presented to M, its read-write head marks off exactly

$\qquad$ $L(m)$ cells of the storage tape and then halts) & $^{\exists}i(2 \leq i \leq m)$

$\qquad [\bar{h}_2(x[(1,1),(1,L(m)^{k+1})]) = \bar{h}_2(x[(i,1),(i,L(m)^{k+1})])] \}$,

where Σ is the input alphabet of M, and $\bar{h}_1$ $(\bar{h}_2)$ is the projection which is

obtained by extending the mapping $h_1:\Sigma \times \{0,1\} \to \Sigma$ $(h_2:\Sigma \times \{0,1\} \to \{0,1\})$ such

that for any $c=(a,b) \in \Sigma \times \{0,1\}$, $h_1(c)=a$ $(h_2(c)=b)$.

Below, we shall show that $T_k[L,M] \in \mathcal{L}[2\text{-ATM}^S(L(m),L(m)^k)]$ and $T_k[L,M] \notin$

$\mathcal{L}[2\text{-ATM}^S(L(m),L'(m)^k)]$. The set $T_k[L,M]$ is accepted by a $2\text{-ATM}^S(L(m),L(m)^k$

$)$ M_1 which acts as follows. Suppose that an input x with $\ell_1(x) = \ell_2(x) = m$ $(m$

$\geq 2)$ is presented to M_1. M_1 directly simulates the action of M on $\bar{h}_1(x)$.

If M does not halt, then M_1 also does not halt, and will not accept x. If

M_1 finds out that M halts (in this case, note that M_1 has marked off exa-

ctly $L(m)$ cells of the storage tape because M constructs the function L),

then M_1 existentially chooses some i $(2 \leq i \leq m)$ and moves its input head on

the first column of the i-th row of x. After that, M_1 universally tries to

check that, for each $1 \leq j \leq L(m)^k$, $\bar{h}_2(x[(i,(j-1)L(m)+1),(i,jL(m))]) = \bar{h}_2(x[(1,$

$(j-1)L(m)+1),(1,jL(m))])$. That is, on the i-th row and $((j-1)L(m)+1)$-st

column of x $(1 \leq j \leq L(m)^k)$, M_1 enters a universal state to choose one of two

further actions. One action is to pick up and store the segment $\bar{h}_2(x[(i,$

$(j-1)L(m)+1),(i,jL(m))])$ on some track of the storage tape (of course, M_1

uses exactly $L(m)$ cells marked off), to compare the segment stored above
with the segment $\bar{h}_2(x[(1,(j-1)L(m)+1),(1,jL(m))])$, and to enter an accepting state only if both segments are identical. The other action is to
continue moving to the i-th row and $(jL(m)+1)$-st column of x (in order to
pick up the next segment $\bar{h}_2(x[(i,jL(m)+1),(i,(j+1)L(m))])$ and compare it
with the corresponding segment $\bar{h}_2(x[(1,jL(m)+1),(1,(j+1)L(m))])$). Note
that the number of pairs of segments which should be compared with each
other in the future can be easily seen by using $L(m)$ cells of the storage
tape. It will be obvious that the input x is in $T_k[L,M]$ if and only if
there is an accepting computation tree of M_1 on x with $L(m)^k$ leaves. Thus
$T_k[L,M] \in \mathcal{L}[2\text{-ATM}^S(L(m),L(m)^k)]$.

We next show that $T_k[L,M] \notin \mathcal{L}[2\text{-ATM}^S(L(m),L'(m)^k)]$. Suppose that there is
a $2\text{-ATM}^S(L(m),L'(m)^k)$ M_2 accepting $T_k[L,M]$. Let s and t be the numbers of
states (of the finite control) and storage tape symbols of M_2, respectively. We assume without loss of generality that when M_2 accepts a tape x in
$T_k[L,M]$, it enters an accepting state only on the upper left-hand corner
of x, and that M_2 never falls off an input tape out of the boundary symbol
#. (Thus M_2 satisfies the property (A) described before.) For each $m \geq 2$,
let $w(m) \in \Sigma^{(2)}$ be a fixed tape such that (i) $\ell_1(w(m))=\ell_2(w(m))=m$ and (ii)
when $w(m)$ is presented to M, it marks off exactly $L(m)$ cells of the storage tape and halts. (Note that for each $m \geq 2$, there exists such a tape
$w(m)$ because M constructs the function L.) For each $m \geq 2$, let

$$V(m)=\{x \in (\Sigma \times \{0,1\})^{(2)} \mid \ell_1(x)=\ell_2(x)=m \ \& \ \bar{h}_2(x[(1,1),(m,L(m)^{k+1})]) \in$$
$$\{0,1\}^{(2)} \ \& \ \bar{h}_2(x[(1,L(m)^{k+1}+1),(m,m)]) \in \{0\}^{(2)} \ \& \ \bar{h}_1(x)=w(m)\}^4_,$$
$$Y(m)=\{y \in \{0,1\}^{(2)} \mid \ell_1(y)=1 \ \& \ \ell_2(y)=L(m)^{k+1}\},$$
$$R(m)=\{row(x) \mid x \in V(m)\},$$

where for each x in $V(m)$,

$$row(x)=\{y \in Y(m) \mid y=\bar{h}_2(x[(i,1),(i,L(m)^{k+1})]) \text{ for some } i \ (2 \leq i \leq m)\}.$$

---

[4] By the assumption that $L(m)^{k+1} \leq m$ $(m \geq 1)$, $V(m)$ is well defined.

Since $|Y(m)|=2^{L(m)^{k+1}}$, it follows that

$$|R(m)| = \begin{cases} \binom{2^{L(m)^{k+1}}}{1} + \binom{2^{L(m)^{k+1}}}{2} + \ldots + \binom{2^{L(m)^{k+1}}}{m-1} & \text{if } 2^{L(m)^{k+1}} > m-1 \\[2ex] \binom{2^{L(m)^{k+1}}}{1} + \ldots + \binom{2^{L(m)^{k+1}}}{2^{L(m)^{k+1}}} = 2^{2^{L(m)^{k+1}}} - 1 & \text{otherwise} \end{cases}$$

Note that $B=\{p \mid$ for some x in $V(m)$, p is the pattern obtained from x by cutting the segment $x[(1,1),(1,L(m)^{k+1})]$ off$\}$ is a set of $(m,L(m)^{k+1})$-chunks over $\Sigma \times \{0,1\}$. Since M_2 can use at most $L(m)$ cells of the storage tape and M_2 is $L'(m)^k$ leaf-size bounded when M_2 reads a tape in $V(m)$, from Lemma 3.2, there are at most

$$E(m) = (2^{b[m]^{L'(m)^k+1}})^{d[m]}$$

M_2-equivalence classes of $(m,L(m)^{k+1})$-chunks (over $\Sigma \times \{0,1\}$) in B, where $b[m]=(L(m)^{k+1}+2)u[m]+1$, $d[m]=(L(m)^{k+1}+3)u[m]$, and $u[m]=sL(m)t^{L(m)}$. We denote these M_2-equivalence classes by $C_1, C_2, \ldots, C_{E(m)}$. Since $\lim_{m\to\infty} L(m)L'(m)^k/\log m = 0$ and $\lim_{m\to\infty} L'(m)/L(m) = 0$ (by assumption), it follows that for large m, $|R(m)| > E(m)$. For such m, there must be some Q, Q' (Q≠Q') in $R(m)$ and some C_i ($1 \leq i \leq E(m)$) such that the following statement holds: "There exist two tapes x,y in $V(m)$ such that

(i) $x[(1,1),(1,L(m)^{k+1})]=y[(1,1),(1,L(m)^{k+1})]$ and $\bar{h}_2(x[(1,1),(1,L(m)^{k+1})])=\bar{h}_2(y[(1,1),(1,L(m)^{k+1})])=\rho$ for some ρ in Q but not in Q',

(ii) $row(x)=Q$ and $row(y)=Q'$, and

(iii) both p_x and p_y are in C_i, where p_x (p_y) is the $(m,L(m)^{k+1})$-chunk over $\Sigma \times \{0,1\}$ obtained from x (from y) by cutting the segment $x[(1,1),(1,L(m)^{k+1})]$ (the segment $y[(1,1),(1,L(m)^{k+1})]$) off."

As is easily seen, x is in $T_k[L,M]$, and so x is accepted by M_2. Therefore, from Lemma 3.1, it follows that y is also accepted by M_2, which is a contradiction. (Note that y is not in $T_k[L,M]$.) Thus $T_k[L,M] \notin \mathcal{L}[2\text{-ATM}^s(L(m), L'(m)^k)]$. This completes the proof of the theorem.   Q.E.D.

Corollary 3.1   Let $k \geq 1$ be a positive integer. Let $L:N \to N$ and $L':N \to N$ be any

functions satisfying the condition that $L'(m) \leq L(m)$ $(m \geq 1)$ and satisfying

conditions (1), (2), and (3) described in Theorem 3.1. Then

$$\mathcal{L}[2\text{-ATM}^S(L(m),L'(m)^k)] \subsetneqq \mathcal{L}[2\text{-ATM}^S(L(m),L(m)^k)].$$

For each r in N, let $\log^{(r)}m$ be the function defined as follows.

$$\log^{(1)}m = \begin{cases} 0 & (m=0), \\ \lceil \log m \rceil & (m \geq 1) \end{cases}$$

$$\log^{(r+1)}m = \log^{(1)}(\log^{(r)}m).$$

where $\lceil \log m \rceil$ denotes the smallest integer greater than or equal to $\log m$.

As shown in Theorem 3 in [12], the function $\log^{(r)}m$ $(r \geq 1)$ is two-dimensio-

nally space-constructible. It is easy to see that for each $r \geq 1$, $\log^{(r+1)}m \leq$

$\log^{(r)}m$ $(m \geq 1)$ and $\lim\limits_{m \to \infty} \log^{(r+1)}m/\log^{(r)}m = 0$. Further, for each $r \geq 2$ and

each $k \geq 1$, $\lim\limits_{m \to \infty} \log^{(r)}m(\log^{(r+1)}m)^k/\log m = 0$. From these facts and Corolla-

ry 3.1, we have

Corollary 3.2.   For any $r \geq 2$ and any $k \geq 1$,

$$\mathcal{L}[2\text{-ATM}^S(\log^{(r)}m,(\log^{(r+1)}m)^k)] \subsetneqq \mathcal{L}[2\text{-ATM}^S(\log^{(r)}m,(\log^{(r)}m)^k)].$$

It is unknown whether a result analogous to Corollary 3.2 also holds for

$r=1$ and $k \geq 1$. It will also be interesting to investigate leaf-size hierarchy

properties of the classes of sets accepted by 2-ATM^S's with spaces of size

greater than $\log m$.

REFERENCES

[1] A.K.Chandra, D.C.Kozen and L.J.Stockmeyer, Alternation, J.ACM 28 (1)

(1981) 114-133.

[2] R.E.Ladner, R.J.Ripton and L.J.Stockmeyer, Alternating pushdown auto-

mata, Proc.19th IEEE Symp. on Foundations of Computer Science, Ann Ar-

bor, MI (1978).

[3] W.L.Ruzzo, Tree-size bounded alternation, J.Comput.Systems Sci.21 (1980

) 218-235.

[4] W.Paul and R.Reischuk, On alternation, Part I, Acta Inform.14 (1980)

243-255.

[5] K.N.King, measures of parallelism in alternating computation trees, Proc.13th Ann.ACM Symp. on Theory of Computing (1981) 189-201.

[6] K.Inoue, I.Takanami and H.Taniguchi, Two-dimensional alternating Turing machines, Theoretical Computer Sci.27 (1983) 61-83.

[7] K.Inoue, I.Takanami and H.Taniguchi, A note on alternating on-line Turing machines, Information Processing Letters 15(4) (1982) 164-168.

[8] J.Hromkovic, On the power of alternation in automata theory, J.Comput. Systems Sci.31(1) (1985) 28-39.

[9] A.Ito, K.Inoue, I.Takanami and H.Taniguchi, Two-dimensional alternating Turing machines with only universal states, Inform. and Cont.55 (1-3) (1982) 193-221.

[10] K.Inoue, A.Ito, I.Takanami and H.Taniguchi, A space-hierarchy result on two-dimensional alternating Turing machines with only universal states, Inform.Sci.35 (1985) 79-90.

[11] K.Inoue and I.Takanami, Three-way tape-bounded two-dimensional Turing machines, Inform.Sci.17 (1979) 195-220.

[12] K.Morita, H.Umeo, H.Ebi and K.Sugata, Lower bounds on tape complexity of two-dimensional tape Turing machines, IECE Japan Trans.Section D (1978) 381-386.

SIMPLE PROGRAMS WITH A FIXED NUMBER OF VARIABLES SEEM STILL HARD TO ANALYZE

Shigeki Iwata
Information Science Laboratory
Tokai University
Hiratsuka 259-12 Japan
and
Takumi Kasai
Department of Computer Science
University of Electro-Communication
Chofu 182 Japan

ABSTRACT.

We consider the halting problem of simple programs with fixed number k of variables. The problem is solvable within $(k+2) \log n$ space. We show that the problem is not solvable within deterministic $((k-7)/2-\varepsilon) \log n$ space for any $\varepsilon > 0$. Under the conjecture that, for large k, there is a problem in deterministic $k \log n$ space which requires polynomial time with large degree to solve, the halting problem is not practically computable in the sense that it requires a large amount of time to solve.

1. Introduction.

It is believed that any NP complete problem can not be solved practically. Authors has established in [1] that some two-person game problem $G(k)$ has $\Omega(n^k)$ deterministic time lower bound. Thus the problem $G(k)$ is not practically solved for large k. Also in [5] they presented some problems solvable within nondeterministic log-space, having nondeterministic $k \log n$ space lower bound.

We show a problem in this paper, solvable within

deterministic log-space, which can not be solved in less than k log n deterministic space, and not supposed practically computable.

We use deterministic Turing machines as our computational model, which has a read-only input tape with endmarkers, and a single read-write work tape with binary alphabet, which has a leftmost cell but is infinite to the right.

Let $DSPACE_2(S(n))$ $(DTIME(T((n))))$ denote the class of languages accepted by Turing machines within $S(n)$ space ($T(n)$ time, respectively).

We introduce the set of programs consisting of the following statements:

    x:=c,
    if x=c goto ℓ,
    halt,

where x is a variable, c is a constant, and ℓ is a statement label. The number of variables which appear in a program is not greater than a fixed number k. We show that the halting problem of programs can not be solved within $((k-7)/2-\varepsilon)$ log n space for any $\varepsilon > 0$. The problem is solvable within $(k+2)$ log n space.

There seems to exist a language among k log n space computable problems, which is not computable in time of small degree polynomial. If we assume that for any a > 0 there is $L_k \in DSPACE_2(k \log n)$ such that $L_k \notin DTIME(n^a)$, then the halting problem is shown to have nontrivial polynomial time lower bound and not practically computable.

2. Definitions and Reduction Lemma.

We make some definitions in this section. Let Σ denote the alphabet $\{0,1\}$. We say that $L \subset \Sigma^*$ <u>requires</u> k log n space if L can not be solved in $(k-\varepsilon)$ log n space for any $\varepsilon > 0$. The function $f:\Sigma^* \to \Sigma^*$ is $S(n)$ <u>space</u> <u>computable</u> if there is a Turing machine M such that for each input $w \in \Sigma^*$, (1) the space of the computation of M does not exceed $S(n)$ tape cells, and (2) the computation produces $f(w)$ on the output tape then halts.

Definition. Let S and Z be monotone increasing functions on nonnegative integers. For L_1, $L_2 \subset \Sigma^*$, we say that L_1 is (S, Z)-<u>reducible to</u> L_2 if there is a S(n) space computable function $f:\Sigma^* \to \Sigma^*$ such that

(1) $w \in L_1$ if and only if $f(w) \in L_2$

(2) for any $w \in \Sigma^*$, $|f(w)| \leq Z(|w|)$.

The following lemma is a variation of [6, Proposition 3].

Lemma 1. Assume that $L \subset \Sigma^*$ is accepted by a S(n) space bounded Turing machine M with the set $\{0, 1, \#\}$ of tape symbols such that the work tape of M contains at most k occurances of # during the computation. Then there is a constant c_k such that L can be solved within

$$S(n)+c_k\lceil \log S(n)\rceil$$

space by a Turing machine M' with the set $\{0, 1\}$ of tape symbols.

By Lemma 1 and [2, Theorem 4], we obtain,

Lemma 2. Let L_1, $L_2 \subset \Sigma^*$. Then there is a constant c such that if L_1 is (S,Z)-reducible to L_2, and L_2 is solvable within $S_2(n)$ space, then L_1 can be solved within

$$\hat{S}(n)+c\lceil \log \hat{S}(n)\rceil$$

space, where $\hat{S}(n)=S_2(Z(n))+2\lceil \log Z(n)\rceil+S(n)$.

Outline of proof. The term $S_2(Z(n))$ comes from space bound on L_2 and the fact that reduced string f(w) is of length at most $Z(|w|)$. $2\lceil \log Z(n)\rceil$ comes from storing the current position of head of Turing machine for L_2 on input f(w) and the position for producing succesive symbol in obtaining current scanned symbols of f(w). S(n) comes from the computation of f(w). The rest of the proof comes from Lemma 1.

3. Simple programs with fixed number of variables.

We introduce simple programs and show some results in this section. The problem we consider is similar as in [3].

Let V be a finite set of <u>variables</u>, and A be a finite

set of constants. A k-memory program P_k is a finite
sequence $1:I_1; 2:I_2; ...; t:I_t;$ of labeled instructions such
that

    (1) each I_i is of the forms

        z:=a,

        if z=a goto ℓ,

        halt,

where z is a variable in V and a is a constant in A,
and ℓ is a label ($1 \leq \ell \leq t$);

    (2) I_t=halt,

    (3) $|V|=k$.

The length of P_k is determined by counting one for an
element in $V \cup \{ :=, =, if, goto, halt \}$, and the length of
the binary representation for labels and constants. Let
$HALT_k$ denote the halting problem of given k-memory program.
Jones and Muchnick [3] showed that the halting problem of a
given program is PSPACE complete if the number of variables
is not restricted. We show that the problem $HALT_k$ requires
$((k-7)/2)$ log n space, where the number of variables is
bounded by k.

    Theorem 1. Let $L \subseteq DSPACE_2(k \log n)$. Then there is a
constant c such that L is $((2+\varepsilon) \log n, cn^2 \log^3 n)$-reducible
to $HALT_{k+1}$ for any $\varepsilon > 0$.

    Proof. Since $L \in DSPACE_2(k \log n)$, there is a k log n
space bounded Turing machine M which accepts L. We devide
the work tape of M into k blocks, each of which is of length
$\lceil \log n \rceil$. We assume that at the beginning of computation of
M, every cell of the work tape contains 0 and that both
heads of tapes are at their leftmost positions. A
configuration of M consists of the current state, the
current head positions of the input and work tape, and
contents of the work tape.

    We constructs a (k+1)-memory program P_{k+1} from M and
its input to simulate computation of M. Let $z_0, z_1, ..., z_k$
be k+1 variables of the program. See Figure 1. For $0 \leq i \leq$
k-1, z_i contains information of (1) head position of the
work tape in the i-th block if the head scans a symbol in
the block, and (2) contents of the i-th block of the work

tape. The head position part of z_i remains 0 if the head of the work tape is not in the i-th block. This part of z_i requires loglog n bits to hold the head position, and the contents part of z_i requires log n bits to store contents of the block. Thus Z_i may have at most n log n distinct values. z_k contains either a constant 'accept', or (1) head position of the input tape, (2) the input symbol, and (3) the state of M. Let A = $\{a_0, a_1, \ldots, a_{m-1}\}$ be the set of constants which z_i (0 $\leq$ i $\leq$ k) takes as values. Note that m = O(n log n). The k+1 variables of P_{k+1} represent configuration of M, except what block the work tape head stays. The head position of the work tape is controlled by the program P_{k+1}.

For our convenience, we use macro notations for P_{k+1} such as %for and %if statements.

    %for i:=0 to k do S_i %end

generates k+1 statements

    S_0; S_1; ...; S_k

and

    %if   Q   then   S   %fi

generates S if condition Q holds, and generates nothing if Q does not hold. We use labels of the form $\ell( )$. We write goto statement immediately after an assignment statement, since

    z:= a; goto ℓ(label);

is equivalent to

    z:= a; if z=a goto ℓ(label);

Also we write goto ℓ(reject) instead of two consecutive statements

    z_k:=a;   if z_k=a goto ℓ(reject);

Here z_k:=a is a dummy statement to make unconditional branch.

The program P_{k+1} consists of five sections below:
(1) Initialization,
(2) Classification according to z_i and z_k,
(3) Simulation of one step of M,
(4) Treatment of work head position moving to the left block,
(5) Acceptance.

(1) Initialization.

P_{k+1} initializes k+1 variables so that they represent the initial configuration of M except the head position of the work tape; every head position part of z_i ($0 \leq i \leq k-1$) is set to 0. Let a_0 (a) be a constant meaning that the head position part of a_0 is 0 and every tape cell of a block is 0 (the input head position is 0, input symbol is the leftmost bit of the input tape, and state is the initial state, respectively). The program of this section is:

```
%for i:=0 to k-1 do
    z_i:=a_0;
%end
z_k:=a;
```

(2) Classification.

Suppose that the work tape head is in the i-th block. At most km^2 cases are classified according to z_i and z_k by executing if-goto statements. The program is as follows;

```
    %for i:=0 to k-1 do
 l(i):     %for j:=0 to m-1 do
               if z_i=a_j goto l(i,j);
           %end
           %for j:=0 to m-1 do
 l(i,j):       %for h:=0 to m-1 do
                   if z_k=a_h goto l(i,j,h);
               %end
           %end
    %end
```

(3) Simulation.

We simulate one step computation of M from $z_i=a_j$ and $z_k=a_h$. Note that we have enough information for the next move of M. Our program assigns new values to z_i and z_k. If the next move is not defined, P_{k+1} branches to l(reject). If the work head moves to the right block, we note that head position part of z_{i+1} is already 0, which means that the head is on the leftmost cell in the (i+1)-th block. If it moves to the left block, P_{k+1} branches to the label of the form ℓ(left,i). If M enters an accepting state then P_{k+1} assigns a constant 'accept' to z_k, and branches to ℓ(accept). The program of this section is:

```
%for i:=0 to k-1 do
     %for j:=0 to m-1 do
          %for h:=0 to m-1 do
ℓ(i,j,h):        %if the next move for zᵢ=aⱼ, z_k=a_h is defined
                 then
                      z_k:= the new value of z_k after one step
                           of M;
                      if z_k='accept' goto ℓ(accept);
                      zᵢ:= the new value of zᵢ after one step
                           of M;
                      %if the work head remains in the same block
                           then goto ℓ(i) %fi;
                      %if it moves to the right block
                           then goto ℓ(i+1) %fi;
                      %if it moves to the left block
                           then goto ℓ(left, i-1) %fi;
                 %fi
                 %if the next move is not defined
                      then goto ℓ(reject) %fi
          %end
     %end
%end
```

(4) Treatment.

When the head of the work tape moves to the left block, say to the i-th block, P_{k+1} changes the head position part of z_i so that the head position of the work tape is on the rightmost cell of the i-th block. The program for the section is:

```
       %for i:=0 to k-2 do
  ℓ(left,i): %for j:=0 to m-1 do
                   if z_i=a_j goto ℓ(left, i, j);
                 %end
                 %for j:=0 to m-1 do
  ℓ(left,i,j):  z_i := head position part indicates that the
                      head is at the rightmost cell, and
                      contents of the block is as the same
                      as old z_i;
                   goto ℓ(i)
                 %end
       %end
```

(5) Acceptance.

The last two statements are for M to reject or to accept its input.

```
  ℓ(reject):  goto ℓ(reject);
  ℓ(accept):  halt;
```

It is clear that M accepts its input if and only if P_{k+1} halts. We calculate the size of P_{k+1}. The length of programs in each section is $O(m^2 \log m)$. Since $m = O(n \log n)$, the length of P_{k+1} is bounded by $O(n^2 \log^3 n)$.

Consider the space amount for the construction. To generate programs in the one step simulation section, $(2+\varepsilon)$ log n space for any $\varepsilon > 0$ is sufficient, since counters for i, j, h need $(2 \log n + O(1))$ space, and we also use these counters for calculation of new values of z_i and z_k. For producing programs of other sections, $(2+\varepsilon)$ log n space is sufficient. Thus the space amount is $(2+\varepsilon)$ log n for any $\varepsilon > 0$.

Therefore, L is $((2+\varepsilon) \log n, cn^2 \log^3 n)$-reducible to $HALT_{k+1}$.

Remark. In the above construction of $HALT_{k+1}$, the time required for the reduction is $O(n^{2+\varepsilon})$ for any $\varepsilon > 0$.

We obtain the next corollary from Theorem 1 and Lemma 2.

Corollary 1. $HALT_k$ requires $((k-7)/2) \log n$ space for any $k > 7$.

Proof. Suppose that $HALT_k$ can be solved within $((k-7-\varepsilon_1)/2) \log n$ space for some $\varepsilon_1 > 0$. From Theorem 1, for any $(k-1) \log n$ space computable language L, there is a constant c such that L is $((2+\varepsilon) \log n, cn^2\log^3 n)$-reducible to $HALT_k$ for any $\varepsilon > 0$. Then by Lemma 2, there is a constant c_1 such that L can be solved within

$$\hat{S}(n) + c_1 \lceil \log \hat{S}(n) \rceil$$

space, where $\hat{S}(n) = ((k-7-\varepsilon_1)/2)\log(cn^2\log^3 n) + 2\log(cn^2\log^3 n) + (2+\varepsilon)\log n$. By simple calculation, it can be obtained that L is solvable within $((k-1)+\varepsilon-\varepsilon_1+\varepsilon_2) \log n$ space for any $\varepsilon_2 > 0$. Since ε and ε_2 are arbitrary, L can be solved within space less than $(k-1)\log n$. Then every language solvable within $(k-1)\log n$ space is solvable within space less than $(k-1)\log n$, this is a contradiction [6].

Hence $HALT_k$ requires $((k-7)/2) \log n$ space.

If the length of P_k is n then the number of constants in P_k is less than n and contents of k variables can be represented within $(k+\varepsilon) \log n$ space for any $\varepsilon > 0$. Considering another $\log n$ space for instruction counter, P_k can be solved within $(k+1+\varepsilon) \log n$ space, thus P_k is in

$$DSPACE_2((k+1+\varepsilon) \log n) - DSPACE_2(((k-7)/2) \log n)$$

for any $\varepsilon > 0$.

4. Remarks on time complexity.

Now let us consider time complexity of $HALT_k$. For small $a > 0$ and for large k, it seems that there exists a laguage $L_k \in DSPACE_2(k \log n)$ such that $L_k \notin DTIME(n^a)$. Thus we present,

Conjecture. For any a, there is an integer k such that
$$DSPACE_2(k \log n) \notin DTIME(n^a).$$

Note that if the above conjecture does not hold then we obtain $P \neq DL = \cup_k DSPACE_2(k \log n)$.

Now we define (time T, Z)-reducibility [1]: $L_1 \subset \Sigma^*$ is

(time T, Z)-reducible to $L_2 \subset \Sigma^*$ if there is T(n) time computable function $f: \Sigma^* \rightarrow \Sigma^*$ such that (1) $w \in L_1$ if and only if $f(w) \in L_2$, and (2) for any $w \in \Sigma^*$, $|f(w)| \leq Z(|w|)$.
Then we have the following lemma:

Lemma 3[1]. Let L_1 be (time T, Z)-reducible to L_2 and L_2 is T_2 time computable then L_1 is $T_2(Z(n))$ time computable.

We have constructed $HALT_{k+1}$ in the proof of Theorem 1. The time for the construction is bounded by n^{2+} time for any $\varepsilon > 0$. Thus we obtain,

Corollary 2. Let $L \in DSPACE_2(k \log n)$. Then there is a constant c such that L is (time $n^{2+\varepsilon}$, $cn^2 \log^3 n$)-reducible to $HALT_{k+1}$, for any $\varepsilon > 0$.

By Corollary 2 and Lemma 3, we obtain that if there is a fixed constant a such that for all k, $HALT_k \in DTIME(n^a)$, then
$$DSPACE_2(k \log n) \subset DTIME(n^{2a+\varepsilon})$$
for any $\varepsilon > 0$, violating the conjecture. Thus under the conjecture, for any a there is an integer k such that
$$HALT_k \notin DTIME(n^a).$$
This means that $HALT_k$ has a lower bound of n^a time, and it will not be practically computed for large k, under the conjecture.

REFERENCES

[1] A. Adachi, S. Iwata, and T. Kasai, Some combinatorial game problems require $\Omega(n^k)$ time, J. Assoc. Comput. Mach. 31, 361-376 (1984).

[2] N. Jones, Space-bounded reducibility among combinatorial problems, J. of Comput. System Sci. 11, 68-85 (1975).

[3] N. Jones and S. Muchnick, Even simple programs are hard to analyze, J. Assoc. Comput. Mach. 24, 338-350 (1977).

[4] T. Kasai, A. Adachi, and S. Iwata, Classes of pebble games and complete problems, SIAM J. Comput. 8, 574-586 (1979).

[5] T. Kasai, and S. Iwata, Gradually intractable problems and nondeterministic log-space lower bounds, Math. System Theory 18, 153-170 (1985).

[6] J. Seiferas, relating refined space complexity classes, J. of Comput. System Sci. 14, 100-129 (1977).

head position of the work
tape in the i-th block

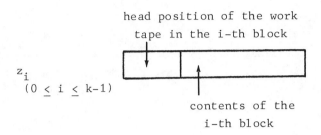

z_i
$(0 \le i \le k-1)$

contents of the
i-th block

'accept'

z_k

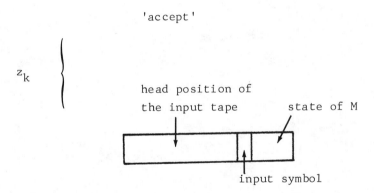

head position of
the input tape   state of M

input symbol

Figure 1   Variables of the program

Theory of the Multiplicative Penalty Function Method
for Linear Programming

Masao IRI

Department of Mathematical Engineering and Instrumentation Physics
Faculty of Engineering, University of Tokyo, Tokyo 113, Japan

and

Hiroshi IMAI

Department of Computer Science and Communication Engineering
Kyushu University, Fukuoka 812, Japan

Abstract

This paper surveys theory of the multiplicative penalty function method for solving a large scale linear programming problem. The method is a simple Newton-like descent algorithm for minimizing a multiplicative penalty function defined on the interior of the feasible region. The multiplicative penalty function is convex and, under a mild assumption, is strictly convex. The algorithm is shown to give local superlinear convergence to the optimum and, under some assumption, global linear convergence. It is similar to Karmarkar's in that it is an interior feasible direction method and self-correcting, while it is quite different from Karmarkar's in that it gives superlinear convergence and that projective geometry is not needed but only affine geometry suffices. Also discussed are techniques for directly handling the linear programming problem of which the optimum value of the objective function is not a priori known and for determining constraints which are inactive at all optimum solutions in the multiplicative penalty function method.

DISCRETE ALGORITHMS AND
COMPLEXITY

417

1. Introduction

Since Khachian's epoch-making work [8, 9], attempts have been made to develop fast algorithms for linear programming, different from the simplex method [1]. In 1984, Karmarkar [7] gave a new polynomial-time algorithm, which is an interior feasible direction method of minimizing a potential function by a kind of gradient projection method in a projectively transformed space. Although both Khachian's method and Karmarkar's are based on nonlinear programming techniques, the latter makes an epoch in that it sheds light on an interior feasible direction method for linear programming.

In this paper we survey theory of the multiplicative penalty function for linear programming, which was first introduced by the first author [3, 4], and subsequently has been refined and extended [2, 5, 6].

The method is of interior iterative type, and is a simple Newton-like descent algorithm for minimizing a multiplicative penalty function appropriately defined for a linear programming problem. An optimum solution to the original linear programming problem can be obtained by minimizing the multiplicative penalty function. The multiplicative penalty function to be minimized is convex, and, under a mild assumption, it is strictly convex. The proposed algorithm converges superlinearly when the optimum value of the objective function is known in advance, and, under some assumption, global linear convergence of the algorithm is guaranteed.

The above-mentioned results are described with the proofs in §§2~5, following Iri and Imai [6]. We also describe some results on extensions given in Imai [2] for directly handling the linear programming problem of which the optimum value of the objective function is not known and for determining constraints which are inactive at all optimum solutions in §6.

Results of some preliminary computational experiments are given in [2, 5, 6], which show that the number of iterations required by the algorithm is small and thus evidence the effectiveness of the algorithm.

2. Problem

The problem we shall consider in the following is to minimize the objective function

$$c(x) \equiv \sum_{\kappa=1}^{n} c_\kappa x^\kappa - c_0 \tag{2.1}$$

under the inequality constraints

$$a^i(x) \equiv \sum_{\kappa=1}^{n} a_\kappa^i x^\kappa - a_0^i \geq 0 \qquad (i = 1, \ldots, m), \tag{2.2}$$

where c_0, c_κ, a_0^i and a_κ^i $(\kappa = 1, \ldots, n; \, i = 1, \ldots, m)$ are given constants.

Following Karmarkar [7] we assume without loss in generality that the interior Int X of the feasible region

$$X \equiv \{ \, x \in \mathbf{R}^n \mid a^i(x) \geq 0 \; (i = 1, \ldots, m) \}, \tag{2.3}$$

is nonempty and a strictly interior point $x^{(0)} \in$ Int X:

$$a^i(x^{(0)}) > 0 \qquad (i = 1, \ldots, m) \tag{2.4}$$

is given, and that an optimum solution exists and the optimum (i.e., the minimum) value of the objective function is a priori known to be equal to zero:

$$c(\hat{x}) = \min\{ \, c(x) \mid x \in X \} = 0. \tag{2.5}$$

Note that (2.5) implies that $c(x) \geq 0$ at every point x in the feasible region X.

Furthermore, we exclude from our consideration some trivial cases by adopting further assumptions (i)~(iii) as follows, where we denote the set of optimum solutions by $\widehat{X}$:

$$\widehat{X} = \{x \in X \mid c(x) = 0\}. \tag{2.6}$$

(i) $\qquad\qquad \widehat{X} \neq X$, i.e., $c(x) > 0$ in Int X. $\tag{2.7}$

(ii) $\widehat{X}$ is bounded.

(iii) At a basic optimum solution (the existence of which is assured by assumption (ii)) there is at least one inactive constraint.

The condition (i) can be easily checked.

The condition (ii) is here assumed so that the sequence produced by the proposed algorithm does not diverge to infinity. As long as the sequence converges to a point of $\widehat{X}$, the condition (ii) is not necessary. If the tendency of the sequence diverging is detected, we may add an extra constraint so that the set of optimum solutions becomes bounded. In fact, as is well known [8], if there is an optimum solution at all, there is one such that the values of the components do not exceed a bound determined readily from the input data.

The condition (iii) is satisfied, for example, if the feasible region is bounded. The case in which (iii) fails to be satisfied can be handled trivially (see Proposition 3.5).

3. A Multiplicative Penalty Function and Its Derivatives

We define a new function $F(x)$ made up of the objective function $c(x)$ and the constraint functions $a^i(x)$, which will play the central role in our algorithm, as

$$F(x) \equiv c(x)^{m+1} \Big/ \prod_{i=1}^{m} a^i(x), \tag{3.1}$$

which is defined only in the interior Int X of the feasible region X.

Under the assumptions we took in §2, it is readily seen that

$$F(x) > 0 \quad \text{in} \ \text{Int} \ X. \tag{3.2}$$

Apparently, this is the affine analogue of Karmarkar's potential function [7], but it has a number of nice properties (the convexity property in particular) which can easily be observed as follows.

Proposition 3.1. If $F(x^{(\nu)}) \to 0$ for a sequence of interior feasible points $x^{(\nu)} \in$ Int X ($\nu = 0, 1, 2, \ldots$), then the distance between $x^{(\nu)}$ and $\widehat{X}$ converges to 0 (and hence, if there is a unique optimum, the sequence converges to it).

Proof: If the set of points $\{x^{(\nu)}\}$ is bounded, so are the $a^i(x^{(\nu)})$'s. Therefore $F(x^{(\nu)}) \to 0$ implies $c(x^{(\nu)}) \to 0$, and, due to the assumption (i), the distance between $x^{(\nu)}$ and $\widehat{X}$ tends to 0. If the set of points $\{x^{(\nu)}\}$ is not bounded, it might be possible that, because $a^i(x^{(\nu)})$ became large, $c(x^{(\nu)})$ did not converge to 0 even if

$F(x^{(\nu)}) \to 0$. However, even in such a case, there would be a constant $b^i(> 0)$ for each i such that $a^i(x)/c(x) \le b^i$, since there is no infinite feasible ray parallel to $\widehat{X}$ due to the assumption (ii), which would lead us to a contradiction that $F(x^{(\nu)}) = c(x^{(\nu)})^{m+1}/\prod_{i=1}^m a^i(x^{(\nu)}) \ge b \cdot c(x^{(\nu)})$ (where $b = \prod_{i=1}^m b^i$) did not converge to 0. $\square$

We might have chosen, instead of $m + 1$, a number greater than the number of active constraints at the optimum point in order only to have Proposition 3.1, but it will be seen that the choice of "$m+1$" or larger is essential also to the strict convexity of $F(x)$ as will be seen in (3.9) and the proof to Proposition 3.3.

The converse of Proposition 3.1 does not hold in general, but we have the following proposition instead.

Proposition 3.2. If the sequence $\{x^{(\nu)}\}$ converges to the optimum in a certain closed polyhedron P such that $\widehat{X} \subset P \subset \widehat{X} \cup \text{Int } X$ (including as a special case the convergence along a straight line), then $F(x^{(\nu)})$ tends to 0 as $\nu \to \infty$.

Proof: Since P is a closed polyhedron and Int X is an open polyhedron, for any $x \in P$ with $c(x) = \epsilon(> 0)$, there is a constant $b^i(> 0)$ such that $a^i(x) > b^i \cdot c(x)$ for each i. Hence $F(x) < c(x) \cdot \prod_{i=1}^m b^i$. $\square$

Thus, in order to find an optimum solution to our linear programming problem we may find a sequence of points $x^{(0)}, x^{(1)}, \ldots$ in Int X such that the sequence $F(x^{(0)})$, $F(x^{(1)}), \ldots$ rapidly converges to zero.

It is interesting to see that the derivatives of $F(x)$ have nice expressions as follows. To begin with we differentiate the logarithm of $F(x)$:

$$\log F(x) = (m + 1) \log c(x) - \sum_{i=1}^m \log a^i(x), \qquad (3.3)$$

to get

$$\eta_\kappa(x) \equiv \frac{\partial}{\partial x^\kappa} \log F(x) = \frac{1}{F(x)} \frac{\partial}{\partial x^\kappa} F(x) = (m + 1) \frac{c_\kappa}{c(x)} - \sum_{i=1}^m \frac{a_\kappa^i}{a^i(x)}. \qquad (3.4)$$

The vector $\boldsymbol{\eta} = \eta_\kappa$, which is actually the gradient of $F(x)$ divided by $F(x)$, will simply be called the "gradient" in the following. Denote

$$
\left.\begin{aligned}
\tilde{c}_\kappa(x) &\equiv \frac{c_\kappa}{c(x)}, \\
\tilde{a}^i_\kappa(x) &\equiv \frac{a^i_\kappa}{a^i(x)}, \\
\bar{a}_\kappa(x) &\equiv \frac{1}{m}\sum_{i=1}^m \tilde{a}^i_\kappa(x).
\end{aligned}\right\}
\tag{3.5}
$$

Then, we can write

$$
\eta_\kappa(x) = (m+1)\tilde{c}_\kappa(x) - m\bar{a}_\kappa(x).
\tag{3.6}
$$

Further differentiation will yield:

$$
\begin{aligned}
B_{\lambda\kappa}(x) &\equiv \frac{\partial^2}{\partial x^\lambda \partial x^\kappa}\log F(x) = \frac{1}{F(x)}\frac{\partial^2}{\partial x^\lambda \partial x^\kappa}F(x) - \eta_\lambda(x)\eta_\kappa(x) \\
&= -(m+1)\tilde{c}_\lambda(x)\tilde{c}_\kappa(x) + \sum_{i=1}^m \tilde{a}^i_\lambda(x)\tilde{a}^i_\kappa(x).
\end{aligned}
\tag{3.7}
$$

Thus, the Hessian matrix of $F(x)$ divided by $F(x)$, which we shall simply call "the Hessian" of $F(x)$ in the following, is

$$
H_{\lambda\kappa}(x) \equiv \frac{1}{F(x)}\frac{\partial^2}{\partial x^\lambda \partial x^\kappa}F(x) = B_{\lambda\kappa}(x) + \eta_\lambda(x)\eta_\kappa(x).
\tag{3.8}
$$

It is an amusing exercise to rewrite the expression for $H_{\lambda\kappa}$ using (3.6) and (3.7) by completing squares as follows.

$$
\begin{aligned}
H_{\lambda\kappa}(x) =\,& m^2[\tilde{c}_\lambda(x) - \bar{a}_\lambda(x)][\tilde{c}_\kappa(x) - \bar{a}_\kappa(x)] \\
&+ \sum_{i=1}^m [\tilde{c}_\lambda(x) - \tilde{a}^i_\lambda(x)][\tilde{c}_\kappa(x) - \tilde{a}^i_\kappa(x)] \\
=\,& m(m+1)[\tilde{c}_\lambda(x) - \bar{a}_\lambda(x)][\tilde{c}_\kappa(x) - \bar{a}_\kappa(x)] \\
&+ \sum_{i=1}^m [\tilde{a}^i_\lambda(x) - \bar{a}_\lambda(x)][\tilde{a}^i_\kappa(x) - \bar{a}_\kappa(x)].
\end{aligned}
\tag{3.9}
$$

The expression (3.9) itself shows that $H_{\lambda\kappa}$ is nonnegative definite, so that $F(x)$ is convex in Int X. Furthermore, under the assumption (iii) of §2, the positive definiteness of $H_{\lambda\kappa}$ can be proved as follows, where we note the well known fact that nonnegative (resp. positive) definiteness of the Hessian over an open domain implies the convexity (resp. strict convexity) over the domain.

Proposition 3.3. $H_{\lambda\kappa}$ is positive definite so that $F(x)$ is strictly convex in Int X.

Proof: We have already seen that $H_{\lambda\kappa}$ is nonnegative definite. If $H_{\lambda\kappa}$ is not positive definite at a point $x \in \text{Int } X$, there is a nonvanishing vector ξ such that

$$\sum_{\lambda=1}^{n} \sum_{\kappa=1}^{n} H_{\lambda\kappa} \xi^{\kappa} \xi^{\lambda} = m(m+1) \left\{ \sum_{\kappa=1}^{n} [\tilde{c}_{\kappa}(x)\xi^{\kappa} - \bar{a}_{\kappa}(x)\xi^{\kappa}] \right\}^2$$
$$+ \sum_{i=1}^{m} \left\{ \sum_{\kappa=1}^{n} [\tilde{a}_{\kappa}^i(x)\xi^{\kappa} - \bar{a}_{\kappa}(x)\xi^{\kappa}] \right\}^2 = 0, \qquad (3.10)$$

which means

$$\sum_{\kappa=1}^{n} \tilde{c}_{\kappa}(x)\xi^{\kappa} = \sum_{\kappa=1}^{n} \tilde{a}_{\kappa}^i(x)\xi^{\kappa} \equiv g \qquad (i = 1, \ldots, m). \qquad (3.11)$$

From the set $I = \{ i \mid a^i(\hat{x}) = 0 \}$ of active constraints at a basic optimum solution $\hat{x}$ we can then choose $\hat{I}$ such that $\{ a_{\kappa}^i \mid i \in \hat{I} \}$ is a maximal independent subset (i.e., a basis) of $\{ a_{\kappa}^i \mid i \in I \}$. Then, since

$$g = \sum_{\kappa=1}^{n} \tilde{a}_{\kappa}^i(x)\xi^{\kappa} = \frac{1}{a^i(x)} \sum_{\kappa=1}^{n} a_{\kappa}^i \xi^{\kappa} = 0 \quad \text{for} \quad i \in \hat{I} \qquad (3.12)$$

would imply $\xi^{\kappa} = 0$, g cannot vanish. Furthermore, for any linear form

$$b(x) = \sum_{\kappa=1}^{n} b_{\kappa} x^{\kappa} - b_0, \qquad (3.13)$$

there is a set of coefficients β_i such that

$$b_{\kappa} = \sum_{i \in \hat{I}} \beta_i a_{\kappa}^i \qquad (3.14)$$

and

$$b(x) - b(\hat{x}) = \sum_{i \in \hat{I}} \beta_i [a^i(x) - a^i(\hat{x})] = \sum_{i \in \hat{I}} \beta_i a^i(x). \qquad (3.15)$$

If there is an inactive constraint $a^{i_0}(\hat{x}) \neq 0$, then, taking $a^{i_0}(x)$ for $b(x)$, we have

$$ga^{i_0}(x) \neq g[a^{i_0}(x) - a^{i_0}(\hat{x})]$$
$$= g \sum_{i \in \hat{I}} \beta_i a^i(x) = \sum_{i \in \hat{I}} \sum_{\kappa=1}^{n} \beta_i a_{\kappa}^i \xi^{\kappa}$$
$$= \sum_{\kappa=1}^{n} a_{\kappa}^{i_0} \xi^{\kappa} = ga^{i_0}(x), \qquad (3.16)$$

which is a contradiction. $\square$

Proposition 3.4. The direction ξ determined by

$$\sum_{\kappa=1}^{n} H_{\lambda\kappa}(x)\xi^{\kappa} = -\eta_{\lambda}(x) \qquad (3.17)$$

is a strict descent direction of $F(x)$ at $x \in \text{Int } X$.

Proof: We have $\sum_{\lambda=1}^{n} \eta_\lambda \xi^\lambda = -\sum_{\lambda=1}^{n} \sum_{\kappa=1}^{n} H_{\lambda\kappa}(x) \xi^\kappa \xi^\lambda$, so that we have from the strict convexity of $H_{\lambda\kappa}$

$$\sum_{\kappa=1}^{n} \eta_\kappa \xi^\kappa < 0. \quad \square \tag{3.18}$$

Proposition 3.5. If the assumption (iii) does not hold, $F(x)$ is linear along the rays emanating from a unique optimum solution $\hat{x}$.

Proof: There is a unique optimum solution since, otherwise, the assumption (ii) would imply the assumption (iii). For any feasible x, we have

$$\left. \begin{aligned} a^i(x) &= a^i(x) - a^i(\hat{x}) = \sum_{\kappa=1}^{n} a_\kappa^i \cdot (x^\kappa - \hat{x}^\kappa), \\ c(x) &= c(x) - c(\hat{x}) = \sum_{\kappa=1}^{n} c_\kappa \cdot (x^\kappa - \hat{x}^\kappa). \end{aligned} \right\} \tag{3.19}$$

Therefore, on the line $x(t) = \hat{x} + t\xi$ with a constant vector ξ, we have

$$F(x(t)) = t \cdot \left(\sum_{\kappa=1}^{n} c_\kappa \xi^\kappa \right)^{m+1} \Big/ \prod_{i=1}^{m} \left(\sum_{\kappa=1}^{n} a_\kappa^i \xi^\kappa \right), \tag{3.20}$$

i.e., the function $F(x)$ is linear along the rays emanating from $\hat{x}$. $\quad \square$

4. Algorithm

The algorithm we propose is straightforward on the basis of the observation we made in the previous section.

1° Start from the given initial point $x^{(0)} \in \text{Int } X$.

2° Iteration: —

At the ν-th approximation $x^{(\nu)}$, compute $F^{(\nu)} = F(x^{(\nu)})$ (from the viewpoint of numerical computation we should not compute $F^{(\nu)}$ itself but $\log F^{(\nu)}$), $\eta_\kappa^{(\nu)} = \eta_\kappa(x^{(\nu)})$ and $H_{\lambda\kappa}^{(\nu)} = H_{\lambda\kappa}(x^{(\nu)})$ by (3.3), (3.4), (3.7) and (3.8) (or (3.9)), and then solve the system of linear equations

$$\sum_{\kappa=1}^{n} H_{\lambda\kappa}^{(\nu)} \xi^{(\nu)\kappa} = -\eta_\lambda^{(\nu)} \qquad (\lambda = 1, \dots, n) \tag{4.1}$$

to determine the vector $\xi^{(\nu)\kappa}$.

Perform the line search in the direction of $\xi^{(\nu)}$ to find the minimum of $F(x)$ on that line, i.e., determine t^* by

$$\left[\frac{\mathrm{d}}{\mathrm{d}t}F(x^{(\nu)}+t\xi^{(\nu)})\right]_{t=t^*}=0 \tag{4.2}$$

and set

$$x^{(\nu+1)}=x^{(\nu)}+t^*\xi^{(\nu)}. \tag{4.3}$$

In the algorithm proposed in the above, it is theoretically assumed that we can obtain the exact value of t^*. Computationally, the line search in each iteration step can be done very quickly, and, from the point of view of the polynomiality of the algorithm, even the bisection search would be sufficient to determine t^* to within the "threshold of resolution" [8]. Practically, we may adopt any reasonable method and more hasty stopping rule therefor. Here, we have

$$\left.\begin{aligned}
f(t) &= F(x^{(\nu)}+t\xi^{(\nu)}) = [c(x^{(\nu)})+\gamma t]^{m+1}\Big/\prod_{i=1}^{m}[a^i(x^{(\nu)})+\alpha^i t],\\
\gamma &= \sum_{\kappa=1}^{n}c_\kappa\xi^{(\nu)\kappa}, \quad \alpha^i = \sum_{\kappa=1}^{n}a_\kappa^i\xi^{(\nu)\kappa} \quad (i=1,\ldots,m),\\
\frac{1}{f(t)}\frac{\mathrm{d}}{\mathrm{d}t}f(t) &= (m+1)\frac{\gamma}{c(x^{(\nu)})+\gamma t} - \sum_{i=1}^{m}\frac{\alpha^i}{a^i(x^{(\nu)})+\alpha^i t},\\
\frac{1}{f(t)}\frac{\mathrm{d}^2}{\mathrm{d}t^2}f(t) &= \left[\frac{1}{f(t)}\frac{\mathrm{d}}{\mathrm{d}t}f(t)\right]^2\\
&\quad -(m+1)\left[\frac{\gamma}{c(x^{(\nu)})+\gamma t}\right]^2 + \sum_{i=1}^{m}\left[\frac{\alpha^i}{a^i(x^{(\nu)})+\alpha^i t}\right]^2.
\end{aligned}\right\} \tag{4.4}$$

Note here that $[\mathrm{d}f/\mathrm{d}t]_{t=0} = -F(x^{(\nu)})\sum_{\lambda=1}^{n}\sum_{\kappa=1}^{n}H_{\lambda\kappa}^{(\nu)}\xi^{(\nu)\kappa}\xi^{(\nu)\lambda} < 0$.

Since $f(t)$ itself is strictly convex and tends to infinity near the boundary $t=\bar{t}$ where

$$\bar{t} = \min_i\{-a^i(x^{(\nu)})/\alpha^i \mid \alpha^i < 0\}, \tag{4.5}$$

we may first search for the smallest t_1 for which $\mathrm{d}f/\mathrm{d}t > 0$ among the sequence $((1-\frac{1}{2})\bar{t}, (1-\frac{1}{4})\bar{t}, (1-\frac{1}{8})\bar{t},\ldots)$ and then, starting from t_1, apply the Newton iteration

$$t_{j+1} = t_j - \left[\frac{\mathrm{d}f}{\mathrm{d}t}\right]_{t=t_j}\Big/\left[\frac{\mathrm{d}^2 f}{\mathrm{d}t^2}\right]_{t=t_j} \tag{4.6}$$

to the equation

$$\frac{d}{dt}f(t) = 0, \tag{4.7}$$

to get the sequence $(t_1, t_2, \ldots)$ rapidly converging to t^*:

$$t_j \to t^* \qquad (j = 1, 2, \ldots). \tag{4.8}$$

5. Convergence

In the following we shall show that the sequence $(x^{(0)}, x^{(1)}, \ldots)$ converges to an optimum $\hat{x}$ quadratically in the non-degenerate case at the final stages of iteration. To show this, we first note that the direction $\xi^{(\nu)}$ determined by (4.1) is a "nice" direction. Let us denote $x^{(\nu)} - \hat{x}$ by $\epsilon^{(\nu)}$:

$$\epsilon^{(\nu)\kappa} = x^{(\nu)\kappa} - \hat{x}^\kappa. \tag{5.1}$$

Before all, we see that

$$\left.\begin{aligned}
\sum_{\kappa=1}^{n} \tilde{c}_\kappa(x^{(\nu)})\epsilon^{(\nu)\kappa} &= \frac{c(x^{(\nu)}) - c(\hat{x})}{c(x^{(\nu)})} = 1, \\
\sum_{\kappa=1}^{n} \tilde{a}_\kappa^i(x^{(\nu)})\epsilon^{(\nu)\kappa} &= \frac{a^i(x^{(\nu)}) - a^i(\hat{x})}{a^i(x^{(\nu)})} = 1 - \frac{a^i(\hat{x})}{a^i(x^{(\nu)})} \ (\le 1).
\end{aligned}\right\} \tag{5.2}$$

Then we have

$$\sum_{\kappa=1}^{n} \eta_\kappa^{(\nu)}\epsilon^{(\nu)\kappa} = (m+1)\sum_{\kappa=1}^{n} \tilde{c}_\kappa(x^{(\nu)})\epsilon^{(\nu)\kappa} - \sum_{i=1}^{m}\sum_{\kappa=1}^{n} \tilde{a}_\kappa^i(x^{(\nu)})\epsilon^{(\nu)\kappa}$$

$$= (m+1) - m + \sum_{i=1}^{m} \frac{a^i(\hat{x})}{a^i(x^{(\nu)})} = 1 + \sum_{i=1}^{m} \frac{a^i(\hat{x})}{a^i(x^{(\nu)})} \ (\ge 1), \tag{5.3}$$

$$\sum_{\kappa=1}^{n} H_{\lambda\kappa}^{(\nu)}\epsilon^{(\nu)\kappa} = -(m+1)\tilde{c}_\lambda(x^{(\nu)})\sum_{\kappa=1}^{n} \tilde{c}_\kappa(x^{(\nu)})\epsilon^{(\nu)\kappa}$$

$$+ \sum_{i=1}^{m} \tilde{a}_\lambda^i(x^{(\nu)})\sum_{\kappa=1}^{n} \tilde{a}_\kappa^i(x^{(\nu)})\epsilon^{(\nu)\kappa} + \eta_\lambda^{(\nu)}\sum_{\kappa=1}^{n} \eta_\kappa^{(\nu)}\epsilon^{(\nu)\kappa}$$

$$= -(m+1)\tilde{c}_\lambda(x^{(\nu)}) + \sum_{i=1}^{m}\left[\tilde{a}_\lambda^i(x^{(\nu)})\left(1 - \frac{a^i(\hat{x})}{a^i(x^{(\nu)})}\right)\right]$$

$$+ \eta_\lambda^{(\nu)}\left(1 + \sum_{i=1}^{m} \frac{a^i(\hat{x})}{a^i(x^{(\nu)})}\right)$$

$$= -\eta_\lambda^{(\nu)} - \sum_{i=1}^{m} \frac{a^i(\hat{x})}{a^i(x^{(\nu)})}\tilde{a}_\lambda^i(x^{(\nu)}) + \eta_\lambda^{(\nu)} + \left(\sum_{i=1}^{m} \frac{a^i(\hat{x})}{a^i(x^{(\nu)})}\right)\eta_\lambda^{(\nu)}$$

$$= \left(\sum_{i=1}^{m} \frac{a^i(\hat{x})}{a^i(x^{(\nu)})}\right)\eta_\lambda^{(\nu)} - \sum_{i=1}^{m} \frac{a^i(\hat{x})}{a^i(x^{(\nu)})}\tilde{a}_\lambda^i(x^{(\nu)}). \tag{5.4}$$

If we denote the set of active constraints at $\hat{x}$ by

$$I = \{\, i \mid a^i(\hat{x}) = 0 \,\} \tag{5.5}$$

as in §3, we have from (5.4)

$$\sum_{\kappa=1}^{n} H_{\lambda\kappa}^{(\nu)} \epsilon^{(\nu)\kappa} = w(x^{(\nu)}) \Big[\eta_\lambda^{(\nu)} - \sum_{i\notin I} \frac{w^i(x^{(\nu)})}{w(x^{(\nu)})} \tilde{a}_\lambda^i(x^{(\nu)}) \Big], \tag{5.6}$$

where

$$\left. \begin{aligned} w^i(x) &= a^i(\hat{x})/a^i(x), \\ w(x) &= \sum_{i\notin I} w^i(x). \end{aligned} \right\} \tag{5.7}$$

(Note that $w^i(x) = 0$ for $i \in I$.) Comparing (4.1), (5.1) and (5.6), we might expect that, if $\epsilon^{(\nu)}$ is small enough,

$$y^{(\nu)} \equiv x^{(\nu)} + w(x^{(\nu)})\xi^{(\nu)} \tag{5.8}$$

would be a better approximation to $\hat{x}$. More rigorously, we can prove the quadratic convergence in the non-degenerate case.

Proposition 5.1. Suppose that there is a unique optimum basis (i.e., neither primal nor dual degenerate) with the corresponding solution $\hat{x}$, to which $x^{(\nu)}$ converges. Then, if $\|x^{(\nu)} - \hat{x}\|$ is sufficiently small, $\|x^{(\nu+1)} - \hat{x}\| = \mathrm{O}(\|x^{(\nu)} - \hat{x}\|^2)$, implying the quadratic convergence.

Proof: By means of an affine transformation which moves $\hat{x}$ to $\mathbf{0}$ and makes the matrix a_κ^i into the basis form with respect to $\hat{x}$, the problem is expressed in the form:

$$\min\{\sum_{\kappa=1}^{n} \bar{c}_\kappa x^\kappa \mid \sum_{\kappa=1}^{n} \bar{a}_\kappa^i x^\kappa - \bar{a}_0^i \geq 0 \ (i = 1,\ldots,m)\}, \tag{5.9}$$

where $\bar{c}_\kappa > 0$ $(\kappa = 1,\ldots,n)$ and $\bar{a}_\kappa^i = \delta_\kappa^i$, $\bar{a}_0^i = 0$ $(\kappa = 1,\ldots,n; \ i = 1,\ldots,n; \ \delta_\kappa^i = 1$ if $\kappa = i$ and $\delta_\kappa^i = 0$ otherwise), and $\bar{a}_0^i < 0$ $(i = n+1,\ldots,m)$ and $\mathbf{0}$ is the unique optimum basic solution. We have only to prove that, in the problem (5.9), for the νth solution $x^{(\nu)}$, if $\|x^{(\nu)}\|$ is sufficiently small, $\|x^{(\nu+1)}\| = \mathrm{O}(\|x^{(\nu)}\|^2)$.

Setting $\epsilon = x^{(\nu)}$, consider another problem scaled by ϵ:

$$\min\{\sum_{\kappa=1}^{n} c_\kappa x^\kappa \mid a^i(x) \equiv \sum_{\kappa=1}^{n} a_\kappa^i x^\kappa - a_0^i \geq 0 \ (i = 1,\ldots,m)\}, \tag{5.10}$$

where $c_\kappa = \bar{c}_\kappa \epsilon^\kappa$, $a_\kappa^i = \bar{a}_\kappa^i \epsilon^\kappa$, and $a_0^i = \bar{a}_0^i$. In order to prove the proposition, it suffices to prove that, in the problem (5.10), for $x^{(\nu)} = e$ ($e^\kappa = 1$ for $\kappa = 1, \ldots, n$), we have $\|x^{(\nu+1)}\| = O(\|\epsilon\|)$.

Let us first note that $y \equiv y^{(\nu)}$ defined by (5.8) satisfies the equations:

$$\sum_{\kappa=1}^n H_{\lambda\kappa}(e) y^\kappa = - \sum_{i=n+1}^m w^i(e) \frac{a_\lambda^i}{a^i(e)}.$$

The right-hand side of this equation is $O(\|\epsilon\|)$. As we shall show in the following claim, the eigenvalues of $H_{\lambda\kappa}(e)$ are all of magnitude $\Theta(1)$, so that $\|y\| = O(\|\epsilon\|)$.

Claim. When $\|\epsilon\|$ is sufficiently small, all the eigenvalues $\sigma_1 \geq \cdots \geq \sigma_n > 0$ of $H_{\lambda\kappa}(e)$ is of order $\Theta(1)$.

Proof of Claim: From (3.9) we have

$$H_{\lambda\kappa}(e) = (-m\frac{c_\lambda}{c(e)} + 1)(-m\frac{c_\kappa}{c(e)} + 1) + \sum_{i=1}^n (-\frac{c_\lambda}{c(e)} + \delta_\lambda^i)(-\frac{c_\kappa}{c(e)} + \delta_\kappa^i)$$
$$+ (m-n)\frac{c_\lambda}{c(e)}\frac{c_\kappa}{c(e)} + O(\|\epsilon\|)$$
$$= \sum_{i=1}^{n+2} D_\lambda^i D_\kappa^i + O(\|\epsilon\|),$$

where

$$D_\kappa^i = \delta_\kappa^i - \frac{c_\kappa}{c(e)} \quad (i = 1, \ldots, n),$$
$$= 1 - m\frac{c_\kappa}{c(e)} \quad (i = n+1)$$
$$= \sqrt{m-n}\frac{c_\kappa}{c(e)} \quad (i = n+2).$$

When $\|\epsilon\|$ is sufficiently small, we may apply the Binet-Chauchy Formula to the principal term of the above expression for $H_{\lambda\kappa}(e)$ to get

$$\prod_{\kappa=1}^n \sigma_\kappa = |\det H_{\lambda\kappa}(e)|$$
$$= \left[(m-n)(m-n+1)\sum_{\kappa=1}^n \left(\frac{c_\kappa}{c(e)}\right)^2 + \sum_{\lambda<\kappa}(m-n)\left(\frac{c_\lambda - c_\kappa}{c(e)}\right)^2\right]\left[1 + O(\|\epsilon\|)\right]$$
$$\geq \frac{(m-n)(m-n+1)}{n}\left[1 + O(\|\epsilon\|)\right]$$

where we made use of the fact that $\sum_{\kappa=1}^n c_\kappa/c(e) = 1$.

Furthermore, we have

$$
\sum_{\kappa=1}^{n} \sigma_\kappa = \|D_\kappa^i\|_E^2 \big[1 + \mathrm{O}(\|\epsilon\|)\big]
$$

$$
= \sum_{i=1}^{n+2} \sum_{\kappa=1}^{n} |D_\kappa^i|^2 \big[1 + \mathrm{O}(\|\epsilon\|)\big]
$$

$$
= \Big\{ m(m+1) \sum_{\kappa=1}^{n} \Big(\frac{c_\kappa}{c(e)}\Big)^2 - 2(m-n+1) \Big\} \big[1 + \mathrm{O}(\|\epsilon\|)\big]
$$

$$
\leq \big[m(m+1) - 2(m-n+1)\big]\big[1 + \mathrm{O}(\|\epsilon\|)\big]
$$

$$
= \big[m(m-1) + 2(n-1)\big]\big[1 + \mathrm{O}(\|\epsilon\|)\big].
$$

Since

$$
\sum_{\kappa=1}^{n} \sigma_\kappa \geq \sigma_1 \geq \sigma_2 \geq \cdots \geq \sigma_n = \prod_{\kappa=1}^{n} \sigma_\kappa \Big/ \prod_{\kappa=1}^{n-1} \sigma_\kappa \geq \prod_{\kappa=1}^{n} \sigma_\kappa \Big/ \Big(\sum_{\kappa=1}^{n} \sigma_\kappa\Big)^{n-1}
$$

and

$$
\prod_{\kappa=1}^{n} \sigma_\kappa \Big/ \Big(\sum_{\kappa=1}^{n} \sigma_\kappa\Big)^{n-1} \geq \frac{(m-n)(m-n+1)}{n[m(m-1) + 2(n-1)]^{n-1}} \big[1 + \mathrm{O}(\|\epsilon\|)\big],
$$

the claim follows. (End of Proof of Claim)

Let z be the first point on a constraint hyperplane $a^i(x) = 0$ $(i = 1, \ldots, n)$ that is met by a ray emanating from e towards y in the direction of $\xi^{(\nu)}$. Since $\|y\| = \mathrm{O}(\|\epsilon\|)$, we have $\|z\| = \mathrm{O}(\|\epsilon\|)$. The line search over the line segment connecting e and z is to find the minimum point τ^* of

$$
f(\tau) = c(x)^{m+1} \Big/ \prod_{i=1}^{m} a^i(x)
$$

where $x = \tau e + (1 - \tau)z$ $(0 \leq \tau \leq 1)$. Setting $\gamma = \sum_{\kappa=1}^{n} c_\kappa(e^\kappa - z^\kappa)$ and $\alpha^i = \sum_{\kappa=1}^{n} a_\kappa^i(e^\kappa - z^\kappa)$, we have

$$
\frac{1}{f(\tau)} \frac{df}{d\tau} = \frac{(m+1)\gamma}{c(z) + \gamma\tau} - \sum_{i=1}^{m} \frac{\alpha^i}{a^i(z) + \alpha^i \tau}
$$

$$
\geq \frac{(m+1)\gamma}{c(z) + \gamma\tau} - \frac{m}{\tau}.
$$

We note that $\dfrac{(m+1)\gamma}{c(z) + \gamma\tau} - \dfrac{m}{\tau} = 0$ when $\tau = \tau' \equiv \dfrac{mc(z)}{\gamma}$. When $\|\epsilon\|$ is sufficiently small, we have $\tau' = \mathrm{O}(\|\epsilon\|)$ and $\dfrac{df}{d\tau}\Big|_{\tau=\tau'} \geq 0$. From the convexity of $f(\tau)$, $\tau^* \leq \tau'$. Thus, we have $\tau^* = \mathrm{O}(\|\epsilon\|)$, and hence $\|x^{(\nu+1)}\| = \mathrm{O}(\|\epsilon\|)$ for $x^{(\nu+1)} = \tau^* e + (1 - \tau^*)z$.

$\square$

In the degenerate case $\hat{x}$ is optimum but may not be basic. In that case $H^{(\nu)}_{\lambda\kappa}$ multiplied by $c(x^{(\nu)})^2$ may have small eigenvalues. However the corresponding eigenvectors are seen to be nearly parallel to $\widehat{X}$, so that, as far as the components orthogonal to $\widehat{X}$ are concerned, we can get to a conclusion similar to the above.

It is also seen from (5.7) and (5.8) that, if $x^{(\nu)}$ is close enough to $\hat{x}$, the t^* determined by the line search in the algorithm is expected to be nearly equal to

$$w(x^{(\nu)}) = \sum_{i \notin I} w^i(x^{(\nu)}) = \sum_{i \notin I} \frac{a^i(\hat{x})}{a^i(x^{(\nu)})} \approx m - \mid I \mid \equiv \hat{t}. \qquad (5.11)$$

(See (5.5) for the definition of I. Note that $|I| = n$ in the nondegenerate case.)

When $x^{(\nu)}$ is not sufficiently close to $\hat{x}$, we cannot expect a superlinear convergence, but only a linear one at best. The following is not a rigorous proof of the linear convergence, but would suggest a theoretical explanation for the empirical behaviour of the algorithm, i.e. the linear convergence, observed in the computational experiments, and give an intuitive sketch on which a more formal proof may be constructed.

Proposition 5.2. Suppose that, in an arbitrary direction $\boldsymbol{\xi}$ starting from $x^{(\nu)}$, the value of the function $F(x^{(\nu)} + t\boldsymbol{\xi})$ can be sufficiently well approximated as

$$F(x^{(\nu)} + t\boldsymbol{\xi}) \approx F(x^{(\nu)}) + t \sum_{\kappa=1}^{n} \xi^\kappa \frac{\partial}{\partial x^\kappa} F(x^{(\nu)}) + \frac{t^2}{2} \sum_{\kappa=1}^{n} \sum_{\lambda=1}^{n} \xi^\kappa \xi^\lambda \frac{\partial^2}{\partial x^\lambda \partial x^\kappa} F(x^{(\nu)}).$$

for t satisfying the inequality

$$\frac{t^2}{2} \sum_{\kappa=1}^{n} \sum_{\lambda=1}^{n} H^{(\nu)}_{\lambda\kappa} \xi^\kappa \xi^\lambda \leq K^2 \qquad (5.12)$$

with an appropriate value of K. Then,

$$\frac{F(x^{(\nu+1)})}{F(x^{(\nu)})} < 1 - K(1 - K).$$

Proof: Under the assumption, we have

$$\frac{f(t)}{f(0)} = \frac{F(x^{(\nu)} + t\boldsymbol{\xi})}{F(x^{(\nu)})} \approx 1 + t \sum_{\kappa=1}^{n} \eta^{(\nu)}_\kappa \xi^\kappa + \frac{t^2}{2} \sum_{\kappa=1}^{n} \sum_{\lambda=1}^{n} H^{(\nu)}_{\lambda\kappa} \xi^\kappa \xi^\lambda$$

so long as t satisfies (5.12). This means that $f(t)/f(0)$ can be approximated by the linear function in t

$$1 + t \sum_{\kappa=1}^{n} \eta_\kappa^{(\nu)} \xi^\kappa \tag{5.13}$$

up to an error less than K^2. We consider the problem of minimizing (5.13) under the condition (5.12), for which the solution is obvious:

$$t = \sqrt{2K^2 \Big/ \sum_{\kappa=1}^{n} \sum_{\lambda=1}^{n} H_{\lambda\kappa}^{(\nu)} \xi^\kappa \xi^\lambda} \tag{5.14}$$

if $\sum_{\kappa=1}^{n} \eta_\kappa^{(\nu)} \xi^\kappa < 0$. The minimum value of (5.13) depends on ξ, and, as is readily seen, the minimum of that minimum value with ξ varied is attained if ξ is chosen equal to $\xi^{(\nu)}$ determined by (4.1).

By determining $\xi^{(\nu)}$ and t in that manner, we shall get

$$\hat{r} = \frac{f(t)}{f(0)} \approx 1 + t \sum_{\kappa=1}^{n} \eta_\kappa^{(\nu)} \xi^{(\nu)\kappa} + K^2$$

$$= 1 - K \sqrt{2 \sum_{\kappa=1}^{n} \sum_{\lambda=1}^{n} H_{\lambda\kappa}^{(\nu)} \xi^{(\nu)\kappa} \xi^{(\nu)\lambda}} + K^2. \tag{5.15}$$

If we chose $\xi = \hat{x} - x^{(\nu)} (= -\epsilon^{(\nu)})$ and determined t by (5.14) accordingly, we should have

$$\sum_{\kappa=1}^{n} \eta_\kappa^{(\nu)} \xi^\kappa = -1 - w(x^{(\nu)}),$$

$$\sum_{\kappa=1}^{n} \sum_{\lambda=1}^{n} H_{\lambda\kappa}^{(\nu)} \xi^\kappa \xi^\lambda = w(x^{(\nu)}) \Big[1 + w(x^{(\nu)}) + \sum_{i \notin I} \frac{w^i(x^{(\nu)})}{w(x^{(\nu)})} \big(-1 + w^i(x^{(\nu)})\big) \Big]$$

$$= w(x^{(\nu)}) + w(x^{(\nu)})^2 - w(x^{(\nu)}) + \sum_{i \notin I} w^i(x^{(\nu)})^2$$

$$= w(x^{(\nu)})^2 + \sum_{i \notin I} w^i(x^{(\nu)})^2$$

(cf. (5.2), (5.3), (5.6) and (5.7)), or

$$r = \frac{f(t)}{f(0)} \approx 1 - t(1 + w(x^{(\nu)})) + K^2$$

$$= 1 - \frac{\sqrt{2} K (1 + w(x^{(\nu)}))}{\sqrt{w(x^{(\nu)})^2 + \sum_{i \notin I} w^i(x^{(\nu)})^2}} + K^2. \tag{5.16}$$

Since $w^i(x^{(\nu)}) > 0$ and $w(x^{(\nu)}) = \sum_{i \notin I} w^i(x^{(\nu)})$, we have

$$\sum_{i \notin I} w^i(x^{(\nu)})^2 \le w(x^{(\nu)})^2,$$

so that we have

$$\sqrt{w(x^{(\nu)})^2 + \sum_{i \notin I} w^i(x^{(\nu)})^2} \leq \sqrt{2}w(x^{(\nu)}), \tag{5.17}$$

or

$$r \leq 1 - \frac{K(1 + w(x^{(\nu)}))}{w(x^{(\nu)})} + K^2 = 1 - K - \frac{K}{w(x^{(\nu)})} + K^2. \tag{5.18}$$

Since the $\hat{r}$ in (5.15) is by definition not greater than the r in (5.18), we finally have

$$\hat{r} < 1 - K(1 - K). \quad \square \tag{5.19}$$

Thus, if the assumption of the Proposition 5.2 is satisfied, at each iteration step, we have the value of the function $F(x^{(\nu)})$ reduced at least by a constant factor $1 - K(1 - K)$ approximately:

$$\frac{F(x^{(\nu+1)})}{F(x^{(\nu)})} < 1 - K(1 - K), \tag{5.20}$$

the factor being equal, for example, to $\frac{3}{4}$, $\frac{13}{16}$ and $\frac{57}{64}$ with $K = \frac{1}{2}$, $\frac{1}{4}$ and $\frac{1}{8}$, respectively.

6. Some Extensions

Define $\hat{c}_0$ to be $\min\{\sum_{\kappa=1}^n c_\kappa x^\kappa \mid x \in X\}$. In the preceding sections 2~5, we assumed that $c(\hat{x}) = 0$ for $\hat{x} \in \widehat{X}$, that is, $c_0 = \hat{c}_0$. Even if $\hat{c}_0$ is not known in advance, we can transform a given problem into a linear programming problem of known optimum objective value by combining it with its dual problem. However, this transformation makes the size of the problem to be solved larger.

Imai [2] proposes a method of handling a linear programming problem with unknown optimum value in the framework of multiplicative penalty function method without combining it with the dual. In this section we describe some of the results in [2] without proof. Since c_0 throughout this section is variable, we explicitly denote the dependence of $c(x)$, $F(x)$ on c_0 as $c(x, c_0)$, $F(x, c_0)$, etc.

6.1. Minima of the multiplicative penalty function and the duality

For $c_0 < \hat{c}_0$, $F(x, c_0)$ is still strictly convex and, from the assumption (ii) in §2, $F(x, c_0)$ diverges to infinity along any ray in Int X even when X is unbounded, from which we have the following.

Proposition 6.1. For $c_0 < \hat{c}_0$, there exists a unique optimum solution, to be denoted by $x(c_0)$, which minimizes $F(x, c_0)$ in Int X. At $x(c_0)$, we have $\eta_\kappa(x(c_0), c_0) = 0$ $(\kappa = 1, \ldots, n)$. $\square$

Denote the given linear programming problem (2.1) and (2.2) by (P). The linear programming problem (D), dual to (P), is as follows:

$$\text{to maximize} \quad \sum_{i=1}^{m} a_0^i y_i,$$

$$\text{s.t.} \quad \sum_{i=1}^{m} a_\kappa^i y_i = c_\kappa \qquad (\kappa = 1, \ldots, n), \tag{D}$$

$$y_i \geq 0 \qquad (i = 1, \ldots, m)$$

For $c_0 < \hat{c}_0$, define $y(c_0)$ by

$$y_i(c_0) = \frac{1}{m+1} \frac{c(x(c_0), c_0)}{a^i(x(c_0))} \geq 0 \qquad (i = 1, \ldots, m).$$

Concerning $x(c_0)$ and $y(c_0)$, we have the following.

Proposition 6.2. For $c_0 < \hat{c}_0$, $y(c_0)$ is a feasible solution to (D), and we have

$$\sum_{i=1}^{m} a_0^i y_i(c_0) = c_0 + \frac{1}{m+1} c(x(c_0), c_0) \leq \hat{c}_0 \leq c_0 + c(x(c_0), c_0) = \sum_{\kappa=1}^{n} c_\kappa x^\kappa(c_0),$$

so that

$$\sum_{\kappa=1}^{n} c_\kappa x^\kappa(c_0) - \hat{c}_0 \leq m(\hat{c}_0 - c_0). \quad \square$$

Proposition 6.3. As $c_0 \uparrow \hat{c}_0$, $x(c_0)$ converges to an optimum solution to (P) and $y(c_0)$ converges to an optimum solution to (D). Also, at that time, $\sum_{\kappa=1}^{n} c_\kappa x^\kappa(c_0)$ and $\sum_{i=1}^{m} a_0^i y_i(c_0)$ are decreasing and increasing, respectively. $\square$

Furthermore, the following duality holds between $x(c_0)$ and $y(c_0)$.

Proposition 6.4. Suppose that the problem (P) is in the so-called canonical form: $a_\kappa^i = \delta_\kappa^i$ and $a_0^i = 0$ for $i = 1, \ldots, n$, where $\delta_\kappa^i = 1$ if $i = \kappa$ and $\delta_\kappa^i = 0$ if $i \neq \kappa$. Set $b^j = a_0^j$ for $j = n+1, \ldots, m$. In this case, the linear programming problem dual to (P) can also be expressed as follows:

$$\text{to minimize} \quad b(z) \equiv b^0 - \sum_{j=n+1}^{m} b^j z_j,$$

$$\text{s.t.} \quad a_\kappa(z) \equiv c_\kappa - \sum_{j=n+1}^{m} a_\kappa^j z_j \geq 0 \qquad (\kappa = 1, \ldots, n),$$

$$z_j \geq 0 \qquad (j = n+1, \ldots, m)$$

For $b^0 > \hat{c}_0$, the multiplicative penalty function

$$G(z) = b(z)^{m+1} \Big/ \Big(\prod_{\kappa=1}^{n} a_\kappa(z) \cdot \prod_{j=n+1}^{m} z_j \Big).$$

defined in the interior of its feasible region has a unique minimum solution, which will be denoted by $z(b^0)$.

Then, for $y(c_0)$ defined via $x(c_0)$ for (P) and $z(b^0)$ thus defined, we have the following.

$$z\Big(c_0 + \frac{m+2}{m+1} c(x(c_0), c_0)\Big) = y(c_0). \quad \Box$$

6.2. Determining constraints inactive at all optimum solutions

For $x \in \mathbf{R}^n$ and c_0 with $c_0 < \hat{c}_0$, define $h(x, c_0)$ by

$$h(x, c_0) \equiv \sum_{\lambda=1}^{n} \sum_{\kappa=1}^{n} H_{\lambda\kappa}(x(c_0), c_0)(x^\kappa - x^\kappa(c_0))(x^\lambda - x^\lambda(c_0)).$$

For c_0 and a nonnegative real number ρ, consider an ellipsoid $E(c_0, \rho)$ given by

$$E(c_0, \rho) \equiv \{x \in \mathbf{R}^n \mid h(x, c_0) \leq \rho\}.$$

The ellipsoid $E(c_0, m(m-1))$ centered at $x(c_0)$ has the following nice property.

Proposition 6.5. $\widehat{X} \subseteq E(c_0, m(m-1))$, and hence, if

$$a^i(x(c_0)) > \sqrt{m(m-1) \sum_{\lambda=1}^{n} \sum_{\kappa=1}^{n} G^{\lambda\kappa} a^i_\kappa a^i_\lambda}$$

where $G^{\lambda\kappa}$ is the inverse of $H_{\lambda\kappa}(x(c_0), c_0)$, then the constraint $a^i(x) \geq 0$ is inactive at all optimum solutions (i.e., $a^i(\hat{x}) > 0$ for any $\hat{x} \in \widehat{X}$). $\quad \Box$

References

[1] G. B. Dantig: *Linear Programming and Extensions*. Princeton University Press, Princeton, 1963.

[2] H. Imai: Extensions of the multiplicative penalty function method for linear programming. *Technical Report CSCE-86-C04*, Department of Computer Science and Communication Engineering, Kyushu University, July 1986, revised.

[3] M. Iri: Another "simple and fast" algorithm for linear programming. Paper presented at *the 12th International Symposium on Mathematical Programming*, August 5 ~ 9, 1985, MIT, Boston, U.S.A.

[4] M. Iri and H. Imai: A method of solving linear programming — with reference to the Karmarkar method and the penalty function method. Research Meeting of the MP Research Group of the OR Society of Japan, February 16, 1985.

[5] M. Iri and H. Imai: A multiplicative penalty function method for linear programming — Another "new and fast" algorithm. *Proceedings of the 6th Mathematical Programming Symposium of Japan*, Tokyo, 1985, pp.97–120.

[6] M. Iri and H. Imai: A multiplicative barrier function method for linear programming. *Algorithmica*, to appear.

[7] N. Karmarkar: A new polynomial-time algorithm for linear programming. *Combinatorica*, Vol.4, No.4 (1984), pp.373–395.

[8] L. G. Khachian: A polynomial algorithm in linear programming. *Doklady Akademii Nauk SSSR*, Vol.244, No.5 (1979), pp.1093–1096 (in Russian); English translation in *Soviet Mathematics Doklady*, Vol.20 (1979), pp.191–194.

[9] L. G. Khachian: Polynomial algorithms in linear programming. *Zhurnal Vychislitelnoi Matematiki i Matematicheskoi Fiziki*, Vol.20 (1980), pp.51–68 (in Russian); English translation in *USSR Computational Mathematics and Mathematical Physics*, Vol.20 (1980), pp.53–72.

Linear-time Computability of Combinatorial

Problems on Generalized-Series-Parallel Graphs

E. Hare[*]

S. Hedetniemi[*]

R. Laskar[*]

K. Peters[*]

Clemson University

Clemson, S. C., U. S. A.

and

T. Wimer[*]

Clarion University of Penna.

Clarion, Pa., U. S. A.

ABSTRACT. This paper extends in several ways the notable work of Takamizawa, Nishizeki and Saito in 1982 [16], which in turn was inspired by that of Watanabe, Ae and Nakamura in 1979 [17]. We illustrate an emerging theory/methodology for constructing linear-time graph algorithms by providing such algorithms for finding the maximum-cut and the maximum cardinality of a minimal dominating set for a generalized-series-parallel graph.

1. Introduction and background.

In recent years, many linear-time graph algorithms have been designed to solve NP-complete problems by restricting the input domains to certain families of graphs, e.g., trees, 2-trees, maximal outerplanar

---

* Research supported in part by an Office of Naval Research contract.

DISCRETE ALGORITHMS AND
COMPLEXITY

graphs, Halin graphs, two-terminal series-parallel graphs, permutation graphs, cographs, etc. Related research includes papers by Takamizawa, Nishizeki and Saito [16]; Bern, Lawler and Wong [3]; Arnborg and Proskurowski [1] and [2]; Syslo [15]; Corneil and Keil [5]; Corneil and Kirkpatrick [6]; Corneil, Perl and Stewart [7]; El-Mallah and Colbourn [8]; Kikuno, Yoshida and Kakuda [13]; and a research group at Clemson University [11], [12], [14], [18], [19], [20] and [21]. These results, when considered together, clearly suggest the emergence of rather strong theory which both explains and predicts the existence of several thousand linear-time graph algorithms.

Several methodologies for designing such algorithms have been suggested in this research. These methodologies include a vertex elimination/reduction technique by Arnborg and Proskurowski [1]; a finite-state table technique by Bern, Lawler and Wong [3]; a dynamic programming approach by Corneil and Keil [5]; and a top-down, class refinement technique resulting in a system of recurrences by Takamizawa, Nishizeki and Saito [16] and Wimer, Hedetniemi and Laskar [20].

Takamizawa, Nishizeki and Saito [16] show that, when restricted to two-terminal series-parallel graphs, many NP-complete problems can be solved by linear-time algorithms. Included among these problems are:

(1) the minimum vertex cover and maximum independent set problems;

(2) the maximum (induced) line subgraph problem;

(3) various minimum edge (vertex) deletion problems;

(4) the minimum feedback vertex set problem;

(5) the minimum path cover problem;

(6) the maximum matching problem;

(7) the maximum cycle problem;

(8) the Chinese Postman problem;

(9) the dominating set problem (Kikuno, Yoshida and Kakuda [13]); and

(10) the Steiner tree problem.

They also state that their algorithms may be generalized to handle the corresponding maximum or minimum weight (induced) subgraph problems; directed series-parallel graphs; and extended series-parallel graphs, e.g., n-terminal series-parallel graphs.

Bern, Lawler and Wong [3] observed that a variety of linear-time algorithms can also be designed for certain families of graphs which can be defined recursively in terms of a finite set of basis graphs and certain 'k-terminal' rules of composition. The families of k-terminal graphs, formulated by Bern, Lawler and Wong, included two-terminal series-parallel graphs, rooted trees, 2-connected outerplanar graphs, proto-Halin graphs and bandwidth k graphs. Notable in their paper was the design of the first (linear) algorithm for solving the irredundance problem for trees. Among the NP-complete problems admitting linear-time algorithms for k-terminal families of graphs, Bern, Lawler and Wong mention maximum and minimum maximal-matching, dominating sets, independent dominating sets, irredundant sets, and, in general, any problem involving a property P which is "regular" with respect to the corresponding rules of composition.

The theory/methodology we illustrate here extends the notable work of Takamizawa, Nishizeki and Saito [16] in several ways. First, it applies to any family of graphs that admits a k-terminal recursive definition (see Bern, Lawler and Wong [3] and Hedetniemi and Wimer [12]). At present, the k-terminal families of graphs have been shown to include over two dozen well known families of graphs. Among those not previously mentioned are: k-trees, for fixed k; k x n grids, for fixed k; (partial) k-chordal graphs, for fixed k; cacti; generalized-series-parallel graphs; C_N-trees; filaments; outerplanar graphs; and unicyclic graphs. In [12], Wimer and Hedetniemi more formally defined k-terminal

families of graphs, began a study of a particularly interesting family
called the generalized-series-parallel graphs and presented a variety of
results on the properties of k-terminal families of graphs.

Second, the methodology can handle a variety of problems in
addition to those already mentioned. In [20], Wimer, Hedetniemi and
Laskar mention a number of dominating set problems (optional-, total-,
connected-, edge-, K_2-, and locating-); minimum length Hamiltonian
walks; minimum spanning trees; and maximum number of disjoint triangles.

This paper focuses on the particularly interesting family of
2-terminal graphs, called generalized-series-parallel graphs, which
properly contains two-terminal series-parallel graphs and other families
such as: trees, outerplanar graphs, unicyclic graphs, C_N-trees, C-trees,
2-trees, cacti and filaments (square, triangular and hexagonal). In
Section 2, the definition of generalized-series-parallel graphs is given
and some of the results previously obtained for this family are
indicated. In Section 3, we illustrate the simplicity of the
methodology by constructing a linear-time algorithm for solving the
maximum-cut problem on generalized-series-parallel graphs. In Section
4, we give some indication of the generality of the methodology by using
it to establish the existence of a linear-time algorithm for determining
the maximum cardinality of a minimal dominating set of a generalized-
series-parallel graph.

2. Generalized-series-parallel graphs.

The family of generalized-series-parallel graphs, hereafter
called gsp-graphs, has the following 2-terminal recursive definition.

DEFINITION 1.

  1. K_2 is a gsp-graph with terminals u and v. (K_2 denotes the
     complete graph on two vertices.)

2. If G_1 and G_2 are gsp-graphs with terminals $\{u_1, v_1\}$ and
   $\{u_2, v_2\}$, respectively, then:

   a. the <u>series composition</u> of G_1 and G_2 , obtained by
      identifying v_1 with u_2 and specifying u_1 and v_2 as the
      terminals of the graph formed (see Figure 1), is a
      gsp-graph;

   b. the <u>parallel composition</u> of G_1 and G_2, obtained by
      identifying u_1 with u_2, v_1 with v_2 and specifying u_1 and
      v_1 as the terminals of the graph formed (see Figure 2),
      is a gsp-graph; and

   c. the <u>generalized-series</u> composition of G_1 and G_2,
      obtained by identifying v_1 with u_2 and specifying u_1 and
      v_1 as the terminals of the graph formed (see Figure 3),
      is a gsp-graph.

3. All and only gsp-graphs are obtained from a finite number of
   applications of 1 and 2 above.

G_1 series G_2 =   G

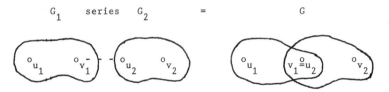

<u>Figure 1.</u> The series composition of G_1 and G_2.

G_1 parallel G_2 =   G

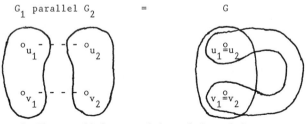

<u>Figure 2.</u> The parallel composition of G_1 and G_2.

G_1 gen-series G_2 =   G

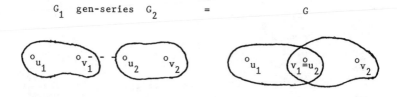

<u>Figure 3.</u> The generalized-series composition of G_1 and G_2.

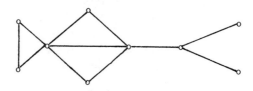

<u>Figure 4.</u> A Generalized-series-parallel graph that is
not a two-terminal series-parallel graph.

<u>DEFINITION 2.</u> The family of <u>two-terminal series-parallel</u> graphs
consists of those generalized-series-parallel graphs that are obtained
by using only the series and parallel compositions of DEFINITION 1.

Figure 4 gives an example of a generalized-series-parallel graph
which is not a two-terminal series-parallel graph. In [11], Wimer and
Hedetniemi presented a variety of results concerning gsp-graphs. They
include the following.

<u>THEOREM 1.</u> [12] The family of generalized-series-parallel graphs
contains each of the following families:

    (i) two-terminal series-parallel graphs;

    (ii) outerplanar graphs;

   (iii) 2-connected outerplanar graphs (2-cops);

    (iv) maximal outerplanar graphs (mops);

    (v) 2-trees;

(vi) cacti;

(vii) trees;

(viii) unicyclic graphs;

(ix) C_N-trees; and

(x) C-trees.

Figure 5 illustrates the inclusion relationships among these families.

An important first component of each of the linear-time algorithms constructed using this methodology is a linear algorithm which produces a decomposition (parse) tree for the input graph. Given a k-terminal family F and a graph $G \in F$, a decomposition tree for G is a labeled, oriented binary tree for which:

1. each leaf is labeled with one of the basis graphs used in the recursive definition of F;

2. each non-leaf (internal vertex) is labeled with one of the composition operations used in the recursive definition of F; and

3. the graph obtained by 'evaluating' the decomposition tree (in much the same way that an arithmetic expression is evaluated) is isomorphic to G.

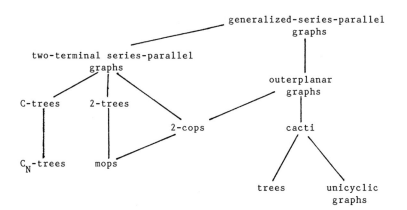

Figure 5. Subfamilies of the generalized-series-parallel family.

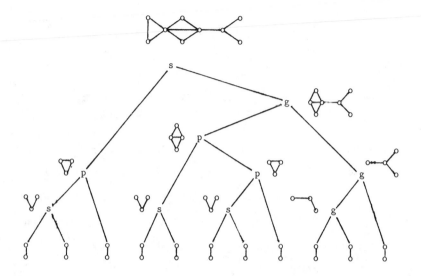

Figure 6. A decomposition tree for the graph in Figure 5.

An important result pertaining to the current discussion is the
following theorem.

THEOREM 2. [12] For the family of generalized-series-parallel graphs,
there exists an O(n) parsing algorithm, i.e., an algorithm that produces
a decomposition tree for any given gsp-graph in linear time.

Figure 6 gives a decomposition tree for the generalized-series-parallel
graph in Figure 5.

All of the algorithms produced by this theory operate like the
algorithm for evaluating arithmetic expressions which uses a postorder
traversal of the expression's evaluation tree. The linear algorithms we
construct are different, however, in that instead of arithmetic
operators at the internal vertices of an evaluation tree, we have
composition operations at the internal vertices of a graph's
decomposition tree, and instead of performing arithmetic operations, we
use a set of recurrence equations to guide the computation. In the next

section we illustrate the simplicity of this theory/methodology by developing a linear-time algorithm for determining the maximum weight cut of an edge-weighted generalized-series-parallel graph.

3. A linear-time maximum-cut algorithm for generalized-series-parallel graphs.

As mentioned in the previous section, each algorithm produced by this methodology operates by evaluating a set of recurrence equations at each non-leaf vertex of a decomposition tree, using values already calculated for the left and right subtrees of that non-leaf vertex. The result, instead of a single value, is a vector of bounded length. Each entry in this vector corresponds to a collection of (graph,set) pairs (what we later call a class) representing a partial solution of some prescribed type.

The edge-weighted maximum-cut problem is known to be NP-complete for arbitrary graphs [9] and polynomial for planar graphs [10]. We introduce the following notation. For any nonempty proper subset of vertices $U \subseteq V(G)$, let $s(U)$ denote the sum of the weights of all the edges that join a vertex in U with a vertex in $V(G) - U$.

DEFINITION 3. For an edge-weighted graph G, the maximum cut of G is
$$mc(G) = \max \left\{ s(U) : U \subseteq V(G) \right\}.$$

In what follows, G represents a gsp-graph with terminals u and v, and U represents a subset of $V(G)$. For the maximum-cut problem on edge-weighted gsp-graphs, we introduce the following classes:

$[1] = \big\{ (G,U)$: a) $u \in U$

                    b) $v \in U$

                    c) $s(U)$ is maximum, subject to the constraint:

                    U satisfies a and b$\big\}$,

$[2] = \{(G,U)$: a) $u \in U$

　　　　　　　　 b) $v \in V(G) - U$

　　　　　　　　 c) $s(U)$ is maximum, subject to the constraint:
　　　　　　　　　　 U satisfies a and b $\}$,

$[3] = \{(G,U)$: a) $u \in V(G) - U$

　　　　　　　　 b) $v \in U$

　　　　　　　　 c) $s(U)$ is maximum, subject to the constraint:
　　　　　　　　　　 U satisfies a and b $\}$, and

$[4] = \{(G,U)$: a) $u \in V(G) - U$

　　　　　　　　 b) $v \in V(G) - U$

　　　　　　　　 c) $s(U)$ is maximum, subject to the constraint:
　　　　　　　　　　 U satisfies a and b $\}$.

Next we derive a set of recurrences establishing relationships among these classes. From the fact that a pair (G,U) appears in a particular class and G is the composition of G_1 and G_2 (either series, parallel, or generalized-series), we can, in a top-down manner, ascertain the possible classes of (G_1,U_1) and (G_2,U_2). We derive a recurrence system for each composition operation. There are four classes and three rules of composition, so that there are twelve recurrences to derive. Since each derivation is straight forward, we only provide one for each composition operation.

　　First of all, assume that the pair (G,U) is in class $[1]$ and G is formed by a series composition of G_1 with G_2. Further, suppose that the terminals of G, G_1 and G_2 are $\{u,v\}$, $\{u_1,v_1\}$ and $\{u_2,v_2\}$, respectively, and that $U = U_1 \cup U_2$ (with the appropriate coalescing of vertices), where $U_1 \subseteq V(G_1)$ and $U_2 \subseteq V(G_2)$. Since u and v are both in U, we see that $u_1 \in U_1$ and $v_2 \in U_2$. If $v_1 \in U_1$, then $u_2 \in U_2$. (In G, $u_2 = v_1$.)

Moreover, both $s(U_1)$ and $s(U_2)$ must be maximum, subject to the restrictions that $u_1 \in U_1$, $v_1 \in U_1$, $u_2 \in U_2$ and $v_2 \in U_2$; otherwise $s(U)$ would not be maximum, subject to the restriction that $u,v \in U$. Notice that $s(U) = s(U_1) + s(U_2)$. It follows that (G_1,U_1) is in class [1] and (G_2,U_2) is in class [1]. On the other hand, if $v_1 \in V(G_1) - U_1$, then $u_2 \in V(G_2) - U_2$, and from an argument similar to the preceding, we conclude that (G_1,U_1) is in class [2] and (G_2,U_2) is in class [3]. The complete set of recurrences for the series composition is as follows:

$$[1] \subseteq [1] \text{ s } [1] \ \cup \ [2] \text{ s } [3],$$

$$[2] \subseteq [1] \text{ s } [2] \ \cup \ [2] \text{ s } [4],$$

$$[3] \subseteq [4] \text{ s } [3] \ \cup \ [3] \text{ s } [1], \text{ and}$$

$$[4] \subseteq [4] \text{ s } [4] \ \cup \ [3] \text{ s } [2].$$

Next we derive the recurrences for the parallel composition operation. Assume, for example, that (G,U) is in class [2] and G is the parallel composition of G_1 with G_2. (The notation for the respective terminals will remain the same.) Since $u \in U$ and $v \in V(G) - U$, we have that $u_1 \in U_1$ and therefore $u_2 \in U_2$. Also, $v_1 \in V(G_1) - U_1$ implies that $v_2 \in V(G_2) - U_2$. Let $w(e)$ represent the weight of the edge e in $E(G)$. Notice that $s(U) = s(U_1) + s(U_2) - w(u_1v_1)$, if $u_1v_1 \in E(G_1)$ and $u_2v_2 \in E(G_2)$; and $s(U) = s(U_1) + s(U_2)$, otherwise. It follows that (G_1,U_1) is in class [2] and (G_2,U_2) is in class [2]. The complete set of recurrences for the parallel composition operation is as follows:

$$[1] = [1] \text{ p } [1], \qquad [2] = [2] \text{ p } [2],$$

$$[3] = [3] \text{ p } [3], \text{ and } [4] = [4] \text{ p } [4].$$

Finally, we derive the recurrences for the generalized-series composition. Since $u,v \in V(G) - U$, we have that $u_1,v_1 \in V(G_1) - U_1$. Thus, $u_2 \in V(G_2) - U_2$. (In G, $v_1 = u_2$.) Now, either $v_2 \in U_2$ or $v_2 \in V(G_2) - U_2$. It follows that either (G_1,U_1) is in class [4] and

(G_2, U_2) is in class [3], or (G_1, U_1) is in class [4] and (G_2, U_2) is in class [4]. The complete set of recurrences for the generalized-series composition operation is as follows:

$[1] \subseteq [1] \; g \; [1] \quad \cup \quad [1] \; g \; [2]$,

$[2] \subseteq [2] \; g \; [3] \quad \cup \quad [2] \; g \; [4]$,

$[3] \subseteq [3] \; g \; [1] \quad \cup \quad [3] \; g \; [2]$, and

$[4] \subseteq [4] \; g \; [3] \quad \cup \quad [4] \; g \; [4]$.

In order to describe the computation at each internal (composition) vertex of a decomposition tree, we introduce the vector

$$X = (\; X(1) \;, \; X(2) \;, \; X(3) \;, \; X(4) \;),$$

where $X(i)$ corresponds to the maximum $s(U)$ associated with class [i]. If XL and XR are the vectors associated with the left and right subtrees, respectively, of a series composition vertex, then the computation proceeds as follows:

$$X(1) \leftarrow \max \{ XL(1) + XR(1) \;, \; XL(2) + XR(3) \},$$

$$X(2) \leftarrow \max \{ XL(1) + XR(2) \;, \; XL(2) + XR(4) \},$$

$$X(3) \leftarrow \max \{ XL(4) + XR(3) \;, \; XL(3) + XR(1) \}, \text{ and}$$

$$X(4) \leftarrow \max \{ XL(4) + XR(4) \;, \; XL(3) + XR(2) \}.$$

For a parallel composition, we use the following recurrence system:

$$X(1) \leftarrow XL(1) + XR(1),$$

$$X(2) \leftarrow \begin{cases} XL(2) + XR(2) - w(u_1 v_1), & \text{if } u_1 v_1 \in E(G_1) \text{ and } u_2 v_2 \in E(G_2) \\ XL(2) + XR(2), & \text{otherwise.} \end{cases}$$

$$X(3) \leftarrow \begin{cases} XL(3) + XR(3) - w(u_1 v_1), & \text{if } u_1 v_1 \in E(G_1) \text{ and } u_2 v_2 \in E(G_2) \\ XL(3) + XR(3), & \text{otherwise.} \end{cases}$$

$$X(4) \leftarrow XL(4) + XR(4).$$

For a generalized-series composition, we use the following:

$$X(1) \leftarrow \max \{ XL(1) + XR(1) \;, \; XL(1) + XR(2) \},$$

$$X(2) \leftarrow \max \{ XL(2) + XR(3) \;, \; XL(2) + XR(4) \},$$

$$X(3) \leftarrow \max \{ XL(3) + XR(1) \;, \; XL(3) + XR(2) \}, \text{ and}$$

$$X(4) \leftarrow \max \{ XL(4) + XR(3) \;, \; XL(4) + XR(4) \}.$$

Associated with each leaf in the decomposition tree is the 'basis' vector (0 , w(e) , w(e) , 0), where w(e) is the weight of the edge

(in G) corresponding to that leaf. Notice that the maximum-cut of an

edge in class [1] or class [4] is 0, whereas the maximum-cut of an edge

in class [2] or class [3] is the weight of that edge. The algorithm can

be outlined as follows:

Step 0. Construct the decomposition tree as in [12].

Step 1. Initialize the vector associated with each leaf to

(0 , w(e) , w(e) , 0).

Step 2. Traversing the decomposition tree in postorder, for each

internal (composition) vertex, calculate the vector X

using the appropriate recurrence system.

Step 3. After the decomposition tree has been traversed,

$$mc(G) = max \{ X(1) , X(2) , X(3) , X(4) \},$$

where X is the vector associated with the root of the

decomposition tree.

In the next section, we take up the problem of determining the

maximum cardinality of a minimal dominating set of a gsp-graph.

4. The maximum cardinality of a minimal dominating set of a
generalized-series-parallel graph.

We exhibit some of the generality of this theory/methodology by

considering the problem of determining the maximum cardinality of a

minimal dominating set of a gsp-graph, i.e., the upper domination

number Γ(G). (See Cockayne, Favaron, Payan and Thomason [4].) In

what follows, N[S] denotes the closed neighborhood of S, that is, if

G = (V,E) is a graph and S ⊆ V(G), then

$$N[S] = \{y \in V(G) : y \in S \text{ or there exists an } x \in S$$
$$\text{such that the edge } xy \in E(G)\}.$$

DEFINITION 4. Given a graph $G = (V,E)$, a subset $S \subseteq V(G)$ is said to be a <u>dominating</u> set of G, if for each $y \in V(G)$, there exists an x in S such that $y \in N[x]$. A dominating set S is said to be a <u>minimal</u> dominating set, if no proper subset S' of S is a dominating set of G.

We show there is a linear-time algorithm for determining $\Gamma(G)$ on the family of gsp-graphs by establishing the existence of an associated set of recurrence systems. First, we formalize some of the notions appearing in the previous section. Let G and H represent gsp-graphs, F represent the family of all gsp-graphs and o represent one of the three composition operations: series, parallel, or generalized-series.

DEFINITION 5. Consider the collection of (graph,set) pairs,
$$A = \{(G,S) : G \in F \text{ and } S \subseteq V(G)\}.$$
A <u>class</u> is a function $f : F \rightarrow 2^A$, where for each $H \in F$,
$$f(H) \subseteq \{(G,S) : (G,S) \in A \text{ and } G = H\}.$$

In other words, a class f associates with each $H \in F$ a well-defined collection of (graph,set) pairs.

DEFINITION 6. Given a property P, a <u>foundation</u> of P with respect to the family F is a collection B of classes such that for each $G \in F$,
$$\{(G,S) : S \text{ has property } P \text{ in } G\} = \cup\{f(G) : f \in B\}.$$

DEFINITION 7. A property P is said to <u>admit</u> a closed system of recurrences with respect to the family F, if there exists a finite collection C of classes for which:

1. C contains a foundation of P with respect to the family F, and

2. for each composition operation o (series, parallel, and generalized-series) and for each $z \in C$, there exists a set Y_{oz}

of pairs of classes in C such that $G = G_1 \circ G_2 \in F$ implies

$z(G) = \cup \{x(G_1) \circ y(G_2) : (x,y) \in Y_{oz}\}.$

The following theorem of Wimer [19] provides that in order to establish the existence of a linear-time algorithm for finding $\Gamma(G)$ on the family of gsp-graphs, it is sufficient to establish that the property: "is a minimal dominating set", admits a closed recurrence system with respect to the family F.

THEOREM 3. [19] If property P admits a closed recurrence system with respect to the family F, then there exists a linear-time algorithm for determining the maximum cardinality of a subset $S \subseteq V(G)$ satisfying property P, where $G \in F$.

Proof. Since F is the family of generalized-series-parallel graphs, from THEOREM 2 we conclude there exists a linear-time parsing algorithm for F. As in DEFINITION 7, let C denote the set of classes appearing in the closed recurrence system for property P. Further, let $G \in F$ and T be its corresponding decomposition tree. Using an inductive argument on the height of decomposition (sub)trees, it is easy to establish that, at each step in the execution of the algorithm outlined in the previous section, the following holds. If H is the generalized-series-parallel graph with decomposition tree equal to the decomposition subtree of T rooted at the composition vertex being processed, then for each class $z \in C$, we have the following. If $(H,S') = (H_1,S_1') \circ (H_2,S_2')$, where $(H,S') \in z(H)$, $(H_1,S_1') \in x(H_1)$ and $(H_2,S_2') \in y(H_2)$, and S' satisfies $|S'| = \max \{|S| : (H,S) \in z(H)\}$, then $|S_1'| = \max \{|S| : (H_1,S) \in x(H_1)\}$ and $|S_2'| = \max \{|S| : (H_2,S) \in y(H_2)\}$. The correctness of the algorithm follows from the fact that C contains a foundation for the property P. $\Box$

We proceed to show that the property P: "is a minimal dominating

set", admits a closed system of recurrences with respect to the family
of generalized-series-parallel graphs in two stages. First, a closed
recurrence system for the property Q: "is a dominating set", is
developed, and then a general technique is used to establish the
existence of a closed recurrence system for property P.

THEOREM 4. The property Q: "is a dominating set", admits a closed
recurrence system with respect to the family of generalized-series-
parallel graphs.

Proof. Consider the set of classes $C = \{[i] : i = 1,2,...,9\}$, where:

$[1](G) = \{(G,S) :$ a) $u \in S$ $[2](G) = \{(G,S) :$ a) $u \in S$

            b) $v \in S$ b) $v \in V - S$

            c) $N[S] = V\}$,   c) $N[S] = V\}$,

$[3](G) = \{(G,S) :$ a) $u \in V - S$ $[4](G) = \{(G,S) :$ a) $u \in V - S$

            b) $v \in S$ b) $v \in V - S$

            c) $N[S] = V\}$,   c) $N[S] = V\}$,

$[5](G) = \{(G,S) :$ a) $u \in V - S$ $[6](G) = \{(G,S) :$ a) $u \in V - S$

            b) $v \in V - S$ b) $v \in V - S$

            c) $N[S] = V - \{u\}\}$,   c) $N[S] = V - \{v\}\}$,

$[7](G) = \{(G,S) :$ a) $u \in V - S$ $[8](G) = \{(G,S) :$ a) $u \in S$

            b) $v \in V - S$ b) $v \in V - S$

            c) $N[S] = V - \{u,v\}\}$,   c) $N[S] = V - \{v\}\}$,

$[9](G) = \{(G,S) :$ a) $u \in V - S$

            b) $v \in S$

            c) $N[S] = V - \{u\}\}$.

Notice that $\{[1], [2], [3], [4]\}$ forms a foundation for property Q

with respect to the family of gsp-graphs. Since the derivation of each
recurrence system for each composition operation is straight forward, we
present only the recurrences for the generalized-series composition:

[1] = [1] g [1] ∪ [1] g [2],

[2] = [2] g [3] ∪ [2] g [9] ∪ [8] g [3] ∪

    [2] g [4] ∪ [2] g [5] ∪ [8] g [4],

[3] = [3] g [1] ∪ [3] g [2],

[4] = [4] g [3] ∪ [4] g [9] ∪ [6] g [3] ∪

    [4] g [4] ∪ [4] g [5] ∪ [6] g [4],

[5] = [5] g [3] ∪ [5] g [9] ∪ [7] g [3] ∪

    [5] g [4] ∪ [5] g [5] ∪ [7] g [4],

[6] = [6] g [9] ∪ [6] g [5],

[7] = [7] g [9] ∪ [7] g [5],

[8] = [8] g [9] ∪ [8] g [5], and

[9] = [9] g [1] ∪ [9] g [2]. □

In [18], Wimer proves the following theorem for properties Q,
which may be expressed in terms of subsets of the vertices of a graph.

THEOREM 5. [18] If property Q admits a closed recurrence system with
respect to a k-terminal family of graphs F, then the property P: "is a
minimal subset S ⊆ V(G) having property Q", also admits a closed
recurrence system with respect to the family F.

The idea behind the proof is conveyed by a simple example.
Suppose that property Q admits the following recurrence system:

    [1] = [1] o [2] ∪ [3] o [2],

    [2] = [2] o [2] ∪ [1] o [1], and

    [3] = [1] o [1] ∪ [2] o [3],

where [1] and [2] form a foundation for Q. We introduce the following notation for the classes for property P:

$[$ i ; X $]$ = $\{(G,S)$: a) (G,S) is in [i] and

                        b) for each proper subset S' of S, the pair

                        (G,S') is <u>not</u> in $\cup\{[i]$: i $\in$ X$\}\}$.

where X represents a subset of $\{1$, 2 , 3$\}$. Notice that classes:

$[$ 1 ; $\{1,2\}$ $]$ and $[$ 2 ; $\{1,2\}$ $]$ form a foundation for property P.

Moreover, some of the recurrences are as follows:

$[$ 1 ; $\{1,2\}$ $]$ = $[$ 1 ; $\{1,2,3\}$ $]$ o $[$ 2 ; $\{1,2\}$ $]$ $\cup$

              $[$ 3 ; $\{1,2,3\}$ $]$ o $[$ 2 ; $\{2\}$ $]$

$[$ 2 ; $\{1,2\}$ $]$ = $[$ 2 ; $\{1,2,3\}$ $]$ o $[$ 2 ; $\{2\}]$ $\cup$

              $[$ 1 ; $\{1\}$ $]$ o $[$ 1 ; $\{1,2\}$ $]$

$[$1 ; $\{1,2,3\}$ $]$ = $[$ 1 ; $\{1,2,3\}$ $]$ o $[$ 2 ; $\{1,2\}$ $]$ $\cup$

              $[$ 3 ; $\{1,2,3\}$ $]$ o $[$ 2 ; $\{2\}$ $]$

$[$ 2 ; $\{2\}$ $]$ = $[$ 2 ; $\{2\}$ $]$ o $[$ 2 ; $\{1,2\}$ $]$ $\cup$ $[$ 1 ; $\{1\}$ $]$ o $[$ 1 ; $\{1,2\}$ $]$ $\cup$

              $[$ 2 ; $\{1,2\}$ $]$ o $[$ 2 ; $\{2\}$ $]$ $\cup$ $[$ 1 ; $\{1,2\}$ $]$ o $[$ 1 ; $\{1\}$ $]$

5. Concluding remarks and acknowledgements.

      This paper is a continuation of a series of papers on the development of a methodology for constructing linear-time graph algorithms on k-terminal families of graphs by Wimer [18], [19] and [21]; Wimer, Hedetniemi and Laskar [20]; Hedetniemi and Wimer [12]; and Hare, Hare and Hedetniemi [11]. This work has (i) extended the lists of both graphs (k-terminal) and NP-complete problems for which linear-time algorithms can be designed; (ii) produced in [19] a linear-time algorithm ($O(2^{k+2}n)$) for solving the domination problem on k-chordal graphs with n vertices, which improves on an $O(n^{k+3})$ algorithm by Corneil and Keil [5]; (iii) produced an $O(2^{2k**2}n + n^3)$ algorithm for solving the domination problem for arbitrary graphs, where the parameter k involves the maximum clique size in an associated 'chordalized' graph; (iv) produced in [21] a variety of linear-time algorithms for series-parallel

graphs, Halin graphs and k-trees; and (v) produced in [18] a linear-time

algorithm for determining the irredundance number of a k-chordal graph.

We dedicate this paper, by its title, to Takamizawa, Nishizeki and

Saito and their collegues Watanabe, Ae and Nakamura; Kikuno, Yoshida and

Kakuda; and Kajitani, Ishizuka and Ueno whose work inspired ours.

6. References.

[1] Arnborg, S. and A. Proskurowski, Linear time algorithms for

    NP-hard problems restricted to partial k-trees, TRITA-NA-8404,

    the Royal Institute of Technology (1984).

[2] Arnborg, S. and A. Proskurowski, Characterization and recognition

    of partial 3-trees, SIAM J. Alg. Disc. Meth. (1985).

[3] Bern, M. W., E. L. Lawler and A. L. Wong, Why certain subgraph

    computations require only linear time, Proc. 26th Symp. on

    Foundations of Computer Science, October, 1985.

[4] Cockayne, E. J., O. Favaron, C. Payan and A. Thomason,

    Contributions to the theory of domination, independence and

    irredundance in graphs, Discrete Math., 33(1981), pp. 249-258.

[5] Corneil, D. G. and J. M. Keil, The complexity of the dominating

    set problem on k-trees, Annals Discrete Math., to appear.

[6] Corneil, D. G., and D. G. Kirkpatrick, Families of recursively

    defined perfect graphs, Congressus Numerantium, 39(1983),

    pp. 237-246.

[7] Corneil, D. G., Y. Perl and L. Stewart, Cographs: recognition,

    applications and algorithms, Congressus Numerantium, 43(1984),

    pp. 249-258.

[8] El-Mallah, E. S. and C. J. Colbourn, Partial k-tree algorithms,
     Proc. of 250th Anniversary Conf. on Graph Theory, Ft. Wayne,
     Ind., March, 1986, to appear.

[9] Garey, M. R. and D. S. Johnson, Computers and Intractability: A
     Guide to the Theory of NP-Completeness, W. H. Freeman, San
     Francisco, 1979.

[10] Hadlock, F. O., Finding a maximum cut of a planar graph in
     polynomial time, SIAM J. Comput., 4(1975), pp. 221-225.

[11] Hare E. O., W. R. Hare and S. T. Hedetniemi, Algorithms for
     computing the domination number of KxN complete grid graphs,
     Congressus Numerantium, to appear.

[12] Hedetniemi, S. T. and T. V. Wimer, k-Terminal recursive families
     of graphs, Proc. 250th Anniversary Conf. on Graph Theory,
     Ft. Wayne, Ind., March, 1986, to appear.

[13] Kikuno, T., N. Yoshida and Y. Kakuda, A linear algorithm for the
     domination number of series parallel graphs, Discrete Appl.
     Math., 5(1983), pp. 299-311.

[14] Peters, K. W., Theoretical and algorithmic results on domination
     and connectivity, Ph. D. Thesis, Clemson University, May, 1986.

[15] Syslo, M. M., NP-complete problems on some tree structured
     graphs: a review, Proc. of the WG '83 (Workshop on graph
     theoretic concepts in computer science, Universitat Osnabruck,
     June, 1983), M. Nagl and J. Perl, Eds., Trauner Verlag, Linz,
     1984, pp. 342-353.

[16] Takamizawa, K., T. Nishizeki and N. Saito, Linear-time
     computability of combinatorial problems on series-parallel
     graphs, J. Assoc. Comput. Mach., 29(1982), pp. 623-641.

[17] Watanabe, T., T. Ae and A. Nakamura, On the node cover problem of

planar graphs, Proc. of the 1979 Int. Symp. on Convexity and

Systems, Tokyo, Japan, 1979, pp. 78-81.

[18] Wimer, T. V., Linear algorithms on k-terminal recursive graphs,

Ph. D. Thesis, Clemson University, 1987 (anticipated).

[19] Wimer, T. V., An O(n) algorithm for domination in k-chordal

graphs, manuscript, May, 1986.

[20] Wimer, T. V., S. T. Hedetniemi and R. Laskar, A methodology for

constructing linear graph algorithms, Congressus Numerantium,

50(1985), pp. 43-60.

[21] Wimer, T. V., Linear algorithms for the dominating cycle problems

in series-parallel graphs, 2-trees, and Halin graphs, Congressus

Numerantium, to appear.

COMPETITIVE SNOOPY CACHING[1]

Anna R. Karlin[2]
Computer Science Department
Stanford University

Mark S. Manasse
DEC Systems Research Center
Palo Alto, California

Larry Rudolph
Computer Science Department
Hebrew University

Daniel D. Sleator
Computer Science Department
Carnegie-Mellon University

ABSTRACT

In a snoopy cache multiprocessor system, each processor has a cache in which it stores blocks of data. Each cache is connected to a bus used to communicate with the other caches and with main memory. Each cache monitors the activity on the bus and in its own processor and decides which blocks of data to keep and which to discard. For several of the proposed architectures for snoopy caching systems, we present new on-line algorithms to be used by the caches to decide which blocks to retain and which to drop in order to minimize communication over the bus. We prove that, for any sequence of operations, our algorithms' communication costs are within a constant factor of the minimum required for that sequence; for some of our algorithms we prove that no on-line algorithm has this property with a smaller constant.

1. INTRODUCTION

Snoopy caching is a promising new technique for enhancing the performance of bus-based multiprocessor systems [G,F,PP,KEW,RS,AB,VH]. In these designs, each processor is connected to its own snoopy cache. All of a processor's memory requests are serviced by its cache. These caches and a main memory are connected by a common bus. Since the bus can service only one request at a time, inefficient use of the bus may cause a processor to idle while its cache is waiting for the bus. Each snoopy cache

---

[1] A preliminary version of this paper appeared in the Proceedings of the 27th Annual Symposium on the Foundations of Computer Science, IEEE, Toronto, Canada, 1986. A version of this paper containing all proofs and some further results will appear in *Algorithmica*.

[2] This author received support from an IBM doctoral fellowship, and did part of this work while a research student associate at the IBM Almaden Research Center.

monitors the activity on the bus and in its own processor, and can dynamically choose which variables to keep and which to drop in order to reduce bus traffic.

In practice, programs for multiprocessors exhibit locality of reference just as sequential programs do. Since fetching a variable over the bus requires one bus cycle to send the address and one bus cycle to receive the value, most designs reduce the overhead of address cycles by clustering variables into blocks. A block fetch of size b takes only $b + 1$ bus cycles, thus saving nearly a factor of two if b is reasonably large and the expectation of locality is justified.

To further reduce the cost of reading, a block may reside in more than one cache at a time. Requests by a processor to modify a memory location that is stored in more than one cache require bus communication. This is because each copy of the block must either be marked invalid, or updated to reflect the new value. (If a particular cache decided not to take either of these actions, then the possibility exists that this cache would later return an incorrect value to its processor.) Thus, a bus cycle is required to broadcast information to all the relevant caches.

A snoopy cache system must use some *block retention* strategy to decide for each cache which blocks to keep and which to discard. In choosing such a strategy, we face a tradeoff: if a block is replicated, then the system must pay the cost of updating all copies following a write to that block; if a block is dropped from a processor's cache, then the system must pay for the processor's next request to read a variable in that block.

Most snoopy cache designs use either *exclusive-write* or *pack-rat* as a block retention strategy. In the exclusive-write strategy, a write to a location in a block causes all other copies of the block to be invalidated. In the pack-rat strategy, a block is only dropped from a cache as a result of a conflict with another block.

Exclusive-write can be a bad strategy. Suppose a processor writes to a specific location and then each of n processors reads that location. This pattern is repeated k times. Let p be the number of bus cycles needed to read a block. Since $n - 1$ processors have to re-read the block containing the location on each iteration, the cost per iteration is at least $(n - 1)p$, for a total cost of at least $k(n - 1)p$. The optimal strategy for this sequence is to keep the location shared among all processors with each write updating the contents of all the other caches for a total cost of at most $k + np$. Hence, in the limit, the number of bus cycles used by exclusive-write exceeds the optimal by a factor of $(n - 1)p$.

Pack-rat can also be a bad strategy. Consider the situation in which two processors read a location, and then one of the processors writes the location w times. Since pack-rat keeps the location shared, it must use a bus cycle for each of the writes, for a total cost of at least w. The optimal strategy for this sequence is for all but the writing processor to drop the block immediately after reading it, incurring a total cost of at most $2p$. Hence, in the limit as w increases, pack-rat uses unboundedly more cycles than are needed.

Is there another strategy that performs well in both of these situations? In this paper we answer this question affirmatively. In fact, we prove something far stronger: we construct strategies that perform nearly optimally for any sequence of operations.

An on-line algorithm is *competitive* if its cumulative cost on any sequence is within a constant factor of the cost of the optimal off-line algorithm on the same sequence, and for no smaller constant does such an algorithm exist. Sleator and Tarjan [ST] were the first to demonstrate an interesting competitive algorithm in their analysis of the move-to-front heuristic for maintaining a linear search list. In this paper, we extend their techniques to analyze new competitive block retention algorithms for several snoopy cache models.

We believe that competitive analysis is more useful than other theoretical methods for analyzing snoopy caching strategies. There are sequences on which no snoopy caching strategy does well (which rarely occur in real systems). It is therefore not sensible to use the worst-case performance of two schemes as an indicator of which is better. To do average-case analysis, a statistical model of the sequence of requests is required. It is extremely difficult to devise a realistic model, since the pattern of accesses changes dynamically with time and with different applications. Without prior knowledge of the structure of the sequence of operations, a scheme that is competitive is more attractive than one that is not. A competitive scheme can be only slightly worse than any other scheme, and may be very much better.

The principle used to devise these schemes is roughly the following: the change from a state A to a state A' is made when the cost of making the change equals the extra cost incurred due to being in state A instead of A'. Like the strategies of [RS1], our algorithms keep counters. We use these counters to make these cost estimates and to decide when to change the arrangement of blocks.

We use competitive analysis to compare block retention schemes for particular architectures. Our analyses shed little light on the question of which architecture to choose, or how to choose the parameters of a given architecture.

Section 2 of this paper defines our terminology, notation, and models. Section 3 presents lower bounds. Section 4 describes and analyzes a competitive algorithm for direct-mapped snoopy caching. The approach is described in detail, and is used in subsequent proofs. Section 5 reexamines paging algorithms and is concerned with dynamically mapped (associative) caches. The algorithm presented in this section is not competitive, however its performance is within a constant factor of the optimum algorithm running on a system with less memory. Sections 6, 7 and 8 present and analyze algorithms for different generalizations of direct-mapped snoopy caching.

2. DEFINITIONS, NOTATION, AND MODELS

In a snoopy caching system there is a single address space used by all of the processors. A location in this space is called a *variable*. The operation of the caching system is transparent to the processors; from their point of view the system is simply a memory which allows them to read and write variables.

The caching system partitions the memory space into *blocks*, groups of variables of uniform size. We let p denote the block size, and $[v]$ denote the block containing the variable v.

Each cache may contain a collection of blocks. The number of blocks in a cache is bounded by the cache size, which may be less than the number of blocks in the address space. The collection of blocks in a cache may change with time. Although main memory is large enough to store all of the blocks of the address space, not all the blocks are stored there at all times.

The slots that may contain blocks in a cache are called *cache lines*. A *direct-mapped* cache uses a hash function $h_i(B)$ to determine the unique cache line in which block B will reside. If $h_i(B) = h_i(B')$ then cache i can contain at most one of the blocks B and B' at any time. (Some authors describe this situation by saying that the set size is 1.) In an *associative cache* any line can store any block.

A cache line is said to be *empty* if it does not contain a block. A *cache collision* occurs when a block is needed in a cache line which currently contains another block.

A block may reside in any subset of the caches, and may or may not reside in main memory. If a block is in none of the caches then it must be in main memory. If the block is not contained in main memory, it is *dirty*, and is otherwise *clean*. A block that is contained in more than one cache is *replicated*. A block residing in only one cache is *unique*.

Main memory plays a more passive role than a cache. A request for data is only answered by main memory if no cache responds to the request. This means that main memory does not have to know which blocks are clean or dirty. Main memory is said to *snoop* if, whenever a new value of a variable or block is broadcast on the bus, the memory updates its own copy of the variable or block. If main memory snoops then any replicated block also resides in main memory, since a change to any variable in a replicated block is broadcast over the bus. A snooping main memory sees this broadcast and updates its copy of the variable. Therefore any replicated block is clean. If main memory does not snoop then the moment a variable is changed by a cache containing the block, the block becomes dirty.

All of the caches discussed in this paper *snoop on variables*. That is, if a new value of variable v is broadcast on the bus and a cache contains block $[v]$, then the cache updates its copy of the variable. In some models the caches can *snoop on blocks*. This means that when a block is broadcast over the bus, any cache that wants the block (and has space for it) can grab the block and put it into its cache.

A processor interacts with the caching system by making a sequence of *requests* of two types:

READ$_i(v)$: Processor i requests the value of variable v.

WRITE$_i(v)$: Processor i requests that the value of variable v be updated to some new value.

In response to a request by processor i, the caches execute one or more of the following actions. Each action has an associated cost, which is the number of bus cycles it requires.

Fetchblock(i, B): Block B is added to cache i. The contents of block B are copied to an empty line. This action costs p.

Writeback(i, B): Block B is made clean. The contents of block B in cache i are broadcast on the bus. Main memory copies the block. This action costs p.

Drop(i, B): The line containing block B in cache i is made empty. Block B is present in cache i, and is either clean or replicated. This action costs 0.

Supply(i, v): Variable v is supplied to processor i by cache i. Block $[v]$ is present in cache i. This action costs 0.

Update(i, v): Variable v is updated in all caches containing block $[v]$. Block $[v]$ is present in cache i. Unless block $[v]$ is replicated and main memory snoops, block $[v]$ is removed from main memory. If $[v]$ is unique to cache i, this action costs 0. If $[v]$ is replicated, this action costs 1.

Supplythrough(i, v): Variable v is supplied to processor i. Block $[v]$ is not present in cache i. The value is retrieved over the bus. This action costs 1.

Updatethrough(i, v): Variable v is updated in main memory and all caches containing block $[v]$. $[v]$ need not be present in cache i. The value is broadcast on the bus even if $[v]$ is not present in any other cache. This action costs 1.

A block-retention algorithm responds to a READ request with a sequence of actions terminated by either a *Supply* or *Supplythrough* action. Similarly, the response to a WRITE request is a sequence of actions ending with an *Update* or *Updatethrough*.

We are now ready to extract from this framework several specific models. These models are distinguished by:

- Whether the caches are direct-mapped or associative.

- Whether *Supplythrough* and *Updatethrough* are allowed. If not, $\text{READ}_i(v)$ and $\text{WRITE}_i(v)$ requests can only be satisfied after cache i contains block $[v]$.
- Whether or not main memory snoops. Sometimes our algorithm and its analysis are independent of this parameter. We only specify it in cases where it matters.
- Whether the caches snoop on variables only, snoop on blocks, or snoop on blocks in a limited fashion.

Direct-Mapped Snoopy Caching
- Direct-mapped.
- No *Updatethrough* or *Supplythrough* actions.
- Caches snoop only on variables. (Thus, snooping only occurs during $Update(i, v)$ actions.)

The only freedom a cache has in this model is deciding when it should drop a block. Voluntarily dropping a block is advantageous only if that block becomes unique to a single cache. The only way a block can enter cache i is in response to a $\text{READ}_i(v)$ or $\text{WRITE}_i(v)$ request.

Associative Snoopy Caching
- Associative mapping.
- No *Updatethrough* or *Supplythrough* actions.
- Caches snoop only on variables (*Update* actions).

A block retention strategy for this model has a great deal more freedom than in direct-mapped snoopy caching. If a block is to be read into a full cache then the strategy may select the block to drop in order to make room for the new one. This problem is related to demand paging.

Block Snoopy Caching
- Direct-mapped. We assume that in each cache no two blocks map to the same line, *i.e.*, each cache is as large as main memory.
- No *Updatethrough* or *Supplythrough* actions.
- Caches snoop on variables and blocks. That is, the caches snoop on *Fetchblock*, *Writeback*, and *Update* actions.

Because of the unlimited cache size and the ability to snoop on block transfers, any block that is not unique can be replicated in all caches. As in direct-mapped snoopy caching, the freedom of a block retention scheme is limited to deciding when to drop a block.

Limited Block Snoopy Caching
- Direct mapped (bounded memory).

- No *Updatethrough* or *Supplythrough* actions, except *Updatethrough* is allowed if $[v]$ is present in cache i.
- Caches snoop on variables and blocks. Snooping on blocks is limited to those that were the last to occupy the line. That is, cache i can acquire block B by snooping only if the last action of cache i for any block B' with $h_i(B) = h_i(B')$ was $Drop(i, B)$.
- Main memory snoops.

Our limitation on block snooping makes it useful for recovering from a heavily written-to block. Relaxing this restriction gives an off-line algorithm great power: an on-line algorithm cannot know which of two blocks that hash to the same line will be used next. Since main memory snoops, we allow *Updatethrough* actions so that algorithms can keep blocks clean.

General Snoopy Caching

- Direct mapped.
- *Updatethrough* and *Supplythrough* allowed. The block $[v]$ need *not* be placed in cache i to satisfy a READ$_i(v)$ or WRITE$_i(v)$ request.
- Caches snoop only on variables (*Update* and *Updatethrough* actions).
- Main memory snoops.

In this model a cache can voluntarily drop a block (*i.e.*, not in response to a collision), and can retain a block that collides with the current access request.

As stated above, a block-retention algorithm takes a sequence σ of READ$_i(v)$ and WRITE$_i(v)$ requests and generates a sequence of actions satisfying the constraints in response. An algorithm is *on-line* if it generates its response to a request up to the completing *Supply*, *Supplythrough*, *Update*, or *Updatethrough* before examining any future requests. An on-line algorithm exhibits *local-control* if, after having examined a request by processor i, no actions for caches other than i are taken until either the request is completed or cache i takes an action with non-zero cost. In the remainder of the paper, on-line means on-line local-control.

Let A be any on-line algorithm which takes a sequence σ of READ$_i(v)$ and WRITE$_i(v)$ requests, and generates a sequence of actions satisfying the constraints of the model. $C_A(\sigma)$ denotes the maximum cost of any sequence of actions generated by A on input σ. Let *opt* be any *off-line* algorithm that examines the entire sequence of requests in advance and generates a sequence of actions satisfying the constraints above with minimum cost. Then $C_{opt}(\sigma)$ is the minimum over all algorithms A of $C_A(\sigma)$, since for any sequence σ there is an algorithm that guesses that the input will be σ and performs optimally.

We will sometimes consider separately the costs attributable to *Fetchblock*, *Writeback* and *Update* actions. These costs are denoted FBC, WBC and UC respectively.

It is important to realize that our algorithms are abstractions presented in a manner that simplifies the analysis. Although in this form they appear to require centralized control, there are techniques for implementing them in a distributed fashion‡. We assume that requests are sequential, even though this is not true in a parallel machine, since the bus serializes all communication.

3. LOWER BOUNDS

Theorem 3.1: *Let A be any on-line block-retention algorithm in a model without Supplythrough and Updatethrough. If there are at least two caches then there is an infinite sequence of requests σ such that* $C_A(\sigma(n)) \geq n$, *and*

$$C_A(\sigma(n)) \geq 2 \cdot C_{opt}(\sigma(n))$$

for infinitely many values of n, where σ(n) denotes the first n requests of σ. Moreover, for all n,

$$C_A(\sigma(n)) + p \geq 2 \cdot C_{opt}(\sigma(n))$$

Proof: Consider two caches, 1 and 2, and a block B initially replicated in both caches. The sequence σ will consist of just two types of operations: WRITE$_1(B)$, and READ$_2(B)$.† The first request in σ is a READ$_2(B)$.

We generate the rest of σ by applying the following rule: If A has block B in cache 2, then we issue a WRITE$_1(B)$ request. Otherwise, we issue a READ$_2(B)$ request.

The cost incurred by algorithm A for this sequence is at least one for each WRITE$_1(B)$ request and p for each READ$_2(B)$ request after the first. (Note that since all control is local, A cannot first $Drop(2, B)$ at 0 cost then $Supply$ at 0 cost, when processing a WRITE$_1(B)$ request; processor 2 doesn't "know" that processor 1 has just executed a write until either an update or an invalidation request is sent over the bus.)

We will now describe an off-line algorithm H and show that its cost on $\sigma(n)$ is at most half that of A. Algorithm H uses a look-ahead of only p, and is independent of A. After each read, H chooses to make B unique to cache 1 if and only if the read is followed by at least p consecutive writes.

We prove by induction that after each read $2 \cdot C_H \leq C_A$. It is true after the first read since $C_H = C_A = 0$. If there are k writes between one read and the next, then the cost incurred by A during that interval is $k + p$, and that incurred by H is $\min(k,p)$. Since $2\min(k,p) \leq k + p$, the result follows by induction. ∎

The proof of this theorem shows that if an on-line algorithm does not spend nearly equal amounts reading and writing, then an off-line algorithm can beat it by more than a factor of two. In devising the algorithms in this paper we were guided by the constraint that the cost of reading and writing must be balanced.

Another question to consider is whether there is a "best" on-line algorithm. Here we show in a strong sense that there is no such thing.

Theorem 3.2: *Let A be any on-line block-retention algorithm in a model without Supplythrough and Updatethrough and with at least two caches. For any on-line algorithm A there is another on-line algorithm G such that for all sequences of requests τ,*

$$C_G(\tau) \leq C_A(\tau) + 2p,$$

and for every N there exists a sequence σ such that $C_A(\sigma) \geq N$ and

$$2 \cdot C_G(\sigma) \leq C_A(\sigma).$$

Proof: Given an algorithm A, construct σ and H as in Theorem 3.1. On any input τ algorithm G emulates H while τ is a prefix of σ. As soon as τ deviates from σ, G sets its state to match A's and emulates A thereafter.

During the prefix of τ that is a prefix of σ, G performs like H, and incurs a cost at most p more than A. At the point at which τ and σ first differ, G must change into A's current state, at a cost of at most p. During the remainder of τ, G and A pay exactly the same amount. Therefore G incurs a cost within $2p$ of A. ∎

Theorem 3.3: *Let A be any on-line block-retention algorithm in a model allowing Supplythrough and Updatethrough. If there are at least two caches then there is an infinite sequence of requests σ such that $C_A(\sigma(n)) \geq n$, and*

$$C_A(\sigma(n)) \geq 3 \cdot C_{opt}(\sigma(n))$$

for infinitely many values of n, where $\sigma(n)$ denotes the first n requests of σ.

The proof of this theorem involves constructing a sequence of operations such that the on-line algorithm performs at least three times worse than a particular off-line algorithm H. The proof is more complicated than that of Theorem 3.1. We can also prove a theorem analogous to Theorem 3.2 in this case.

4. DIRECT-MAPPED SNOOPY CACHING

Our block-retention algorithm for the direct-mapped snoopy cache model, *dsc*, uses an array of counts to decide when to drop a block B from cache i. Each element of this array (denoted $w[i, B]$) takes on an integer value between 0 and p. If a block is replicated, then every write to it requires a bus cycle. Each other cache containing the block is partially guilty of causing this bus cycle. Consequently, in the following algorithm, a write to a replicated block reduces a counter in one of the other caches sharing the block. When the counter reaches zero the block is dropped. When a block is brought into a cache its count is set to p.

Two invariants are maintained that relate the state of the caches to the $w[i, B]$ values. First, $w[i, B]$ is 0 if and only if block B is not in cache i. Second, if i is the last processor to modify a dirty block B then $w[i, B] = p$.

Algorithm *Direct-Mapped-Snoopy-Caching*;
    for $t := 1$ to length(σ) **do**
        if $\sigma(t) = \text{READ}_i(v)$ **then**
            $B := [v]$;
            if $w[i, B] = 0$ **then** *Getblock*(i, B);
            else $w[i, B] := q$, where $q \in [w[i, B] \cdots p]$ **fi**;
            Supply(i, v)
        elsif $\sigma(t) = \text{WRITE}_i(v)$ **then**
            $B := [v]$;
            if $w[i, B] = 0$ **then** *Getblock*(i, B)
            else $w[i, B] := p$ **fi**;
            Update(i, v);
            if $\exists\, j \neq i$ **s.t.** $w[j, B] \neq 0$ **then**
                $C_{dsc} := C_{dsc} + 1$;
                $w[j, B] := w[j, B] - 1$;
                if $w[j, B] = 0$ **then** *Drop*(j, B) **fi**
            fi
        fi
    od
end *Direct-Mapped-Snoopy-Caching*;

Procedure *Getblock*(i, B);
    if $\exists\, B'$ **s.t.** $h_i(B') = h_i(B) \,\wedge\, w[i, B'] \neq 0$ **then**
        $\{$ B collides with B', so drop B'. $\}$
        if $w[i, B'] = p$ **then** *Writeback*(i, B'); $C_{dsc} := C_{dsc} + p$ **fi**;
        $w[i, B'] := 0$;
        Drop(i, B')

fi;

$Fetchblock(i, B); c_{dsc} := c_{dsc} + p;$

$w[i, B] := p$

end $Getblock;$

Algorithm dsc is under-determined at two points: when $w[i, B]$ is incremented during a READ$_i(v)$ request, and when j is chosen during a write to a replicated block. It turns out that amortized analysis of the algorithm is insensitive to these choices, so other criteria must be used to make them.

A $Writeback$ is done by this algorithm when the count of a block that must be dropped equals p. This is done to maintain the second of the two invariants. The effect of this is that a $Writeback$ may be done while the block is still replicated. There is no advantage in doing such a $Writeback$. Algorithm dsc can easily be modified to avoid doing this, but its analysis becomes slightly more complicated.

Theorem 4.1:

For any sequence σ and any on-line or off-line algorithm A,

$$c_{dsc}(\sigma) \leq 2 \cdot c_A(\sigma) + k.$$

The constant k depends only on the initial cache states of dsc and A, and is zero if all caches are initially empty.

Proof: When any algorithm is run on a sequence of requests σ with a particular initial state of the caches, it generates a sequence of actions. In order to compare the performance of two algorithms on the sequence σ we will need to correlate the actions of the two algorithms. To do this we construct a sequence of actions τ by merging the actions generated by A and dsc on input σ in a particular order.

We construct the sequence of actions τ as follows: Start with the empty sequence. For each request in σ, we extend τ first by the actions taken by A up to the $Supply$ or $Update$ that completes the request. We label each of these A. We then extend τ by the actions taken by dsc, up to the $Supply$ or $Update$. We label each of these dsc. Finally, we extend τ by the completing $Supply$ or $Update$, which we label with both A and dsc. We will denote by $c_{dsc}(\tau, t)$ the cost of the actions labeled with dsc in the first t steps of τ. $c_{opt}(\tau, t)$ is defined similarly.

We will prove by induction on t that

$$c_{dsc}(\tau, t) - 2 \cdot c_A(\tau, t) \leq \Phi(t) - \Phi(0), \tag{1}$$

where $\Phi(t)$ is a potential function that depends on the cache states of dsc and A after t steps of τ. The theorem follows with $k = -\Phi(0)$, since Φ is chosen to be always nonpositive.

For $t = 0$, both sides of (1) are 0. The inductive step reduces to showing $\Delta C_{dsc} - 2 \cdot \Delta C_A \leq \Delta \Phi$ where $\Delta \cdot = \cdot(t) - \cdot(t-1)$. Let S_A be the set of pairs (i, B) of caches and blocks such that B is kept in cache i by A after t steps of τ. We take the potential function to be

$$\Phi(t) = \sum_{(i,B) \in S_A} (w[i, B] - 2p) + \sum_{(i,B) \notin S_A} (-w[i, B]).$$

Every step in dsc and in A that changes the potential or incurs a cost results in an action in τ. Therefore to prove the theorem it is sufficient to analyze the effect of every type of action in τ. The following case analysis does this.

If step t of τ is an action labeled only with A, then one of the following cases holds:

A. The action is $Fetchblock(i, B)$:

   $\Delta C_A = p$ and so we must show $\Delta \Phi \geq -2p$. Before this action $(i, B) \notin S_A$. After the action $(i, B) \in S_A$. Therefore $\Delta \Phi = w[i, B] - 2p - (-w[i, B]) = 2w[i, B] - 2p \geq -2p$.

B. The action is $Drop(i, B)$:

   $\Delta C_A = 0$ and so we must show $\Delta \Phi \geq 0$. This is the reverse of the previous case. Before the action $(i, B) \in S_A$, and after the action $(i, B) \notin S_A$. The change in potential is $2p - 2w[i, B] \geq 0$.

C. The action is $Writeback(i, B)$:

   $\Delta C_A = p$ and so we must show $\Delta \Phi \geq -2p$. Here $\Delta C_A = p$ and $\Delta \Phi = 0$, maintaining the assertion.

If step t of τ is an action labeled only with dsc, then one of the following cases holds:

A. The action is $Fetchblock(i, B)$:

   $\Delta C_{dsc} = p$, so we must show that $\Delta \Phi \geq p$. The count $w[i, B]$ changes from 0 to p. Because of the way the actions are ordered in τ, when this $Fetchblock(i, B)$ is done it must be the case that $(i, B) \in S_A$. Thus the potential increases by p.

B. The action is $Writeback(i, B)$:

   $\Delta C_{dsc} = p$, so again we must show $\Delta \Phi \geq p$. This time $w[i, B']$ changes from p to 0, and $(i, B') \notin S_A$. $\Delta \Phi = -0 - (-p) = p$.

C. The action is $Drop(i, B')$, and was caused by a collision:

   The cost of the operation is 0, so we need to show that $\Delta \Phi \geq 0$. The count of the block that is dropped, $w[i, B']$, is set to 0. This cannot decrease the potential since $(i, B') \notin S_A$.

D. The action is $Drop(j, B)$, and was caused by a write to a replicated block:

   The cost of the operation is 0 and the potential does not change since $w[j, B]$ is 0.

If step t of τ is an action labeled with both A and dsc then one of the following cases holds:

A. The action is $Supply(i,v)$:

The cost to both dsc and to A is 0, and $\Delta w[i,B] \geq 0$. Since $(i,B) \in S_A$, $\Delta \Phi \geq 0$.

B. The action is $Update(i,v)$: There are three subcases depending on whether or not block B is unique to dsc and whether or not block B is unique to A.

B1. B is unique to dsc:

This is the same as case A except that A may incur a cost of 1 which improves the situation.

B2. B is replicated in dsc and is unique in A:

$\Delta C_{dsc} = 1$ and $\Delta C_A = 0$, so we need to show that $\Delta \Phi \geq 1$. This is the case since $w[j,B]$ is decreased by 1, and $(j,B) \notin S_A$.

B3. B is replicated in dsc and in A:

$\Delta C_{dsc} = \Delta C_A = 1$, so we need to show that $\Delta \Phi \geq -1$. This is the case since $w[j,B]$ changes by 1 causing the potential to change by 1.

∎

The following theorem is a slightly stronger version of Theorem 4.1. The proof (which we omit) uses two separate potential functions (one for *Fetchblock* costs and one for *Update* costs) and requires a slightly more careful accounting of costs.

Theorem 4.2: *For any sequence σ and any on-line or off-line algorithm A,*

$$\text{FBC}_{dsc}(\sigma) \leq \text{FBC}_A(\sigma) + \text{UC}_A(\sigma) + k_1$$

and

$$\text{UC}_{dsc}(\sigma) + \text{WBC}_{dsc}(\sigma) \leq \text{FBC}_A(\sigma) + \text{UC}_A(\sigma) + k_2.$$

The constants k_1 and k_2 depend on the initial cache states of dsc and A. If all caches are initially empty then k_1 and k_2 are zero.

5. ASSOCIATIVE CACHING

We now examine block retention strategies for the *associative cache model*. In this model a block can reside anywhere in the cache. A strategy in the associative cache model has the burden of deciding which block to drop when a new block is read into the cache, as well as having to decide which blocks to drop because of writes to replicated blocks.

We have devised strategies with nearly optimal amortized performance in this model by combining demand paging strategies with the standard snoopy caching strategy of Section 4.†

---

† Our techniques can be applied to the situation in which the cache is k-way set associative. Each set is regarded as an independent cache.

We begin by examining demand paging strategies, and formulating their analysis in terms of potential functions.

Demand Paging

Consider a two-level memory divided into pages of fixed uniform size. Let n be the number of pages of fast memory. A sequence of page accesses is to be performed, and each access requires that the desired page be put into fast memory. If the page is already in fast memory the access costs nothing. If the page is in slow memory we must swap it for a page in fast memory at a cost of one page fault. A paging rule is an algorithm for deciding which page to move from fast memory to slow memory.

We consider the following paging rules:

Least recently used (lru)

When swapping is necessary, replace the page whose last access was longest ago.

First in, first out (fifo)

Replace the page that has been in fast memory the longest.

Flush when full (fwf)

When attempting to read a page into a full fast memory, discard all other pages.

Longest forward distance (min)

Replace the page whose next access is latest.

All of these but *min* are on-line algorithms. *min* is off-line because it requires knowledge of the sequence in advance. It is also optimal in the sense that it minimizes the number of page faults for any sequence [B].

We compare each of the on-line algorithms described above to the *min* algorithm. Let A be any algorithm, n_A the number of pages of fast memory available to A, σ a sequence of page accesses, and $F_A(\sigma)$ the number of page faults made by A on σ. When comparing A and *min*, we assume that $n_A \geq n_{min}$.

Sleator and Tarjan proved the following lower bound:

Theorem 5.1: [ST] *Let A be any on-line algorithm. Then there are arbitrarily long sequences σ such that*

$$F_A(\sigma) \geq \left(\frac{n_A}{n_A - n_{min} + 1} \right) F_{min}(\sigma).$$

Sleator and Tarjan also proved that the performance of *lru* and *fifo* is within an additive constant of this lower bound. In their proof they considered sequences on which *lru* makes n_{lru} faults and showed that for those sequences *min* must make $n_{lru} - n_{min} + 1$ faults. We have new analyses of *lru* and *fifo* using potential functions. Using these methods we show that the bound is also tight for *fwf*. Our results are summarized by the following three theorems.

Theorem 5.2: *For any input sequence σ,*

$$\mathrm{F}_{fwf}(\sigma) \leq \left(\frac{n_{fwf}}{n_{fwf} - n_{min} + 1} \right) \mathrm{F}_{min}(\sigma) + k,$$

where k depends only on the initial state of the caches and is zero if both sets of caches start out empty.

Proof: We maintain an array a of binary variables. $a[P]$ is 1 if and only if page P is in the fast memory maintained by fwf.

Let $\rho = \frac{n_{fwf}}{n_{fwf} - n_{min} + 1}$, and let S_{min} be the set of pages the min algorithm has in fast memory after step t of σ. The potential function

$$\Phi(t) = \sum_{P \in S_{min}} (a[P] - \rho) - \sum_{P \notin S_{min}} a[P](\rho - 1),$$

can be used to prove

$$\Delta \mathrm{F}_{fwf}(\sigma, t) - (\rho) \Delta \mathrm{F}_{min}(\sigma, t) \leq \Delta \Phi,$$

and hence prove the theorem. ∎

Theorem 5.3: *For any sequence σ,*

$$\mathrm{F}_{fifo}(\sigma) \leq \left(\frac{n_{fifo}}{n_{fifo} - n_{min} + 1} \right) \mathrm{F}_{min}(\sigma) + k,$$

where k depends only on the initial state of the caches and is zero if the cache of min is initially empty.

Proof: Consider the following implementation of the *fifo* strategy. For each page P, maintain an integer valued variable $a[P]$ in the range $[0, n_{fifo}]$. $a[P] = 0$ if P is not in fast memory. When page P is read into fast memory, $a[P]$ is set to n_{fifo}, and for all other pages P' in fast memory $a[P']$ is decremented. (The page whose new $a[P]$ value is 0 is the one replaced. This is the page that has been in the fast memory the longest.)

The potential function we use to prove this theorem is:

$$\Phi(t) = \sum_{P \in S_{min}} \frac{a[P] - n_{fifo}}{n_{fifo} - n_{min} + 1}.$$

∎

The same techniques suffice to prove the following theorem.

Theorem 5.4: *For any sequence σ,*

$$\mathrm{F}_{lru}(\sigma) \leq \left(\frac{n_{lru}}{n_{lru} - n_{min} + 1} \right) \mathrm{F}_{min}(\sigma) + k,$$

where k depends only on the initial state of the caches and is zero if the cache of min is initially empty.

Combining Caching with Paging

We may now combine caching strategies with paging strategies. First, as an immediate corollary of Theorems 4.1 and 5.1, we obtain:

Theorem 5.5: *Let A be any on-line algorithm for associative snoopy caching where each cache managed by A has size n_A, and each cache managed by opt has size n_{opt}. Then there are arbitrarily long sequences σ such that*

$$C_A(\sigma) \geq \max\left(\frac{n_A}{n_A - n_{opt} + 1}, 2\right) \cdot C_{opt}(\sigma).$$

Algorithm *scwf*, presented below, nearly achieves this lower bound. This algorithm combines the *fifo* algorithm for paging and the *dsc* algorithm for direct-mapped snoopy caching. For each block B and each cache i we maintain two variables:

$a[i, B]$: a real valued variable in the range $[0, n_{scwf}]$ that roughly represents the maximum number of other blocks cache i can read until block B in cache i is invalidated.

$w[i, B]$: an integer valued variable in the range $[0, p]$. $w[i, B] = 0$ if and only if block B is not present in cache i.

Algorithm *Snoopy-Caching-With-fifo*;
    for $t := 1$ **to** length(σ) **do**
        if $\sigma(t) = \text{READ}_i(v)$ **then**
            $B := [v]$;
            if $w[i, B] = 0$ **then** *Getblock*(i, B) **fi**;
            Supply(i, v)
        elsif $\sigma(t) = \text{WRITE}_i(v)$ **then**
            $B := [v]$;
            if $w[i, B] = 0$ **then** *Getblock*(i, B);
            else $w[i, B] := p$ **fi**;
            Update(i, v);
            if $\exists j$ **s.t.** $w[j, B] \neq 0 \wedge j \neq i$ **then** { block B is replicated }
                $\text{UC}_{scwf} := \text{UC}_{scwf} + 1$;
                $w[j, B] := w[j, B] - 1$; $a[j, B] := \min(a[j, B], \frac{w[j, B]}{p} n_{scwf})$ (∗)
                if $w[j, B] = 0$ **then** *Drop*(j, B) **fi**
            fi
        fi
    od
end *Snoopy-Caching-With-fifo*;

Procedure *Getblock*(i, B);

{ first do *fifo* decrement }
for B' s.t. $w[i, B'] \neq 0$ **do**
   $a[i, B'] := a[i, B'] - 1;$
   if $a[i, B'] \leq 0$ **then**
        { may need space, drop B' }
        if B' dirty and i is the last cache storing it **then**
            $Writeback(i, B');$ $\text{WBC}_{scwf} := \text{WBC}_{scwf} + p$
        fi;
        $Drop(i, B');$ $a[i, B'] := 0;$ $w[i, B'] := 0$
   fi
od;
{ cache is no longer full, get block }
$Fetchblock(i, B);$ $a[i, B] := n_{scwf};$ $w[i, B] := p;$
$\text{FBC}_{scwf} := \text{FBC}_{scwf} + p$
end *Getblock*;

The only link in this algorithm between the variable a accounting for paging and the variable w accounting for writes to replicated blocks is on line ($*$). The effect of this line is to keep the a variable at roughly the same proportion to its maximum value as the w variable is to its maximum value. This technicality is necessary to prevent a large potential swing when a block is invalidated due to replicated writes. As a consequence, we may drop more than one block when a new block is read in.

Theorem 5.6: *Let A be any algorithm (on-line or off-line) for deciding on block retention in an associative snoopy cache. Let n_{scwf} be the size of the caches managed by scwf and n_A be the size of the caches managed by A.*

Then for all sequences σ,

$$\text{FBC}_{scwf}(\sigma) \leq \left(\frac{n_{scwf}}{n_{scwf} - n_A + 1} \right) (\text{FBC}_A(\sigma) + \text{UC}_A(\sigma)) + k_1 \tag{1}$$

$$\text{UC}_{scwf}(\sigma) \leq \text{FBC}_A(\sigma) + \text{UC}_A(\sigma) + k_2. \tag{2}$$

Hence,

$$\text{FBC}_{scwf}(\sigma) + \text{UC}_{scwf}(\sigma) \leq \left(1 + \frac{n_{scwf}}{n_{scwf} - n_A + 1} \right) (\text{FBC}_A(\sigma) + \text{UC}_A(\sigma)) + k,$$

where k_1, k_2, and k are constants that depend on the relative initial cache states of scwf and A. If the caches are initially empty then k_1, k_2, and k are all zero.

Proof: As in the proof of theorem 4.1, we let τ denote the labeled, merged sequence of actions taken by *scwf* and A. At each step t of τ, S_A is the set of pairs (i, B) such that algorithm A has block B stored in cache i. The potential functions

$$\Phi_F(t) = \sum_{(i,B)\in S_A} p \cdot \frac{a[i, B] - n_{scwf}}{n_{scwf} - n_A + 1}$$

and

$$\Phi_U(t) = \sum_{(i,B)\in S_A} (-p) + \sum_{(i,B)\notin S_A} (-w[i, B])$$

are used to show that the invariants

$$\Delta \text{FBC}_{scwf}(\tau, t) - \left(\frac{n_{scwf}}{n_{scwf} - n_A + 1}\right) (\Delta \text{FBC}_A(\tau, t) + \Delta \text{UC}_A(\tau, t)) \le \Delta \Phi_F(\tau, t)$$

and

$$\Delta \text{UC}_{scwf}(\tau, t) - (\Delta \text{FBC}_A(\tau, t) + \Delta \text{UC}_A(\tau, t)) \le \Delta \Phi_U(\tau, t)$$

hold. From these equations (1) and (2) above follow.

We omit the analysis required to verify that the above inequalities hold in all cases.

∎

Corollary:

$$C_{scwf}(\sigma) \le \left(1 + 2 \cdot \frac{n_{scwf}}{n_{scwf} - n_A + 1}\right) (\text{FBC}_A(\sigma) + \text{UC}_A(\sigma)) + k$$

Proof: The cost of writebacks to $scwf$ is bounded by the cost of reads.   ∎

6. GENERAL SNOOPY CACHING

Like associative caching, general snoopy caching is a generalization of direct mapped snoopy caching. Here we maintain the direct mapped feature, but allow a different freedom. A cache can use the *Supplythrough* and *Updatethrough* actions to read or modify a variable in a block that is not in the cache. This gives the cache the freedom to decide both when a block should be fetched as well as when it should be dropped.

Our algorithm for general snoopy caching, *gsc*, maintains two variables, $w[i, B]$ and $x[i, B]$, for each cache i and block B. Each variable assumes an integer value in the range 0 to p. As in *dsc*, $w[i, B] \ne 0$ if and only if block B is in cache i. Furthermore, if $x[i, B] \ne 0$ then block B is not in cache i. Therefore at any time one or both of $w[i, B]$ or $x[i, B]$ is 0. As in *dsc*, $w[i, B]$ decreases as cache i loses interest in keeping its copy of block B. Analogously $x[i, B]$ increases as cache i gains interest in getting its own copy of block B.

In the program below C'_{gsc} denotes the cost incurred by *gsc* for all actions except *Writebacks*. The numbers in braces are labels used in the analysis.

Algorithm *General-Snoopy-Caching*;
    for $t := 1$ **to** length(σ) **do**
        if $\sigma(t) = \text{READ}_i(v)$ **then**
            $B := [v]$;
            if $w[i, B] = 0$ **then** *Adjust*(i, B) **fi**;
            if $w[i, B] = 0$ **then** *Supplythrough*(i, v) $\{1\}$; $\text{C}'_{gsc} := \text{C}'_{gsc} + 1$
            else *Supply*(i, v) $\{2\}$
            fi
        elsif $\sigma(t) = \text{WRITE}_i(v)$ **then**
            $B := [v]$;
            if $w[i, B] = 0$ **then** *Adjust*(i, B) **fi**;
            if $w[i, B] = 0$ **then** *Updatethrough*(i, v) $\{3\}$; $\text{C}'_{gsc} := \text{C}'_{gsc} + 1$
            elsif $w[i, B] < p$ **then**
                $w[i, B] := w[i, B] + 1$;
                Updatethrough(i, v) $\{4\}$; $\text{C}'_{gsc} := \text{C}'_{gsc} + 1$
            elsif $w[i, B] = p$ **then**
                if block B is in another cache j **then**
                    Updatethrough(i, v) $\{5\}$; $\text{C}'_{gsc} := \text{C}'_{gsc} + 1$;
                    $w[j, B] := w[j, B] - 1$;
                    if $w[j, B] = 0$ **then** *Drop*(j, B) $\{6\}$ **fi**
                else *Update*(i, v) $\{7\}$
                fi
            fi
        fi
    od
end *General-Snoopy-Caching*;

Procedure *Adjust*(i, B);
    Choose one of the following three options so that some **then** clause is executed;
    i.e., non-deterministically choose a successful guarded command:
    (a) **if** $x[i, B] < p$ **then** $x[i, B] := x[i, B] + 1$ **fi**
    (b) **if** another block B' is occupying the cache line $h_i(B)$ **then**
        $w[i, B'] := w[i, B'] - 1$;
        if $w[i, B'] = 0$ **then**
            if B' dirty **then** *Writeback*(i, B') $\{8\}$ **fi**;
            Drop(i, B') $\{9\}$
        fi
    fi
    (c) **if** $x[i, B] = p \wedge$ cache line $h_i(B)$ is empty **then**
        Fetchblock(i, B) $\{10\}$; $\text{C}'_{gsc} := \text{C}'_{gsc} + p$;

$$x[i, B] := 0; \; w[i, B] := p$$

fi

end *Adjust*;

Theorem 6.1: *For any sequence σ and any on-line or off-line algorithm A,*

$$\mathrm{c'}_{gsc}(\sigma) \le 3 \cdot \mathrm{c'}_A(\sigma) + k,$$

where the costs do not count Writeback. The constant k depends on the initial cache states of gsc and A. If both cache sets are initially empty then k is zero.

Proof: As before, we let τ denote the labeled, merged sequence of actions taken by *gsc* and *A*. The action taken by *gsc* that satisfies a request (*Supply, Supplythrough, Update,* or *Updatethrough*) and that used by *A* to satisfy the same request are combined together to make a single element of τ, even though they may be different types of actions.

The potential function

$$\Phi(t) = \sum_{(i,B) \in S_A} (2w[i, B] + x[i, B] - 3p) + \sum_{(i,B) \notin S_A} (-w[i, B] - 2x[i, B])$$

will be used. For each action it is possible to verify the assertion

$$\Delta \mathrm{c'}_{gsc} - 3\Delta \mathrm{c'}_A \le \Delta\Phi,$$

which suffices to prove the theorem.

∎

Combined with Theorem 3.3, this shows that algorithm *gsc* is competitive when writeback costs are ignored. We do not know if *gsc* is competitive if these costs are considered. The following corollary shows that it is within a factor of 4 of optimum.

Corollary:

$$\mathrm{c}_{gsc}(\sigma) \le 4 \cdot \mathrm{c'}_A(\sigma) + k,$$

Proof: For every *Writeback*(i, B) there is a sequence of actions leading up to it that have a cost of $3p$: Initially $w[i, B] = x[i, B] = 0$. Before block B is fetched, $x[i, B]$ is increased from 0 to p, at a cost of 1 for each of these actions. Block B is then fetched at a cost of p. Finally before the writeback, $w[i, B]$ is decreased from p to 0, at a total cost of p (for the *Updatethrough*'s to other blocks). Thus we have:

$$\mathrm{WBC}_{gsc} \le \frac{1}{3}\mathrm{c'}_{gsc}.$$

Combining this with the fact that $\mathrm{c}_{gsc} = \mathrm{c'}_{gsc} + \mathrm{WBC}_{gsc}$ and Theorem 6.1 gives the result.

∎

7. BLOCK SNOOPY CACHING

The models we have considered so far allow snooping only on *Update* actions. We now propose a model which allows snooping on *Fetchblock* and *Writeback* actions as well.

In the *block snoopy caching* model, each processor has a cache of infinite size. Every block will be stored in some cache, so in this model there is no main memory. When a block is sent over the bus in response to READ, other caches can grab the data at no additional cost. Since writes are just as costly if a block is replicated in two caches as in all of them, we assume that every block is either unique or replicated all caches.

In algorithm *bsc*, we make a block unique only after some processor writes to it p times without any other processor reading or writing the block. To record the number of uninterrupted writes the last writer has performed on a block B, we maintain the following state variables:

$last[B] = i$, where i is was the last cache to issue an update action to block B.

$w[B] = \min(n,p)$, where n is the number of uninterrupted updates $last[B]$ has issued to block B.

Algorithm *bsc* maintains the invariant that $w[B] = p$ if and only if B is unique to cache $last[B]$.

Algorithm *Block-Snoopy-Caching*;
    for $t := 1$ to length(σ) **do**
        if $\sigma(t) = \text{READ}_i(v)$ **then**
            $B := [v]$;
            if $w[B] = p \wedge last[B] \neq i$ { block B unique to some other cache } **then**
                $Fetchblock(i, B)$; $w[B] := 0$; $C_{bsc} := C_{bsc} + p$
                { B now replicated in all caches }
            elsif $w[B] < p \wedge last[B] \neq i$ { B replicated, but i not last writer } **then**
                $w[B] := 0$
            fi;
            $Supply(i, v)$
        elsif $\sigma(t) = \text{WRITE}_i(v)$ **then**
            $B := [v]$;
            if $w[B] < p \wedge i = last[B]$ { B replicated and i last writer } **then**
                $Update(i, v)$ {1}; $w[B] := w[B] + 1$; $C_{bsc} := C_{bsc} + 1$;
                if $w[B] = p$ **then** { make B unique to i }
                    for j s.t. $j \neq i$ **do** $Drop(j, B)$ **od**
                fi
            elsif $w[B] < p \wedge i \neq last[B]$ { B replicated and i not last writer } **then**

$$w[B] := 1;\ last[B] := i;$$
$$Update(i,v)\ \{2\};\ C_{bsc} := C_{bsc} + 1$$
elsif $w[B] = p\ \wedge\ i \neq last[B]$ { B unique to some other cache } **then**
$$Fetchblock(i,B);\ w[B] := 0;\ C_{bsc} := C_{bsc} + p;$$
$$\{\ B\ \text{now replicated in all caches}\ \}$$
$$last[B] := i;$$
$$Update(i,v)\ \{3\};\ w[B] := w[B] + 1;\ C_{bsc} := C_{bsc} + 1$$
elsif $w[B] = p\ \wedge\ i = last[B]$ { B unique to i } **then**
$$Update(i,v)$$
fi

fi

od

end *Block-Snoopy-Caching*;

Theorem 7.1: *For any sequence σ and any on-line or off-line block-retention algorithm A in the block snoopy caching model,*

$$C_{bsc}(\sigma) \leq 2 \cdot C_A(\sigma) + k$$

where k is a constant that depends on the relative initial cache states of bsc and A. If every block is initially unique to its last writer then $k = 0$.

Proof: As usual we let τ denote the labeled, merged sequence of actions taken by *bsc* and *A*. At time *t*, *L* is the set of blocks *B* which *A* stores only in cache $last[B]$, and *S* is the set of blocks *B* which *A* stores in some cache other than $last[B]$. In this model, *S* is the complement of *L*, since every block is in some cache. The potential function

$$\Phi(t) = \sum_{B \in S} \left(-w[B] - p \right) + \sum_{B \in L} \left(w[B] - p \right)$$

can be combined with a case analysis to prove the theorem.

∎

The lower bound of Theorem 3.1 holds for this model, so algorithm *bsc* is competitive.

8. LIMITED BLOCK SNOOPY CACHING

The block snoopy caching model presented in Section 7 unrealistic, since it assumes infinite caches. In this section, we consider *limited block snoopy caching*, a version of block snoopy caching for direct-mapped caches. In the limited snoopy caching model, a cache is allowed to grab a block only if that block was the last to occupy its cache line. Caches can grab *B* on both *Fetchblock* and *Writeback* actions. It is assumed in this model that main memory snoops on all transactions. (Thus, main memory acts like all other participants on the bus, except that it has no collisions. It is therefore equivalent to giving each block B some cache i in which $h_i(B) = h_i(B')$ implies that $B = B'$, distributing the functionality of main memory.) Hence, a block can become dirty only when it has been written to since it became unique to some cache.

The algorithm we propose, *lbsc*, retains the simplicity of block snoopy caching and the practicality of direct mapped snoopy caching. We believe that it is the most promising algorithm in this paper. This model is not as general as others we consider, but we see no way of having practical on-line algorithms take advantage of greater flexibility.

Algorithm *lbsc* maintains the variables $w[B]$ and $last[B]$ just as algorithm *bsc*, except that $last[B]$ takes on the value -1 if the block B is present only in main memory. Algorithm *lbsc* maintains two additional variables:

$Store[B]$: The set of processors storing block B.

$Reserved[B]$: The set of processors that dropped block B and have not since fetched any new block into cache line $h_i(B)$.

Algorithm *Limited-Block-Snoopy-Caching*;
    for $t := 1$ **to** length(σ) **do**
        if $\sigma(t) = \text{READ}_i(v)$ **then**
            $B := [v]$;
            if $i \notin Store[B]$ **then** { block B not present in i's cache }
                $Getblock(i, B)$
            else { do read at no cost }
                if $w[B] < p \ \wedge \ last[B] \neq i$ { B replicated, but i not last writer }
                then
                    $w[B] := 0$ **fi**
            fi;
            $Supply(i, v)$
        elsif $\sigma(t) = \text{WRITE}_i(v)$ **then**
            $B := [v]$;
            if $i \notin Store[B]$ **then** $Getblock(i, B)$ **fi**;
            if $w[B] < p \ \wedge \ i = last[B]$ { i last writer } **then**
                $w[B] := w[B] + 1$; $Updatethrough(i, v)$; $\mathrm{C}_{lbsc} := \mathrm{C}_{lbsc} + 1$;
                if $w[B] = p$ **then** { make B unique to i }
                    for j s.t. $j \neq i$ **do** $Drop(j, B)$ **od**;
                    $Reserved[B] := Store[B] - \{i\}$; $Store[B] := \{i\}$ $Update(i, v)$
            fi

>   **elsif** $i \neq last[B]$ { B actively replicated } **then**
> $w[B] := 1;\ last[B] := i;\ Update(i,v);\ C_{lbsc} := C_{lbsc} + 1$
>   **elsif** $i = last[B]\ \wedge\ w[B] = p$ **then**
> $Update(i,v)$
>   **fi**
>   **fi**
> **od**
end *Limited-Block-Snoopy-Caching*;

Procedure *Getblock(i, B)*;
  for B' s.t. $h_i(B') = h_i(B)\ \wedge\ i \in Store[B']$ **do**
    if $i = last[B']$ and $w[B'] = p$ **then**
       $Writeback(i, B');\ w[B'] := 0;\ C_{lbsc} := C_{lbsc} + p;$
       $Store[B'] := Store[B'] \cup Reserved[B'];\ Reserved[B'] := \emptyset;\ last[B] := -1$
    fi;
     $Drop(i, B');\ Store[B'] := Store[B'] - \{i\};$
    if $last[B] = i$ **then** $last[B] := -1$ **fi**;
    { the cache line is now empty, do read }
     $Fetchblock(i, B);\ w[B] := 0;$ { B replicated by everyone in reserved set }
     $C_{lbsc} := C_{lbsc} + p;$
     $Store[B] := Store[B] \cup Reserved[B] \cup \{i\};\ Reserved[B] := \emptyset$
  od
end *Getblock*;

Theorem 9.1: *For any sequence σ and any on-line or off-line algorithm A,*

$$C_{lbsc}(\sigma) \leq 2 \cdot C_A(\sigma) + k$$

where k is a constant that depends on the relative initial cache states of lbsc and A. If both cache sets are initially full, and all blocks are dirty then $k = 0$.

Proof: The potential function

$$\Phi(t) = \sum_{B \text{ clean to } A} (-w[B]) + \sum_{B \text{ dirty to } A} (w[B]) - \sum_i p \cdot n_l$$

is used to prove this theorem. The quantity n_l is the number of cache lines in a cache. The third term in the potential is used merely to ensure that the potential is always non-positive. Note that if B is dirty to A, then B is also unique to A.

    We omit the case analysis required to complete the proof.

9. REMARKS

In this paper we have defined several snoopy caching models and devised competitive algorithms for them. It is a surprising fact that on-line algorithms with such a strong near-optimality property even exist. Furthermore this phenomenon seems to be robust. A worthy and tractable goal for future work is to devise competitive algorithms for other snoopy caching problems, and other scheduling problems.

The practical significance of these results remains to be demonstrated. The only concrete evidence that a competitive algorithm is better in practice than one with good average case performance was supplied by Bentley and McGeoch [BM]. They showed that the move-to-front heuristic (a competitive algorithm) for maintaining a list performs better than some other heuristics on sequences obtained from real data, while average case analysis predicts the opposite outcome. We believe that it is likely that the algorithms in this paper (or ones derived from the same principles) will prove to be useful in practice.

ACKNOWLEDGEMENTS

We thank Bill Coates, Butler Lampson, Greg Nelson, and Chuck Thacker for their comments and critiques of the work in progress. Guy Jacobson, Albert Greenberg, and Marc Snir made valuable comments about the exposition, and Zary Segall started us thinking about snoopy caching. We thank DEC Systems Research Center for travel support. Finally, we are deeply indebted to Hania Gajewska for her assistance in writing and editing this paper.

PERSPECTIVES IN COMPUTING

Volumes 1 – 12 were published as **Notes and Reports in Computer Science and Applied Mathematics.**